YAMAHA

Personal Watercraft

1992-97 REPAIR MANUAL

I0803580

SELOC®

Managing Partners Dean F. Morgantini
Barry L. Beck

Executive Editor Kevin M. G. Maher, A.S.E.

Production Managers Melinda Possinger
Ronald Webb

Author Clarence Coles

Manufactured in USA

104 Willowbrook Lane
West Chester, PA 19382
ISBN 13: 978-0-89330-044-6
ISBN 10: 0-89330-044-7
3456789012 9876543210

www.selocmarine.com
1-866-SELOC55

TABLE OF CONTENTS

1
DESCRIPTION & OPERATION

1-1 BRIEF HISTORY

The jet drive system for propelling a craft through the water arrived on the scene in the early 1960's with the jet drive boat. In the early days the jet drive system was mated only with "high performance" powerplants -- engines in the 454 cu. in. class and larger. For this reason, during the "gas crunch" of the 1970's the jet drives were labeled as "inefficient" and as "gas hogs".

In addition to these two negative terms, they earned the reputation as a "bad boy" boat due to their noisy "straight" exhaust, high rpm operation, and their almost unbelievable maneuverability. These combined factors did little to enhance their image and certainly restricted their popularity.

With "new and improved" technology, personal watercraft arrived on the scene around 1973. Modern personal watercraft were developed using the same principles as the jet boats.

Sales of Personal Watercraft have skyrocketed in the past six years, due to their versatility, maneuverability, modest cost (compared to a boat with similar capability). Almost a thousand units have been loaned or donated to law enforcement as well as search and rescue organizations.

Today single, twin, and three cylinder 2-stroke engines are used with single stage pumps (one impeller) to make the craft highly efficient.

Models Covered

The following Yamaha models are covered in this manual, with the engine designation and the approximate years of manufacture given. The manufacturer reserved the right to discontinue a model within a production year. By the same token, the manufacturer may introduce a new model within the year.

The engine designation number is used throughout this manual. Therefore, when working on the fuel, ignition or other system, including the engine, the designation number is used to give the reader confidence she/he is following the proper procedure for the engine being serviced.

MODEL	Years Of Production
Super Jet 650	1992-1993
Super Jet 700	1994-1997
WaveRunner	1991-1992
WaveRunner III 700	1992-1997
VXR 650 & PROVXR 700	1993
WaveRunner 700	1993-1995
WaveRaider 700	1996
WaveRaider Deluxe	1994-1995
WaveRaider 1100	1995-1996
WaveBlaster 700	1994-1995
WaveBlaster 700	1996-1997
WaveBlaster II	1996-1997
WaveVenture 760	1995-1997
WaveVenture 1100	1995-1997
GP 760	1997
GP 1200	1997

OTHER SELOC PERSONAL WATERCRAFT MANUALS

This manual is one in a series covering personal watercraft. Manuals covering models produced through 1991 include:

Volume I -- Kawasaki Jet Skis -- thru 1991
Volume IA -- Kawasaki -- 1992 thru 1997
Volume II -- Bombardier Sea-Doo -- thru 1991
Volume IIA -- Bombardier Sea-Doo -- 1992 thru 1997
Volume III -- Yamaha, Jet-N-Cat and other Cuyuna powered craft including Aqua-Jet, SOS TideRider, Fazer, Fazer II, Scram Jet and Wet Jet -- thru 1991
Volume IIIA -- This manual
Volume IV -- Polaris -- 1992 thru 1997

1-2 PRINCIPLES OF OPERATION

One of the first lessons to be learned in any elementary physics class is Newton's basic law: "for every force, there is an opposite and equal force". This statement is the basic principle of the jet pump. Water is "sucked" and "scooped" in from under the craft by a powerful pump rotating at incredible speed and then discharged, "blown" out, sternward in the opposite direction. In this manner the watercraft is propelled forward.

The personal watercraft covered in this manual are equipped with either a single or twin cylinder water cooled two-stroke engine, matched with a single stage (one impeller) jet pump.

On a very few models, a "gate" is swung down over the pump outlet nozzle forcing the exhausted water back in a forward direction, thus moving the craft sternward.

Personal watercraft jet pumps may be classified as "axial flow" or "mixed flow".

Axial Flow

Water in an axial pump moves on a single axis, as depicted in the adjacent illustration, thus the word "axial". In simple terms, water is ingested and discharged parallel to the axis of impeller rotation. Some manufacturers classify their units as "axial flow" while others with virtually the same water movement label the unit as "mixed flow".

The inside of the impeller housing is parallel to the water flow. Therefore, this

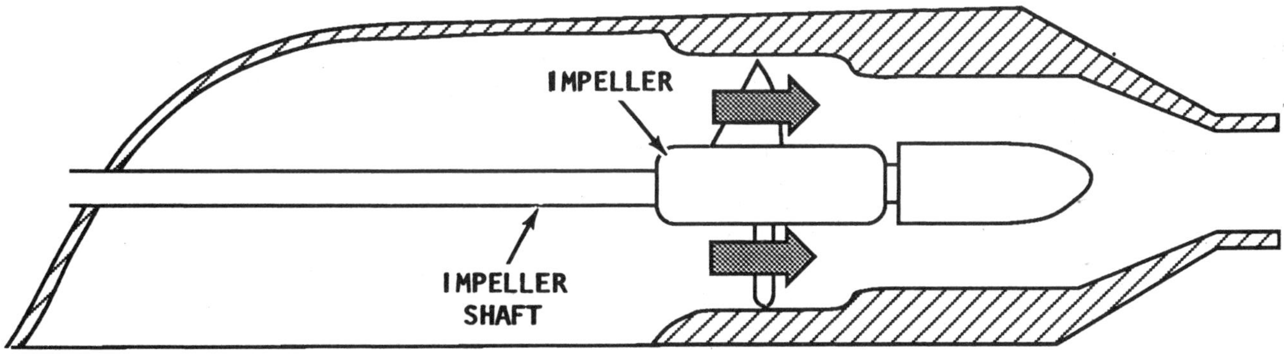

Cross-section line drawing to depict water flow through an axial flow jet pump. The water passes through parallel to the axis of impeller rotation.

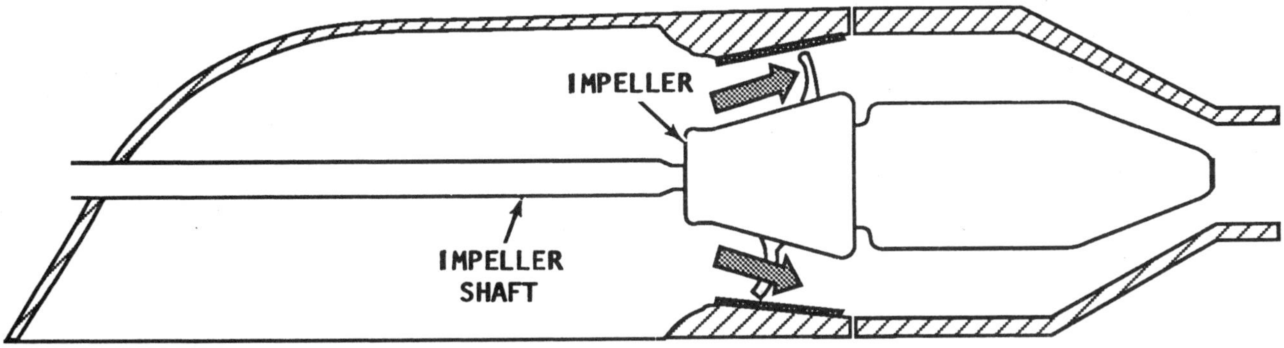

Cross-section line drawing to depict water flow through an mixed flow jet pump. Notice how the water is directed upward at an angle to the axis of impeller rotation.

design pump needs no liner against the impeller housing, as in the case of a mixed flow pump.

Mixed Flow

Many experts consider the mixed flow system to be the most efficient for personal watercraft application. The water flow is discharged at an inclined angle to the axis of impeller rotation, as indicated by the arrows in the accompanying illustration. The impeller blades are inclined in such a manner to cause the water to be thrown off at a 45° angle to the impeller shaft within the impeller duct. From the duct, the water is then forced out through the nozzle housing and nozzle. The vanes in the impeller duct help straighten the water flow through the nozzle.

The inside of the impeller housing is inclined at an angle to the water flow. Therefore, this design pump incorporates a liner against the impeller housing and shim material to space the impeller blades at a specified distance from the liner. Mixed flow pump efficiency decreases by 30% as blade-to-liner clearance increases by 0.04" (1mm).

Axial or Mixed Flow?

Axial and mixed flow pumps are intended for different applications. One is not necessarily better than the other. The axial pump can be operated at higher engine rpm and is more suitable for racing. A mixed flow pump adds thrust for low engine rpm due to the pump design. Therefore, the mixed flow pump performs more efficiently at low engine rpm and is more suitable for a craft equipped to carry extra weight.

In recent years, Yamaha has moved exclusively to the axial pump, and today all their watercraft have an axial pump installed.

A jet pump seldom requires service except for the following:

Impeller-to-liner clearance becomes excessive -- mixed flow only.

Impeller is damaged.

The oil seal around the impeller shaft fails -- allowing water to enter the hull.

1-3 ENGINE AND JET DRIVE

The basic principle and arrangement of engine and pump are almost identical for all manufacturers.

The engine crankshaft is coupled either directly to the pump shaft or through a short driveshaft without any gear reduction. An impeller mounted on the pump shaft draws water into an opening in the hull through a suction and intake casting. Once the craft has attained forward motion, the intake also serves as a "scoop" adding to the volume of water moved through the pump.

Volume and Velocity

The impeller duct is slightly funnel shaped. This design coupled with the capacity of the pump (impeller) causes the volume of water entering the pump to exit the nozzle with increased velocity. This principle is similar to air passing through the venturi of a carburetor.

The amount of water ejected sternward from the nozzle at high velocity is the force propelling the craft through the water. This force can actually be measured and calculated in foot pounds or Newton meters. The greater the velocity of water mass moving through the nozzle, the greater the thrust to move the craft.

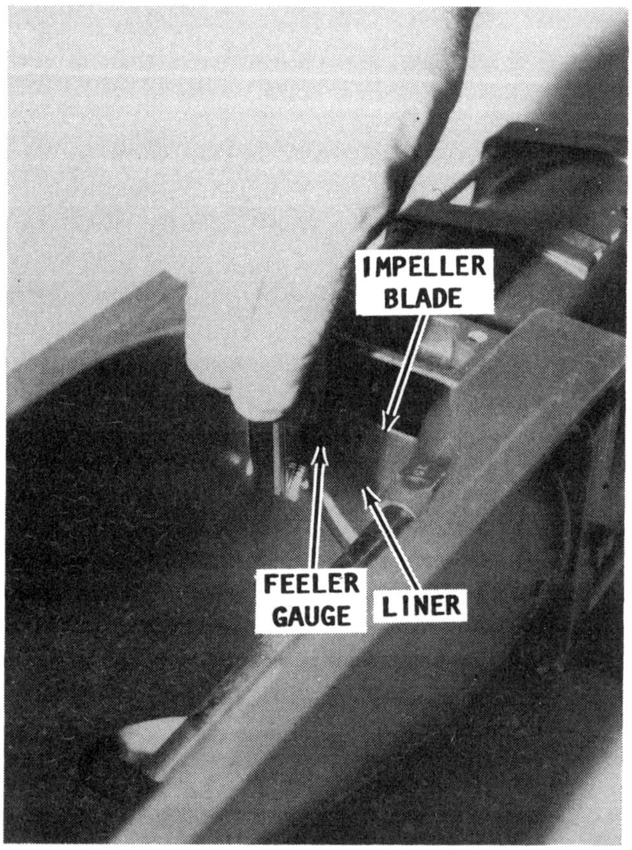

Checking the impeller-to-liner clearance on a mixed flow Yamaha jet pump.

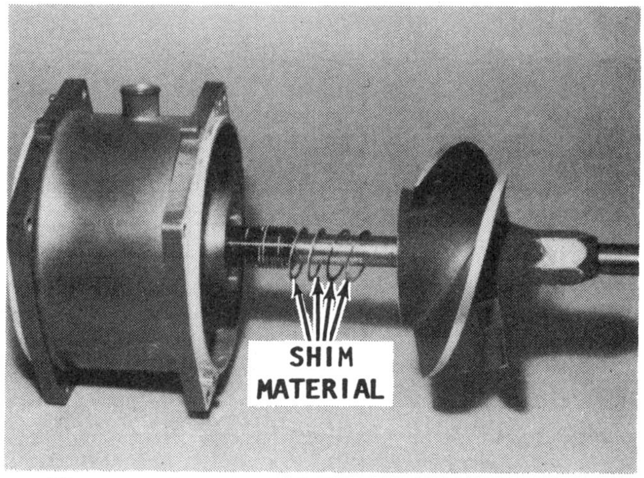

The correct amount of shim material placed on the shaft between the impeller and housing, provides the specified blade-to-liner clearance.

1-4 IMPELLERS

Impellers provide thrust using a combination of water flow and water pressure in a closed environment.

The blades of an impeller overlap, thus water is trapped and forced through the impeller into the duct and nozzle. The water moving past the impeller resists cavitation because it is under pressure. Blades in the impeller duct are angled exactly opposite to those of the impeller. These duct blades redirect the water to establish a concentrated flow through the nozzle. The shape of the duct also aids in funneling the flow through the nozzle.

The vanes, which are an integral part of the housing, redirect the water flow -- parallel to the pump shaft.

The design and overlap of the impeller blades is the working feature of a jet pump. The blades force the water through the housing under pressure. The taper of the nozzle increases water flow velocity, in much the same manner as air passing through the venturi of a carburetor.

Cavitation Burns

Cavitation burns are the worst enemy of an impeller. These burns literally "eat away" material from the impeller, leaving holes and weakening the impeller structure. In extreme cases entire blades have been known to "depart" from the impeller hub because the cavitation burns at the base of the blade were so severe.

Cavitation burns are the result of imperfections (damage) on the impeller blades or air mixed with the water flow.

IMPELLER WORDS

The leading edge of each impeller blade should be checked at regular intervals. Ideally, the edge should be rounded to a 1/32" radius, **NOT** a knife-edge! The cross-section shape of an impeller blade is similar to that of an airplane wing.

If the craft is consistently operated in shallow water with a sandy or "pebbly" bottom, the leading edge of the impeller blades will become rounded or will become chipped with missing pieces.

Very little material may be removed from the impeller blades during reconditioning work. Therefore, if the edge is rounded off or corroded, a file can be carefully used to "dress" the edge.

If an impeller blade is chipped more than 1/4", the impeller should be replaced. Any chip smaller than 1/4" can be evenly filed away along the length of the blade. Whatever work is done to one blade must be done to all blades in order to maintain impeller balance. If the impeller becomes excessively out of balance, a definite vibration condition will be quite noticeable as the craft moves through the water. Such vibration will also cause premature bearing and shaft wear.

Cavitation burns are caused by:

- Wave jumping - air is sucked into the pump as the craft leaves the surface of the water.
- Bad seals between the impeller and intake housings -- allowing air to enter.
- Leading edge of the impeller is damaged.

To explain exactly what causes cavitation burns, first, let us examine the last cause. If the impeller leading edge is damaged and "mushrooms" over the blade, a low pressure area will form under the mushroomed lip.

At atmospheric pressure, water boils at 212°F. Anytime there is an imperfection on the surface of an impeller blade and water passes over that imperfection, the water pressure is lowered. If the pressure is lowered, water will boil at a much lower temperature. Therefore, air bubbles will form in the water boiling under the mushroomed lip. The bubbles will creep down the surface of the blade and accumulate at the impeller hub. A high pressure area is formed at the base of the blade. Here, the air bubbles will collapse and reform back into water with a release of energy. This energy is absorbed by the impeller and results in material being eaten away.

The impeller should be dressed to a slightly rounded edge. It is impossible to achieve a perfectly straight sharp edge, as one side will always be convex and the other side concave. The concave side will form an area of low pressure and encourage cavitation as described above.

The other two causes of cavitation -- defective seals and wave jumping -- occurrs when air is sucked in with the water flow. The same principles apply, as just described. Air bubbles will creep down the surface of the blade and accumulate at the impeller hub. A high pressure area is formed at the base of the blade. Here, the air bubbles will collapse and reform back into water with a release of energy. This energy is absorbed by the impeller and results in material being eaten away.

Cooling Water and Bilge Hoses

On most pumps, two hoses are attached to the jet pump housing or ride plate. One hose channels some of the water flowing

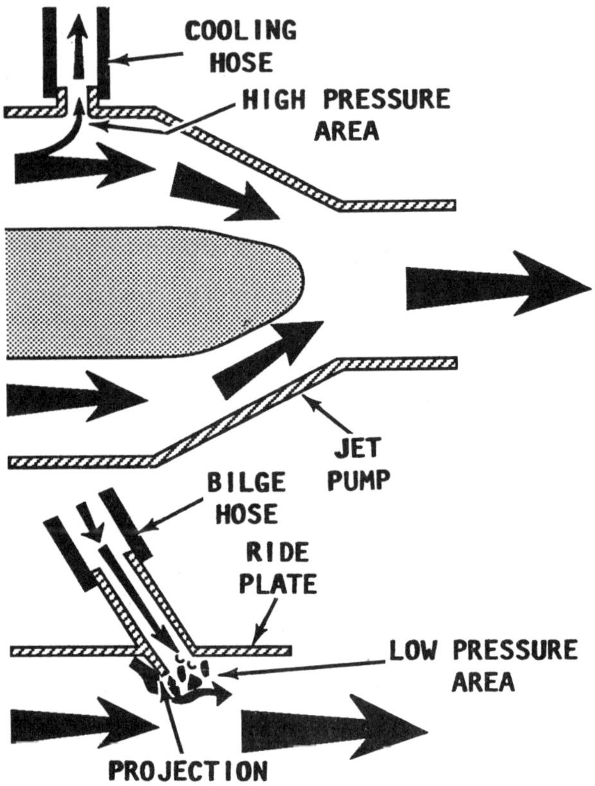

The cooling hose routes water from the pump to the engine. The bilge hose "vacuums" water from the bilge to the pump. The direction of water flow in these two hoses is opposite, as explained in the text.

through the pump to the exhaust manifold -- the hottest part of the engine -- to cool the block during operation. The other hose siphons water out of the bottom of the hull, and is referred to as the bilge system. The cooling hose has water flowing **FROM** the pump. The bilge hose has water flowing **TO** the pump. Both hoses attach in a similar manner.

What determines the direction of water flow?

The answer to this question is in a simple explanation of high and low pressure areas along the surface of the housing or casting, in contact with the water flow.

Close inspection of the area inside the housing at the cooling water hose fitting reveals a smooth rounded shoulder with no obstruction or obstacle to impede the flow of water. A high pressure area develops here and draws the water down the hose attached to the fitting.

Further inspection of the casting at the bilge hose fitting reveals a small protrusion around the opening. This protrusion causes disturbance to the water flow and creates an area of low pressure. This low pressure area will have the effect of emptying air and water from the hose aft with the impeller water flow -- similar to the action of a vacuum cleaner, as depicted in the accompanying illustration. If the other end of the hose is submerged in water inside the hull, the water will be "vacuumed" out. In this manner, the bilge system drains the bilge.

Many an owner -- with good intentions -- thinking his action would smooth water flow and increase pump performance -- has filed the protrusion described in the previous paragraph smooth with the surrounding area of the housing or casting surface. During operation of the water craft, the bilge system worked in **REVERSE.** Water was pumped from the impeller housing into the bilge area, quickly filling bilge and sinking the craft before the rider had time to realize what was happening.

1-5 REPLACEABLE PARTS

Any time the engine or jet pump is disassembled, all manufacturers and the authors heartily recommend all parts included in an overhaul kit be installed. An engine kit usually includes all gaskets, seals, O-rings, and other parts required to rebuild the engine. Pistons, rings, bearings, crankshafts and even blocks should be inspected to determine if they are fit for further service. The pump kits usually include all gaskets, seals, O-rings, and other parts required to restore full efficiency and "like new" condition to the jet pump unit.

1-6 DEBRIS REMOVAL AND ENGINE OVERHEATING

As may be expected, a clogged impeller will slow the craft. The volume of water passing through the nozzle and water velocity will be reduced. A clogged impeller may cause restricted cooling water through the engine.

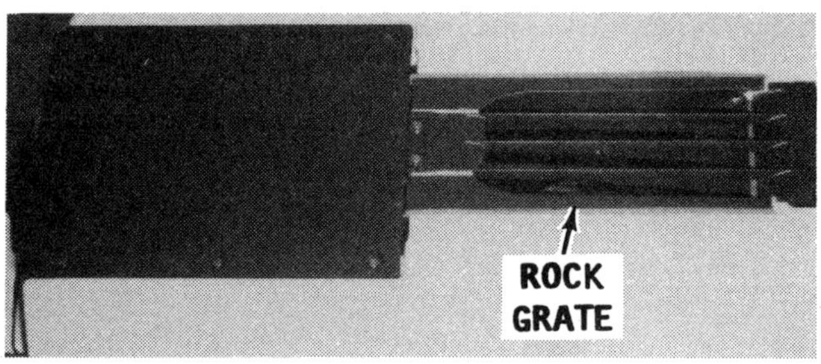

Any obstruction, such as a plastic bag, sucked up against the rock grate will drastically restrict water volume to the pump. A reduction in water flow affects craft performance and may quickly lead to a serious engine overheating condition.

Many times the cooling water supply hose, if not properly secured with a hose clamp, may "blow off". The engine loses its supply of cooling water and internal damage quickly occurs.

Some units are equipped with an over-heating warning horn. If the horn sounds, **SHUT DOWN** the engine immediately and remove the restriction or check the cooling hose connection.

Caution must be exercised when moving the craft off a beach to avoid sucking in mud, sand, pebbles, or rocks through the intake. Such ingestion could cause damage to the impeller, the vanes in the impeller duct, or clog engine cooling passages.

The engine cooling passages must be flushed with clear water on a regular basis. This is accomplished by simply connecting a garden hose to the cooling water hose or fitting on the manifold, if so equipped. Such an easy maintenance practice should become a habit and will prevent accumulation of debris which could restrict engine coolant water flow and cause overheating.

1-7 REVERSE CAPABILITY WAVEVENTURE WAVERUNNER III GP

As mentioned earlier, a gate is installed in such a manner to swing down over the discharge nozzle. The gate is controlled with a cable.

When the gate is in the fully raised position, allowing all water from the nozzle to be discharged sternward -- the craft moves forward.

When the gate is swung down just part way, some of the discharged water moves sternward and the other portion of water is deflected downward and forward under the craft. Positioning the gate in such a manner places the jet pump in a **NEUTRAL** condition, because the water moving aft equals the water moving forward and the craft is static ("dead in the water").

When the gate is moved to the full down position, virtually all discharged water from the nozzle is deflected down and forward -- the craft moves sternward.

Adjustment of the reverse cable is covered in Chapter 11, Control Adjustments.

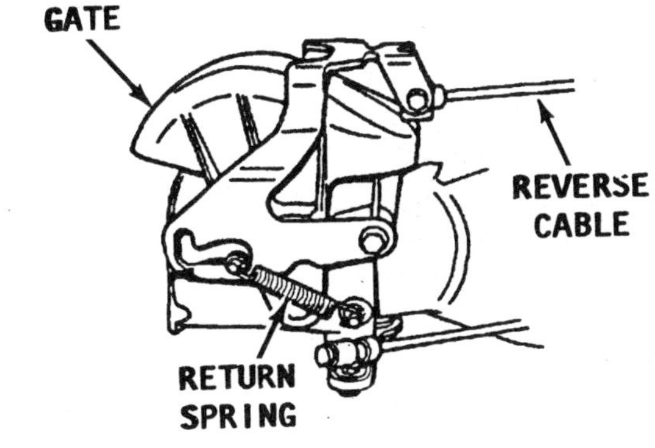

The reverse gate control arrangement on a Yamaha WaveRunner III and Jet-N-Cat III.

1-8 TEST TANKS

Many times the performance of tune-up tasks, or adjustments are called for while the craft is in the water with the engine running. With an outboad or a stern drive, the mechanic always has the boat between him/her and the wet stuff. On a personal watercraft, this is impossible without getting into the water, unless a test tank is used.

The advantages of using a test tank are:

To simulate actual water conditions. The craft may be operated without an exhaust extraction pipe and without using an auxiliary cooling water supply.

To test the engine at high rpm, placing a load on the impeller.

To reveal water leaks in the engine compartment and hull.

To uncover exhaust leaks.

To identify fuel leaks.

To detect engine noises.

To perform carburetor adjustments.

To check for bad impellers -- slippage.

To spot problems which might occur only after running for say 30 minutes, therefore, prevent being stranded in the middle of a lake or far from shore if a serious malfunction should occur.

The only problem a test tank cannot help diagnose is a craft handling problem.

The accompanying illustration depicts the type of test tank manufacturers use, with **approximate** dimensions. This type of tank is partially sunk into the ground. The craft sits in a body of circulating water and the mechanic has access to both sides of the craft without getting wet and has a dry place for tools etc.

The tank design with an island in the center allows water to circulate around the tank. With no circulation the water would

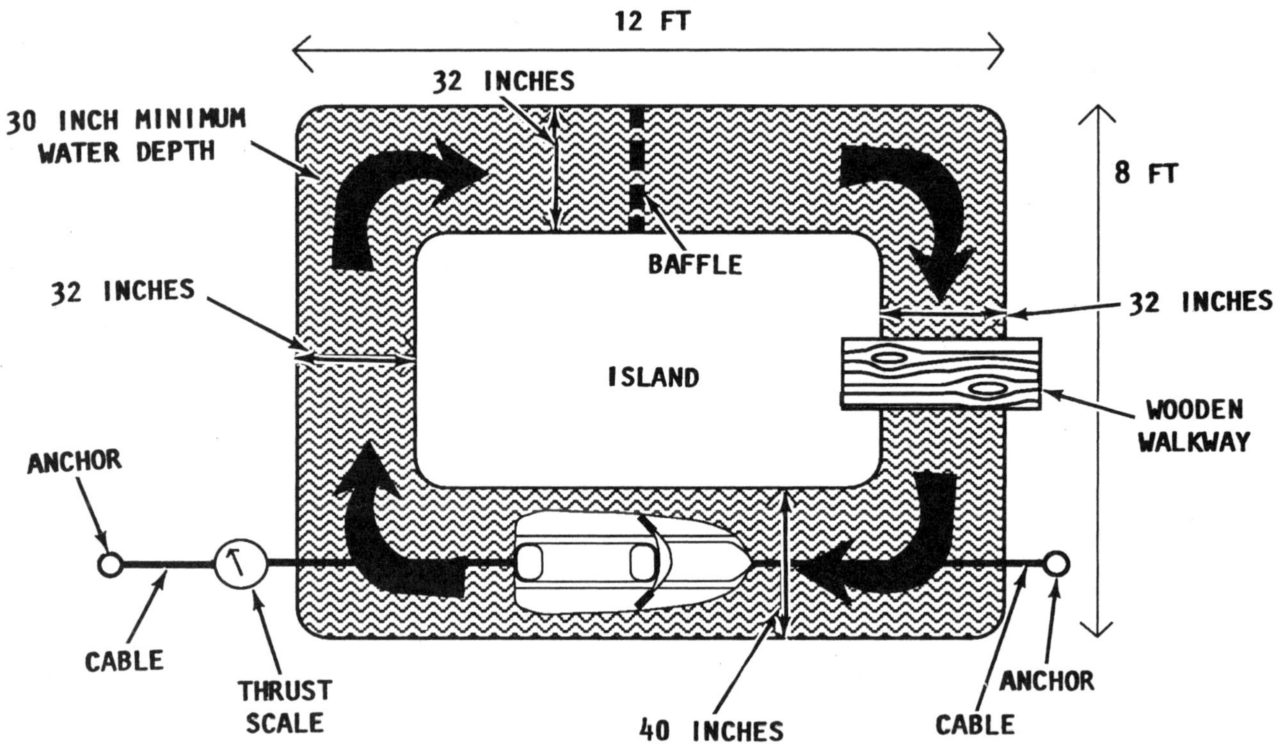

Layout of a typical test tank for testing personal watercraft. Such a tank is most valuable in verifying the completed work following service on the engine or the pump. The tank is described in detail on this and the facing page.

foam and the jet pump would cavitate and loose thrust. A series of baffle plates installed on the opposite side to the craft, slow and straighten the water flow. The walls must be strong enough to hold the weight of the water and to contain the thrust of the pump, but coated to seal the walls and not scratch the sides of the craft.

The bow is secured with a stout line anchored to the edge of the tank to prevent the craft from "wandering". The stern is secured to the opposite edge of the tank to prevent the craft from moving forward. A thrust scale is sometimes attached to the stern line to determine the thrust exerted by the pump.

Seek out dealers with a test tank and attempt to use/rent their facilities to test the completed work.

"Pride of ownership" is certainly reflected in the condition of this Yamaha Personal Watercraft.

1-9 THROTTLE LIMITER

Some manufacturers have equipped their craft with a device to limit throttle opening. If the owner wishes to limit craft speed when on loan to a novice rider, a throttle limiter, next to the twist grip on the handlebar, may be adjusted for this purpose.

Loosen the bolt and slide the lever on the throttle limiter down to the desired position, then tighten the bolt to hold the adjustment.

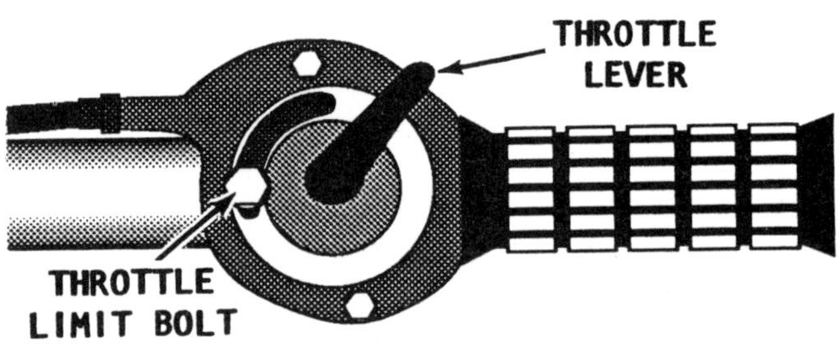

A throttle limiter device may be employed to limit engine rpm and thus craft speed.

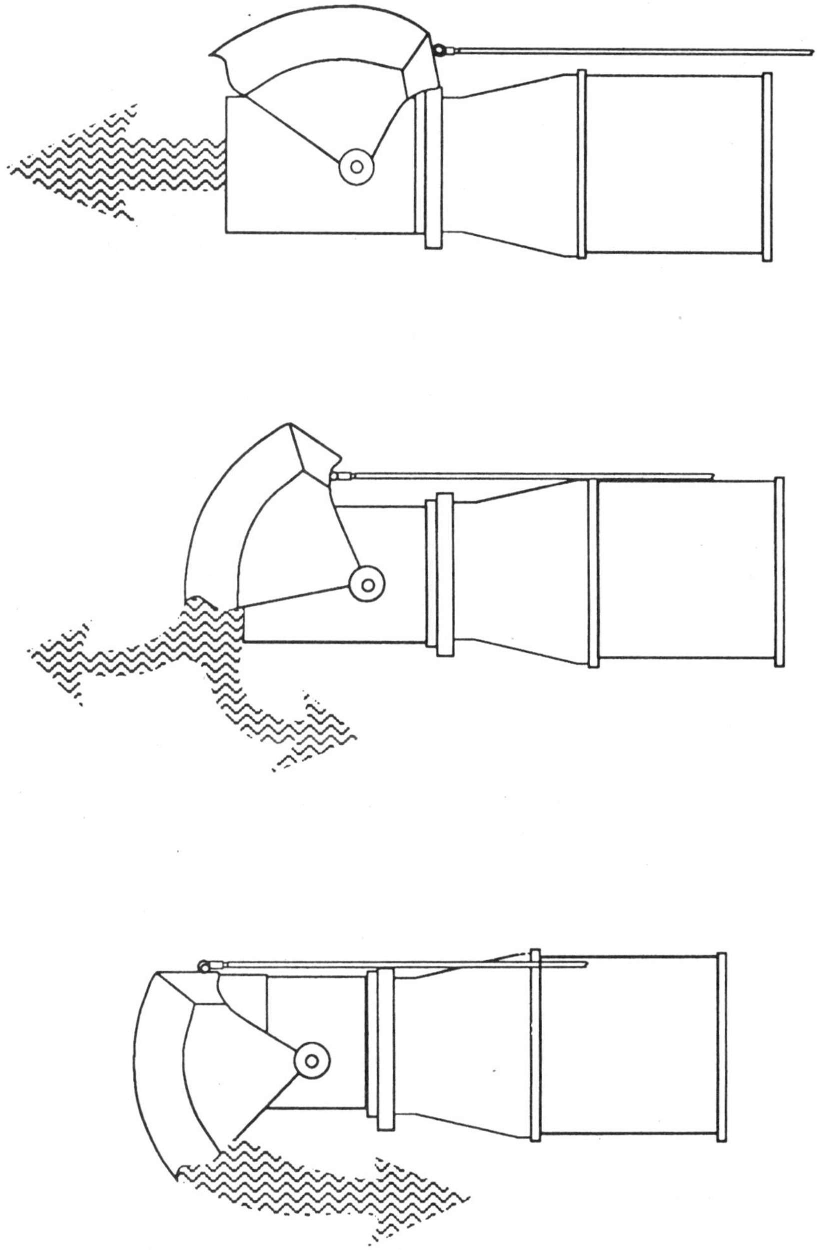

Simple line drawings to illustrate water flow from the nozzle with the reverse gate in the full ***FORWARD*** *position (top), in the* ***NEUTRAL*** *position (center), and in full* ***REVERSE*** *(bottom).*

FUNPIX2

2 SAFETY

2-1 INTRODUCTION

Personal watercrafting is one of the fastest growing leisure activites in the world. Riding a personal watercraft can be an exciting, exhilarating, and safe experience provided the operator exercises prudent behavior and remains in constant control of the vehicle.

Personal watercraft may be likened to a firearm. Weapons do not injure people, but the individual handling them is the true culprit. In a similar manner, if the personal watercraft is operated in an unresponsible manner the driver, passengers, and others using the same waterway may be in danger.

The greatest hazard in operating a personal watercraft stems not from the craft itself, but from the behavior of the operator. The Personal Watercraft Industry Association (PWIA) and the National Marine Manufacturers Association (NMMA) recognize there are a number of problems due to irresponsible craft operators contributing to tarnishment of the sport. Specifically, these problems range from alcohol and substance abuse to excessive noise, speed, and reckless maneuvering. Insensitive operators can disrupt an otherwise enjoyable day for other craft users through misconduct on the water. These individuals often endanger their own lives as well as the lives of others by losing full control of their craft.

Organized events, races, and exhibitions, properly planned and controlled have proven to be a spectacular event appealing to a wide range and number of participants and spectators.

Craft Classification

Any craft equipped with propulsion machinery is classified as a motorboat.

Personal watercraft are classified as "Class A inboard boats" by the Coast Guard and therefore are subject to most of the same laws and requirements as more conventional larger craft. A decal, usually affixed somewhere in the stern area, lists exceptions the Coast Guard has granted for this type of water vehicle.

Information

In 1989, several states recognized the need to impose specific regulations governing operation of personal watercraft. Rules and regulations differ from state to state and are constantly being revised. Therefore, it would be an impossible task to present current legislation on personal watercraft activites. Before the printing ink for this publication was dry, additions, deletions, and revisions would already be in effect.

For current information, the reader may call 1-800-336-BOAT for the name and ad-

Personal watercraft heading down the channel toward "open" water and a fun day with the waves at sea. This couple is conscientious of the 5 mph speed and "no wake" restrictions in the harbor area. Obviously they are also aware of other safety rules by wearing life jackets.

dress of the local Boating Law Administrator. The reader may also contact the PWIA Government Relations Representative, Washington, D.C.

Regulation Enforcement

The U.S. Coast Guard and state enforcement officers have the authority to stop any craft to check for compliance with federal or state law. They can order a craft to return to the closest dock and remain out of the water until the hazardous condition of the craft is corrected.

Examples are:

Inadequate number of Personal Flotation Devices.

Missing/Inoperative fire extinguisher.

Overloading.

Operation at night without proper lights.

Fuel leakage.

Fuel transportation (other than approved fuel tank).

Failure to meet ventilation requirements.

Failure to meet carburetor backfire flame arrestor requirements.

Excessive leakage or accumulation of water in the bilge.

The U.S. Coast Guard and state enforcement officers have the authority to stop any craft if they determine the craft is being operated in a negligent manner. Negligent operation is defined as "the failure to excercise the degree of care necessary to prevent the endangering of life, limb, or property of any person".

Examples are:

Operating while under the influence of drugs or alcohol.

Excessive speed in a congested area.

Excessive speed in stormy or foggy conditions.

Coming too close to another vessel.

Operating in a swimming area where bathers are present.

Towing water skiers where obstructions exist or where a fall might cause skier to be struck by another vessel.

Operating in the vicinity of a dam.

Cutting through a marine parade or regatta.

2-2 MINIMUM LEGAL REQUIREMENTS FOR EQUIPMENT ONBOARD CRAFT

All personal watercraft owners **MUST** provide the following equipment:

One approved Type I, II, III or IV PFD (personal flotation device) for each person on board or being towed on water skis, etc.

An efficient sound producing device.

A B-I approved hand portable fire extinquisher.

Visual distress signals for nighttime use, if operated on coastal waters.

Personal Flotation Devices (PFDs)

The Coast Guard requires an approved life-saving device be worn by each person on board. Devices approved are identified by a tag indicating Coast Guard approval. Such devices may be life preservers, or buoyant vests. Ring buoys, or buoyant cushions are not acceptable.

Life preservers have been classified by the Coast Guard into five type categories. All PFDs presently acceptable on recreational craft fall into one of these five designations. Only four of the five catagories are stipulated by legal requirements. Type V is not acceptable for use on a personal watercraft.

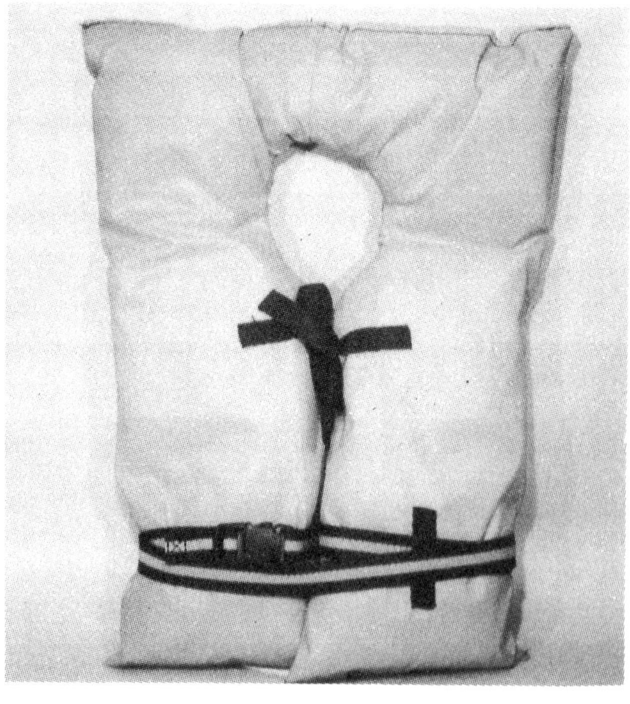

Type I PFD Coast Guard approved life jacket. This type flotation device provides the greatest amount of buoyancy.

A Type III PFD requires the wearer to be active to remain upright in the water. This type device is comfortable and allows the wearer to actually swim while in the water.

A PFD **MUST** be U.S. Coast Guard approved, in good and serviceable condition, and of an appropriate size for the person intending to wear it.

It is an accepted fact that most boating people own life preservers, but too few actually wear them. There is little or no excuse for not wearing one because the modern comfortable designs available today do not subtract from an individual's boating pleasure.

PFDs may have a long serviceable life, if proper care is exercised and the device is not abused. Wipe them clean and dry before storing in a well ventilated area during the off-season. **NEVER** use a PFD as a fender. A crushed PFD loses its buoyancy and becomes useless.

Type I PFD has the greatest required buoyancy and is designed to turn most **UNCONSCIOUS** persons in the water from a face down position to a vertical or slightly backward position. The adult size device provides a minimum buoyancy of 22 pounds and the child size provides a minimum buoyancy of 11 pounds. The Type I PFD provides the greatest protection to its wearer and is most effective for all waters and conditions.

Type II PFD is designed to turn its wearer in a vertical or slightly backward position in the water. The turning action is not as pronounced as with a Type I. The device will not turn as many different type persons under the same conditions as the Type I. An adult size device provides a minimum buoyancy of 15½ pounds, the medium child size provides a minimum of 11 pounds, and the infant and small child sizes provide a minimum buoyancy of 7 pounds.

Type III PFD is designed to permit the wearer to place himself (herself) in a vertical or slightly backward position. The Type III device has the same buoyancy as the Type II PFD but it has little or no turning ability. Many of the Type III PFD are designed to be particularly useful when water skiing, sailing, hunting, fishing, or engaging in other water sports. Several of this type will also provide increased hypothermia protection.

Type IV PFD is designed to be thrown to a person in the water and grasped and held by the user until rescued. It is **NOT** designed to be worn. The most common Type IV PFD is a ring buoy or a buoyant cushion.

ONE LAST WORD

Common sense dictates the "cheap and cheerful" approach does not pay when applied to a life preserving device. Select and buy the very best. The life you save may be your own.

NOW, THESE WORDS

Due to the nature and maneuvering characteristics of personal watercraft, and from a "practical" standpoint, the following paragraph on bells, horns, and whistles hardly apply. The information is included to make the manual "complete" and because according to the U.S. Coast Guard they are required. Also, the authors feel the reader may "skipper" or "crew" on a larger craft and therefore, might be required to use the information presented here.

Bells, Horns and Whistles

All craft must carry some means of producing an efficient sound signal and the sound must be audible for a specific distance and duration, depending on the size of the craft. For personal watercraft, an audible sound must carry for one half mile and be of four to six second duration.

Law enforcement craft are the **ONLY** boats allowed to use sirens.

Personal watercraft operators are required to sound fog and maneuvering signals when underway in fog or rain as a means of communication between craft which are not visible. This system was devised to alert nearby craft of the presence of others in the water and as a means of communicating maneuvering intentions. Signals indicating maneuvering tactics are short one second blasts.

One blast indicates the craft is turning to starboard.
Two blasts indicate the craft is turning to port.

Three blasts indicate the craft is in reverse.
Five or more blasts indicate - stay away - danger.

A prolonged blast lasting 4 to 6 seconds duration every two minutes indicates a straight line course in poor visibility.

These signals should be memorised by every personal watercraft operator, not necessarily because the operator would give them, but in the event of a head on collision with say a large powerboat, the skipper may

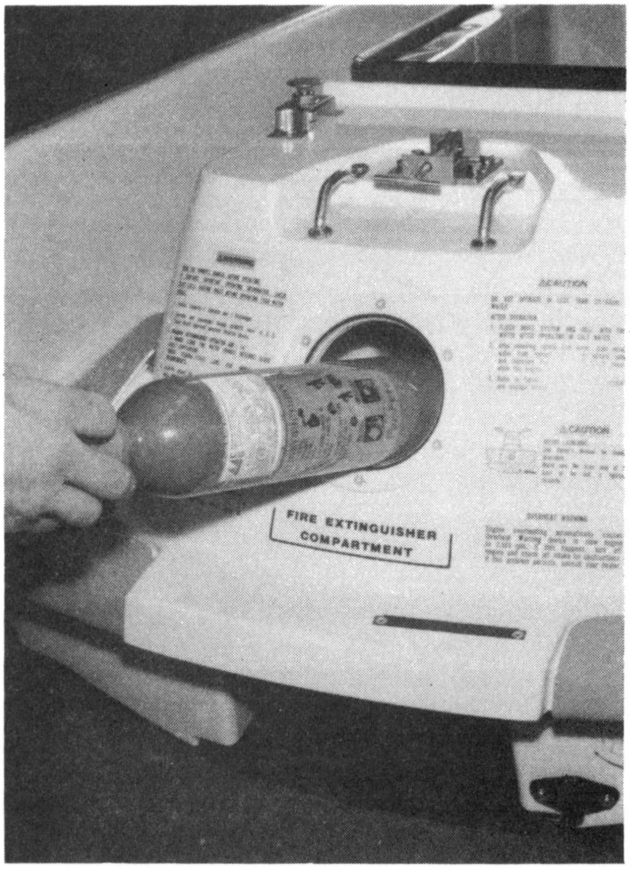

Personal watercraft are required to carry a type B-1 fire extinguisher aboard. The compartment is almost always in the stern, as shown. where it is readily available.

signal his intention to turn either to port or starboard using this system of communication.

Fire Extinguishers

Personal watercraft are classified as "Class A inboard boats" by the Coast Guard and therefore are required to carry a B-I fire extinguisher.

All fire extinguishers must bear Underwriters Laboratory (UL) "Marine Type" approved labels. With the UL certification, the extinguisher does not have to have a Coast Guard approval number.

B-I contains 1-1/4 gallons foam, or 4 pounds carbon dioxide, or 2 pounds dry chemical agent, or 2-1/2 pounds Halon.

READ labels on fire extinguishers. If the extinguisher is U.L. listed, it is approved for marine use.

Any personal watercraft can be rolled over and held under water for a few seconds to extinguish the fire. Turning the craft over in the water will prevent oxygen from entering the engine compartment. Without oxygen, the fire will soon exhaust the remaining oxygen in the compartment and then go out. **DO NOT** open the engine compartment until the smoke has completely stopped, then open with great caution and have a fire extinguisher at hand.

Visual Distress Signals

Coast Guard Regulations require personal watercraft to carry night visual distress signals when used on coastal waters - even though it is illegal to operate a personal watercraft at night.

Coastal waters include: the Great Lakes, the territorial seas and those waters directly connected to the Great Lakes and the territorial seas, up to a point where the waters are less than two miles wide.

These signals assist rescuers in locating and aiding people in distress. This information is useful to every personal watercraft owner, to know how to respond to others in distress.

For night use: Pyrotechnic visual distress signaling devices (red flares, hand held or aerial) **MUST** be Coast Guard Approved, in serviceable condition and stowed to be readily accessible. If they are marked with a date showing the serviceable life, this date must not have passed.

Coast Guard Approved pyrotechnic devices carry an expiration date. This date can **NOT** exceed 42 months from the date of manufacture and at such time the device can no longer be counted toward the minimum requirements.

The only non-pyrotechnic visual distress signaling device approved by the coast guard for use at night is an electric distress light -- not a flashlight but an approved electric distress light which **MUST** automatically flash the international **SOS** distress signal (. . . - - - . . .)four to six times each minute.

2-3 MINIMUM LEGAL REQUIREMENTS FOR REGISTRATION OF CRAFT

Federal regulations require all personal watercraft to be issued a registration number and have the number displayed in a specific manner on the craft.

The "Certificate of Number" is issued by the state and must be carried on board at all times. The Hull Identification Number (HIN) is necessary to register the craft with the state.

The registration number must be displayed as follows:

The figures must be read from left to right.

The figures must be displayed on the forward half of each side of the bow of the craft.

The figures must be in bold, block letters of good proportion and must not be less than 3 inches high.

The figures must be of contrasting color to the craft hull, or background.

The figures must be as high above the waterline as practical.

No figures other than those assigned to the craft can be displayed on the forward half of the craft.

Letters must be separated from numbers by spaces or hyphens.

Validation decals (if required by state) must be displayed within 6 inches of the registration number.

Elaborate color schemes and custom detailing are very much a part of the fun of owning a personal watercraft. **HOWEVER,** the paint design must not obstruct the registration numbers or the validation decal. Like an automobile without a license plate, sooner or later a craft with no visible registration numbers will attract the attention of the law.

Hull Identification Number

Federal regulations require all personal watercraft to have a Hull Identification Number (HIN) permanently attached to the craft in two separate locations: on the starboard side of the transom, above the waterline. The HIN must also be displayed in an unexposed location, which is usually left to the discretion of the manufacturer.

2-4 SAFETY PRACTICES

Riding Techniques

Of all watercraft, large and small, the personal watercraft are the most responsive to steering and maneuverability. Therefore, a personal watercraft operator should take it upon herself/himself to stay clear of other boaters and especially swimmers.

A beginner should operate the craft at a low speed until the operator feels comfortable and is aware of its limitations and responses to steering.

While riding the craft, keep feet, hands, hair, and clothing away from the pump intake.

Full Throttle Operation

Prolonged operation at full throttle will raise the cylinder head temperature by

The validation decal, required by most states, and the registration number, required by all states, must be displayed port and starboard on the forward portion of the hull.

about 100° above normal. Some units are equipped with a thermo-switch engine temperature sensor. This sensor is connected directly to the CDI unit and grounded to the engine kill switch. If the engine temperature exceeds a maximum value specifed by the manufacturer, the ignition will be grounded and the engine shut down to prevent damage through overheating.

Jumping Waves

In the very early days of personal watercraft, jumping could cause extensive internal engine damage. When the craft left the water, unchecked engine rpm rapidly increased to as high as 12,000 rpm. As soon as the craft re-entered the water, engine rpm instantly decreased to about 6,000 rpm. This sudden increase and decrease in engine speed dramatically shortened engine life. In those days, repeated jumps were known to cause bent crankshafts, sheared flywheel keys, and broken connecting rods.

Yamaha engineers developed an rpm limiter system as an integral part of the CDI unit. This limiter prevents high engine rpm and an almost "runaway" condition, during wave or ramp jumping. On "stock", out the door factory units, this limiter restricts engine speed to about 7100 rpm. Thus, wave jumping, using a ramp, and a host of other almost unbelievable manuevers can be performed without undue stress on the engine. Today, with an rpm limiter system installed, a bent crankshaft or broken connecting rod is almost non-existent.

Several decals may be affixed to the stern of the hull to indicate compliance with or exceptions granted to normal Coast Guard regulations.

Alcohol and Substance Use

Operating a personal watercraft while under the influence of either alcohol or drugs is both illegal and life threatening. This fact cannot be stated too strongly. Such substances affect vision and slow reaction times. The danger is quadrupled in a craft on the water compared to on the shore.

Age Restrictions

Children under 14 years of age should not operate a watercraft unless accompanied on a two passenger craft by an adult experienced operator. Specific minimum age limits have been imposed by many states.

Speed Restrictions

Where no speed limits are posted, commonsense dictates the craft should be operated so it will pose no danger to other water users or the operator. Many states now have enforced speed limits for certain areas and conditions.

When entering "no wake" or 5 mph zones, such as fishing areas, swimming areas or marinas, the operator must slow to headway speed, the slowest speed at which appropriate steering capability can be maintained.

Individuals responsible for law enforcement on the water are keeping an ever vigilant eye on personal watercraft in many areas. Horseplay such as "wetting down" or "buzzing" other water users may result in a "ticket" for negligent operation.

Operation at Night

Personal watercraft are not equipped with lights and therefore, it is illegal to operate such a craft on the water after sunset.

Shallow Water Operation

Under normal conditions, personal watercraft may be operated in very shallow waters, and it is possible to maneuver the craft directly onto a slopping beach.

Caution must be exercised when moving the craft off a beach to avoid sucking in mud, sand, pebbles, or rocks through the intake. Such ingestion could cause damage to the impeller, the vanes in the pump bowl, or clog engine cooling passages.

WARNING
Expelled sand and small pebbles may cause INJURY to persons in the area.

A grated section set into the hull bottom helps prevent the ingestion of small rocks and pebbles.

Carry about a foot of stiff wire aboard for use in probing into the impeller area to dislodge debris where fingers cannot reach.

Engine Compartment Ventilation

All motorboats (personal watercraft included) built after April 25, 1940 and before August 1, 1980, powered by a gasoline engine or by fuels having a flashpoint of 110° F or less **MUST** have the following, which is quoted from a recent Coast Guard publication:

> At least two ventilation ducts fitted with cowls or their equivalent for the purpose of properly and efficiently ventilating the bilges of every engine and fuel tank compartment. Each duct must be at least two inches in internal diameter.
>
> There shall be at least one exhaust duct installed so as to extend from the lower portion of the bilge to cowls in the open air, and at least one intake duct installed so as to extend to a point at least midway to the bilge or at least below the level of the carburetor air intake.

Flame Arrestors

A flame arrestor, as the name suggests, safeguards against flame caused by engine backfire.

A gasoline engine installed in a motorboat or motor vessel after April 25, 1940, except outboard motors, must have a Coast Guard Approved flame arrestor fitted to the carburetor. This requirement applies to personal watercraft because the engine is enclosed.

Fuel System

All parts of the fuel system should be selected and installed to provide maximum service and protection against leakage.

The capacity of the fuel filter must be large enough to handle the demands of the engine as specified by the engine manufacturer.

All fittings and outlets must come out the top of the tank.

In order to obtain maximum circulation of air around fuel tanks, the tank should not come in contact with the hull except through the necessary supports. The supporting surfaces and hold-downs must fasten the tank firmly and they should be insulated from the tank surfaces. This insulation material should be non-abrasive and non-absorbent material.

Taking On Fuel

The fuel tank should be kept almost full to allow for expansion, but still prevent water from entering the system through condensation caused by temperature changes. Water droplets forming are one of the greatest enemies of the fuel system. By keeping the tank almost full, the air space in the tank is kept to an absolute minimum and there is less room for moisture to form. It is a good practice not to store fuel in the tank over an extended period, say for six months. Today, fuels contain ingredients that change into gums when stored for any length of time. These gums and varnish products will cause carburetor problems and poor spark plug performance. An additive (Sta-Bil) is available and can be used to prevent gums and varnish from forming.

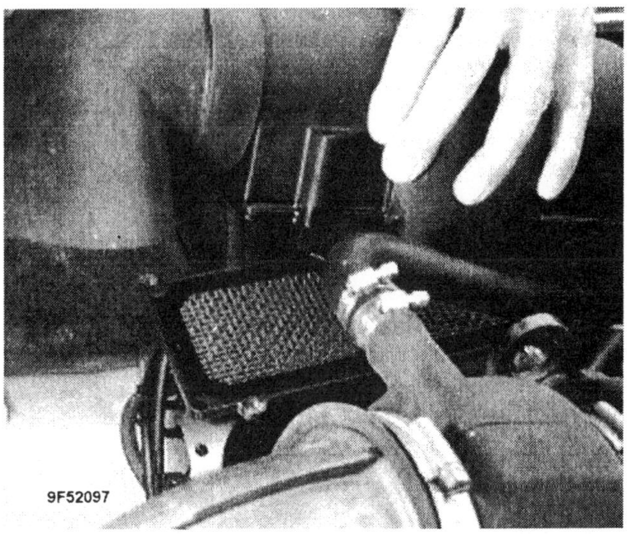

Carburetors on personal watercraft are required to be fitted with a flame arrestor because the engine compartment is an enclosed area.

Excessive Noise

Every manufacturer designs a stock exhaust system to keep noise to a minimum. A poorly maintained or modified exhaust system will produce excessive and disturbing noise. This is a form of air polution and is illegal in most states.

Automotive Replacement Parts

When replacing fuel, electrical, and other parts, check to be sure they are marine type and Coast Guard Approved. Automotive parts are not made to the high standards of marine parts. The carburetors must **NOT** leak fuel; electrical equipment **MUST** be able to operate in a gas fume enclosed area without exploding; etc. Automotive parts could cause a fire endangering the operator, passengers, and the craft. The part may look the same and even have a similar number, but if it is not **MARINE** it is not safe to use and will not pass Coast Guard inspection.

Overloading

Each personal watercraft is designed to carry a specific number of persons. Attempting to board more passangers than the craft is designed to carry, will upset weight distribution causing a marked decrease in performance and possible loss of control.

2-5 BOATING ACCIDENT REPORTS

New federal and state regulations require an accident report to be filed with the nearest state boating authority within 48 hours if a person is lost, disappears, or is injured to the degree of needing medical treatment beyond first aid. The time limit is reduced to 24 hours if the accident results in a loss of life.

Accidents involving only property or equipment damage **MUST** be reported within 10 days, if the damage is in excess of $500.00. Some states require reporting of accidents with propery damage less then $500.00 or a total boat loss. A $1,000.00 **PENALTY** may be assessed for failure to submit the report.

WORDS OF ADVICE

Take time to make a copy of the report to keep for your records or for the insurance company. Once the report is filed, the Coast Guard will not give out a copy, even to the person who filed the report.

The report must give details of the accident and include:

1- The date, time, and exact location of the occurrence.

2- The name of each person who died, was lost, or injured.

3- The number and name of the vessel.

4- The names and addresses of the owner and operator.

If the operator cannot file the report for any reason, each person on board **MUST** notify the authorities, or determine that the report has been filed.

In nautical terms, the front of the craft is the **bow**; the rear is the **stern**; the right side, when facing forward, is the **starboard** side; and the left side is the **port** side. One easy way to remember this basic fundamental is to consider the words "port" and "left" both have four letters and go together.

All directional references in this manual use this terminology. Therefore, the direction from which an item is viewed is of no consequence, because **starboard** and **port** **NEVER** change no matter where the individual is located, or standing, even on his or her head.

2-6 SECURITY

As mentioned in the opening paragraphs of this chapter, personal watercrafting is one of the fastest growing leisure activites in the world. Like most personal possessions, personal watercraft have value and valuables are subject to be lost to unscrupulous characters -- thieves. The best advice for a personal watercraft owner is "lock it or lose it".

Do not leave the craft unattended on the beach or dock. **ALWAYS** remove the kill switch tether from the switch and of course, the ignition key, if the unit is equipped with these features. Certain aftermarket security devices are available for installation to prevent theft of personal watercraft. These include: A "secret" ignition grounding switch, which grounds one side of the ignition coil, and a hidden fuel shut-off valve.

Most owners transport their craft on trailers or in the bed of a pickup truck. If loaded on a trailer, chain and lock the craft to the trailer. Invest in a hitch lock so the trailer cannot be detached from the towing vehicle. If the craft is loaded on a pickup truck, chain and lock it to the bed, or to a large and heavy object.

3
TUNING

3-1 INTRODUCTION

The efficiency, reliability, fuel economy and enjoyment available from engine performance are all directly dependent on having the engine tuned properly. The importance of performing service work in the sequence detailed in this chapter cannot be overemphasized. Before making any adjustments, check the specifications in the Appendix. **NEVER** rely on memory when making critical adjustments.

Before beginning to tune any engine, check to be sure the engine has satisfactory compression. An engine with worn or broken piston rings, burned pistons, or scored cylinder walls, cannot be made to perform properly no matter how much time and expense is spent on the tune-up. Poor compression must be corrected or the tune-up will not give the desired results.

A practical maintenance program that is followed throughout the year, is one of the best methods of ensuring the engine will give satisfactory performance at any time.

The extent of the engine tune-up is usually dependent on the time lapse since the last service. A complete tune-up of the entire engine would entail almost all of the work outlined in this manual. A logical sequence of steps will be presented in general terms. If additional information or detailed service work is required, the chapter containing the instructions will be referenced.

Each year higher compression ratios are built into modern marine engines and the electrical systems become more complex, especially with electronic (capacitor discharge) units. Therefore, the need for reliable, authoritative, and detailed instructions

this chapter and the referenced chapters fulfill that requirement.

3-2 TUNE-UP SEQUENCE

During a major tune-up, a definite sequence of service work should be followed to return the engine to the maximum performance desired. This type of work should not be confused with attempting to locate problem areas of "why" the engine is not performing satisfactorily. This work is classified as "troubleshooting". In many cases, these two areas will overlap, because many times a minor or major tune-up will correct the malfunction and return the system to normal operation.

A clean, properly tuned, and adequately maintained power unit can multiply by many fold the enjoyment derived from owning and operating a personal water-

The following list is a suggested sequence of tasks to perform during the tune-up service work. The tasks are merely listed here. In most cases, procedures are given in subsequent sections of this chapter. For more detailed instructions, see the referenced chapter, for the unit being seviced.

1- Perform a compression check of each cylinder. See Ignition Chapter.
2- Inspect the spark plugs to determine their condition. Test for adequate spark at the plug. See Ignition Chapter.
3- Start the engine in a body of water or connect a "Flushing Kit" with a garden hose and check the water flow through the engine, See Engine Chapter.
4- Check the carburetor adjustments and the need for an overhaul. See Fuel Chapter.
5- Check the fuel pump for adequate performance and delivery. See Fuel Chapter.
6- Make a general inspection of the ignition system. See Ignition Chapter.
7- Test the cranking motor and the solenoid. See Electrical Chapter.
8- Check the internal wiring.

Performing a compression test on a two cylinder engine. Both spark plug leads have been grounded to prevent placing an unnecessary extra load on the ignition coil.

3-3 COMPRESSION CHECK

A compression check is extremely important, because an engine with low or uneven compression between cylinders **CANNOT** be tuned to operate satisfactorily. Therefore, it is essential that any compression problem be corrected before proceeding with the tune-up procedure.

If the engine shows any indication of overheating, such as discolored or scorched paint, inspect the piston skirts visually thru the transfer ports, using a mirror and flashlight, for possible scoring. It is possible for a cylinder with satisfactory compression to be scored slightly.

Checking Compression

Remove the spark plug wires. **ALWAYS** grasp the molded cap and pull it loose with a twisting motion to prevent damage to the connection. Remove both spark plugs and remember from which cylinder they came for evaluation later. Ground both spark plug leads to the engine to render the ignition system inoperative while performing the compression check.

Diaphragm assembly removed from the carburetor.

Inside view of the fuel pump cover. On a triple installation, the No. 3 carburetor does not have a pump.

Insert a compression gauge into the forward spark plug opening. Crank the engine with the cranking motor, thru at least four complete revolutions of the crankshaft, with the throttle at the wide-open position, to obtain the highest possible reading. Record the highest reading. Repeat the test and record the compression for the other cylinder. The manufacturer specifies the compression pressure for a new engine should be 142.2 psi (981 kpa). A variation between cylinders is far more important than the actual readings. A variation of more than 15 psi between the two cylinders indicates the lower compression cylinder is defective. The problem may be worn, broken, or sticking piston rings, scored pistons or worn cylinders.

Use of an engine cleaner will help to free stuck rings and to dissolve accumulated carbon. Follow the directions on the can.

3-4 SPARK PLUG INSPECTION

Inspect both spark plugs for badly worn electrodes, glazed, broken, blistered, or lead fouled insulators. Replace both the plugs, if either shows signs of excessive wear.

Make an evaluation of the cylinder performance by comparing the spark condition with those shown in the Ignition Chapter. Check each spark plug to be sure they are both of the same manufacturer and have the same heat range rating.

Inspect the threads in the spark plug opening in the head and clean the threads before installing the plug.

When purchasing new spark plugs, **ALWAYS** ask the dealer if there has been a spark plug change for the engine being serviced. Set the spark plug gap to 0.020-0.024" for all models covered in this manual.

*Examples of damaged spark plugs. Notice the broken electrode of the left plug. The broken part **MUST** be found and removed before returning the engine to service to prevent the part from causing extensive and expensive damage to the engine.*

Crank the engine through several revolutions to blow out any material which might have become dislodged during cleaning.

Install the spark plugs and tighten them to a torque value of 14ft lbs (20Nm). **ALWAYS** use a new gasket and wipe the seats in the head clean. The gasket must be fully compressed on clean seats to complete the heat transfer process and to provide a gas tight seal in the cylinder. If the torque value is too high, the heat will dissipate too rapidly. Conversely, if the torque value is too low, heat will not dissipate fast enough.

BROKEN REED
(All Models)

A broken reed is usually caused by metal fatigue over a long period of time. The failure may also be due to the reed flexing too far because the reed stop has not been adjusted properly or the stop has become distorted.

If the reed is broken, the loose piece **MUST** be located and removed, before the engine is returned to service. The piece of reed may have found its way into the crankcase, behind the by-pass cover. If the broken piece cannot be located, the engine

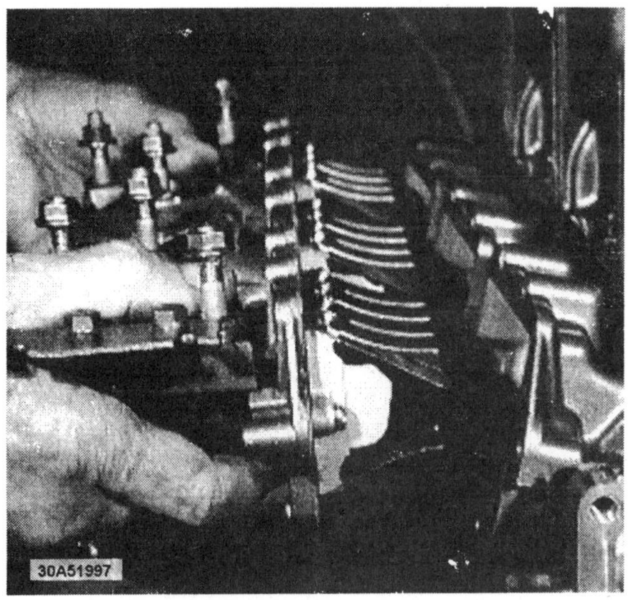

Removing/installing the intake manifold from a Yamaha Model 1100 or 1200 Series engine. The reed blocks are attached to the manifold.

must be completely disassembled until it is located and removed.

An excellent check for a broken reed on an operating engine is to hold an ordinary business card in front of the carburetor. Under normal operating conditions, a very small amount of fine mist will be noticeable, but if fuel begins to appear rapidly on the card from the carburetor, one of the reeds is broken and causing the backflow through the carburetor onto the card.

A broken reed will cause the engine to operate roughly and with a "pop" back through the carburetor.

The reeds must **NEVER** be turned over in an attempt to correct a problem. Such action would cause the reed to flex in the opposite direction and the reed would break in a very short time.

3-5 ELECTRICAL POWER SUPPLY

Remove the battery from the engine compartment for service. Inspect and service the battery, cables and connections. Check for signs of corrosion. Inspect the battery case for cracks or bulges, dirt, acid, and electrolyte leakage.

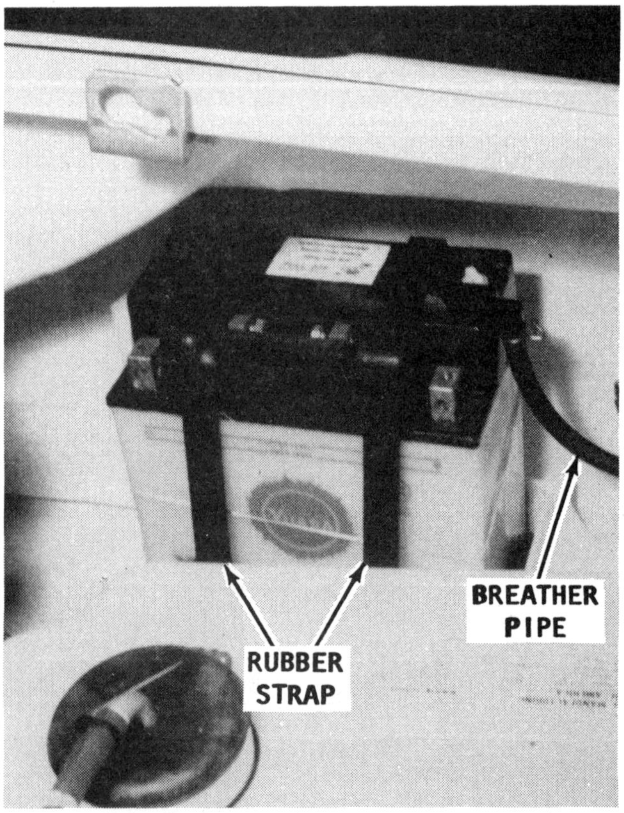

*Due to the violent maneuvers experienced by a personal watercraft — more so than any other type craft -- the battery **MUST** be extremely well-secured with **NO** movement of any kind possible.*

Make sure the breather pipe is attached to the battery and not pinched by any part of the engine compartment.

Clean the top of the battery. The top of a 12-volt battery should be kept especially clean of acid film and dirt, because of the high voltage between the battery terminals and prevent contact between the acid and the two rubber hold down bands. For best results, first wash the battery with diluted ammonia or baking soda solution to neutralize any acid present. Flush the solution off the battery with clean water. Keep the vent plugs tight to prevent the neutralizing solution or water from entering the cells.

Filling the Battery

Remove each filler cap using a pair of pliers. Fill each cell to the proper level with distilled water. The level of electrolyte should be between the upper and lower level marks during operation. When filling the battery, fill to the upper line and allow the battery to stand for twenty minutes. Check the level again and replenish as necessary.

Use a temperature corrected hydrometer to test the specific gravity of the electrolyte. At 20°C (68°F) the hydrometer reading should be 1.26 on the scale. If it is necessary to charge the battery, leave the filler caps lightly resting on the cell openings to allow the gases to escape. The charging current should not exceed 1.9 amps for 10 hours.

After charging, push each filler cap into place and wipe the top of the battery clean before installation.

Clean the battery posts and battery cable ends with a wire brush to ensure good, clean connections. Clean the top surface of the battery and identify the "POS" or "+" and "NEG" or "-" embossed symbols. Correctly connect the battery cables to the battery observing polarity. If the cables are connected backwards, the ignition system **WILL** be destroyed the first time the engine is started.

Check to be sure the battery is fastened securely in position. The hold-down rubber straps should be tight enough to prevent any movement of the battery in the holder under the most violent maneuvers of the watercraft.

If the battery posts or cable terminals are corroded, the cables should be cleaned separately with a baking soda solution and a wire brush. Apply a thin coating of Multi-purpose Lubricant to the posts and cable clamps before making the connections. The lubricant will help to prevent corrosion.

Jumper Cables

If booster batteries are used for starting an engine the jumper cables must be connected correctly and in the proper sequence to prevent damage to either battery, or the rectifier diodes.

ALWAYS connect a cable from the positive terminals of the dead battery to the positive terminal of the good battery **FIRST.** **NEXT,** connect one end of the other cable to the negative terminal of the good battery. Finally, connect the other end of the cable to the far side of the **ENGINE** for a good ground. By making the ground connection on the engine, any spark created will not be near the battery. An arc near the battery could cause an explosion, destroying the battery and causing serious personal injury.

If a trickle charger is used on a dead battery installed in the craft, one battery lead **MUST** be disconnected prior to connecting the charger, to prevent destroying the diodes in the rectifier.

NEVER use a trickle charger as a booster to start the engine because the diodes in the rectifier will be **DAMAGED.**

3-6 CARBURETOR ADJUSTMENT

Fuel and Fuel Tanks

Take time to check the fuel tank and all of the fuel lines, fittings, couplings, valves, flexible tank fill and vent. Turn on the fuel supply valve. If gas was not drained at the end of the previous season, make a careful inspection for gum formation. When gasoline is allowed to stand for long periods of time, particularly in the presence of copper, gummy deposits form. This gum can clog the filters, lines, and passageways in the carburetor.

If the condition of the fuel is in doubt, drain, clean, and fill the tank with fresh fuel, with the proper fuel/oil mixture recommended by the manufacturer.

Low Speed and Idle Mixture Adjustment

The idle mixture and idle speed are set at the factory. Due to local conditions, it may be necessary to adjust the carburetor while the craft is operating in a test tank or secured in a body of water. For maximum performance, the idle mixture and the idle rpm should be adjusted under actual operating conditions.

Set the low speed adjustment screw at the specified number of turns open from a lightly seated position. Refer to the Appendix for the model being serviced.

Start the engine and allow it to warm to operating temperature.

CAUTION

Water must circulate through the jet pump -- to and from the engine, anytime the engine is operating. Circulating water will prevent overheating — which could cause damage to moving engine parts and possible engine seizure.

NEVER, AGAIN NEVER, operate the engine at high speed with a flush device attached. An engine operating at high speed with such a device attached, would **RUNAWAY** from lack of a load on the impeller shaft, causing extensive damage.

Connect a tachometer to the engine.

SPECIAL WORDS ON TACHOMETERS AND CONNECTIONS

A tachometer connected to the engine must be used to accurately determine engine speed during idle and high-speed adjustments.

Theoretically, it should be possible to connect a tachometer to any engine and receive an

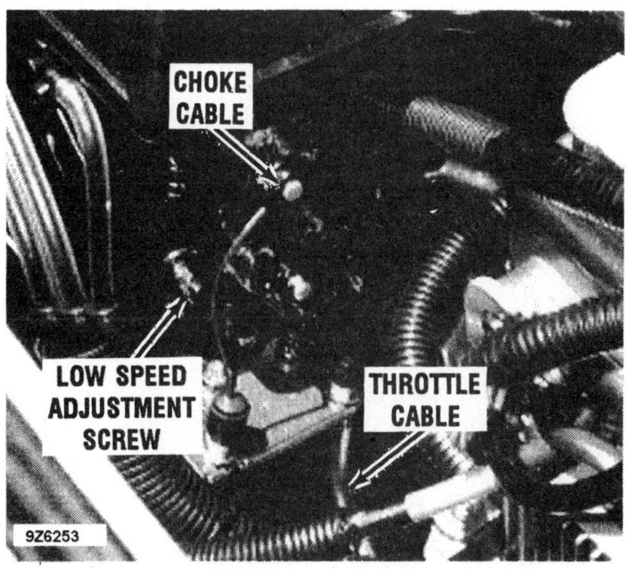

Close view -- with the flame arrestor removed -- of the No. 1 carburetor installed on a Model 1100 or 1200 Series engine with the linkage connected. The choke cable, throttle cable, and low speed adjustment screw are identified.

accurate count of crankshaft revolutions -- **RIGHT? WRONG!**

Unfortunately, this is not the case. Tachometer manufacturers admit, on certain two-stroke applications where points, and an ignition coil are **NOT** used, an attempt to connect a tachometer to the unit could "go up in smoke".

The general rules for connecting a tachometer to a marine two-stroke engine are:

1- The tachometer **MUST** be calibrated at the factory for two-stroke applications. Some tachometers have a dial indicator which may simply be switched from two-stroke to four-stroke and back again.

2- A tachometer may have as many as **FOUR** leads. The meter will always have a minimum of an input lead and a ground lead. The colors of these leads may vary between manufacturers, but the instructions provided with the meter will (or should), identify these leads. The input lead is connected to the primary **NEGATIVE** side of the ignition coil and the ground lead is connected to a suitable engine ground.

3- Some tachometers have a third wire which is considered the "hot" lead. The "hot" lead is attached to the **POSITIVE** battery terminal. On other tachometers, this "hot" lead is only used for an internal light bulb to illuminate the meter face. On still other tachometers this "hot" lead is necessary to the operation of the meter.

Once again, the instructions with the tachometer should identify the "hot" lead.

4- A fourth lead from the tachometer is used as the ground lead to the light bulb.

Making a low speed adjustment with the flame arrestor removed; the craft in a body of water or a flush attachment and garden hose connected; and the engine operating.

The fuel pump diaphragm must be carefully inspected for the tiniest hole or tear. Such damage will "wet foul" the spark plug at idle speed.

FIRST, last, and **ALWAYS**, check the tachometer manufacturer's instructions for use with a two-stroke unit.

Procedure

With the engine operating, **SLOWLY** turn the throttle stop screw until the engine idles at 1,200 rpm. Now, rotate the low speed screw in or out 1/8 turn at-a-time until the cylinders fire evenly and engine rpm increases. Re-adjust the throttle stop screw to reduce the rpm to idle speed.

High Speed Screw Adjustment

Set the high speed adjustment screw at the specified number of turns open from a lightly seated position, for the unit being serviced, as given in the Appendix.

Such a setting is the best setting for sea level. For operation at higher elevations, a leaner mixture is obtained by rotating the screw **CLOCKWISE** 1/8 turn at-a-time until satisfactory engine operation is obtained.

Removing the cranking motor from the engine for service work and/or testing.

3-7 FUEL PUMPS

Many times, a defective fuel pump diaphragm is mistakenly diagnosed as a problem in the ignition system. The most common problem is a tiny pin-hole in the diaphragm. Such a small hole will permit gas to enter the crankcase and wet foul both spark plugs at idle-speed. During high-speed operation, gas quantity is limited, the plug is not fouled and will therefore fire in a satisfactory manner.

If the fuel pump fails to perform properly, an insufficient fuel supply will be delivered to the carburetor. This lack of fuel will cause the engine to run lean, lose rpm or cause piston scoring.

NEVER use liquid Neoprene on fuel line fittings. Always use Permatex when making fuel line connections. Permatex is available at almost all marine and hardware stores.

To service the fuel pump, see the Fuel Chapter.

3-8 CRANKING MOTOR AND SOLENOID

Cranking Motor Test

Check to be sure the battery is fully charged. Would you believe, many cranking motors are needlessly disassembled, when the battery is actually the culprit.

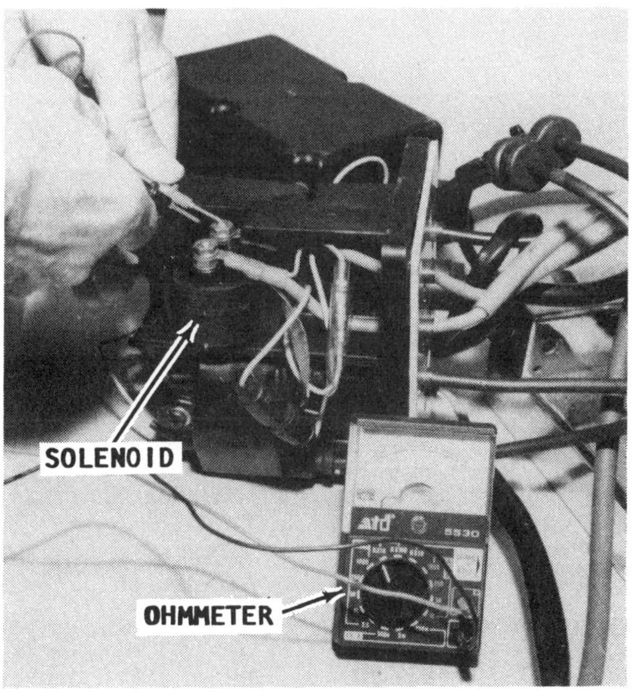

Using an ohmmeter to test the cranking motor solenoid housed inside the electrical box.

Lubricate the pinion gear and screw shaft with No. 10 oil.

Connect one lead of a voltmeter to the positive terminal of the cranking motor. Connect the other meter lead to a good ground on the engine. Check the battery voltage under load by depressing the ignition switch and observing the voltmeter reading.

If the reading is 9-1/2 volts or greater, and the cranking motor fails to operate, repair or replace the unit. See the Electrical Chapter.

Solenoid Test

An ohmmeter is required for this test. Select the Rx1000 ohm scale. Calibrate the meter by making contact with the meter leads to each other, and then rotating the calibration knob on the meter until the needle indicates zero ohms. Separate the meter leads.

Make contact with the Red meter lead to one of the large terminals on the solenoid. Make contact with the Black meter lead to the other large solenoid terminal. **NEVER** connect the battery leads to the large terminals of the solenoid, or the meter will be damaged.

Using battery jumper leads, connect the positive battery lead to the small terminal of the solenoid. Connect the negative battery lead to the small terminal of the solenoid. If the meter needle indicates continuity, the solenoid is serviceable. If the meter fails to indicate continuity, the solenoid is defective and **MUST** be replaced.

3-9 JET PUMP

Very few personal watercraft are equipped with a reverse gate. However, if the unit being serviced has a reverse gate, the gate **MUST** be properly adjusted to obtain maximum performance from the craft. When properly adjusted, the gate will permit the pump to deliver its full potential of thrust with no drag.

Gate Position

The shift rod lever adjustment should be checked from time to time to ensure the gate is firmly against the pump housing, when the unit is in the **FORWARD** position (wide open).

With the gate against the housing, any rattle noises will be avoided as the craft moves through the water. Proper position-

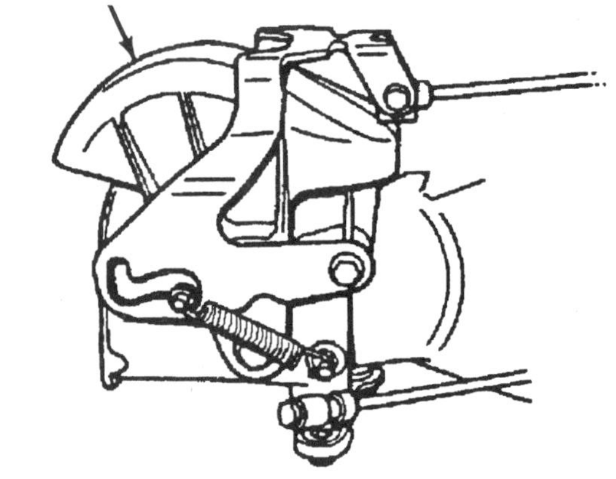

Simple line drawing to illustrate the reverse gate installed on the Yamaha WaveVenture and WaveRunner III GP, both covered in this manual.

ing of the gate in forward gear will prevent wave action from accidently shifting the gate into reverse as the craft is operated through violent maneuvers.

A simple "tuning" task with the jet pump is to make a thorough check of the linkage and gate movement. Such a check will ensure maximum thrust and use of the horsepower developed by the engine.

Impeller

Excessively rounded jet impeller edges will reduce the efficiency of the jet drive.

The term cavitation "burn" is a common expression used throughout the world among people working with pumps, impeller blades, and forceful water movement.

"Burns" on the impeller blades are caused by cavitation air bubbles exploding with considerable force against the impeller blades. The edges of the blades may develop small "dime size" areas resembling a porus sponge, as the aluminum material is actually "eaten" by the condition just described.

Impeller Service

Complete detailed procedures to service the impeller are given in Chapter 10 -- Jet Pump. As the text explains, some damage to the impeller can be corrected, while other more serious damage requires the impeller to be replaced.

The impeller **MUST** remain balanced. Any work on one blade must be also be done to the other blades. Out of balance will cause noticeable vibration. Vibration is a terrible enemy, because it can cause expensive damage to the impeller shaft, bearings and seals.

The "bottom line" on a jet pump is the condition and efficiency of the impeller. Adequate care, maintenance and timely replacement will result in maximum performance. Detailed service procedures for the impeller are presented in Chapter 10 -- Jet Pump.

3-10 MODIFYING FOR HIGHER PERFORMANCE

Normally Seloc manuals only cover stock engine and jet pump components. However, personal watercraft enthusiasts are notorious for modifying their equipment to gain higher performance. Therefore, a large aftermarket industry has grown to accomodate this need for speed. A few well chosen words on modifying for performance seem to be in order.

The following general guidelines will provide improved two stroke performance. The tasks listed below, in order of effectiveness, or possibly a combination of modifications and components, may give the desired results.

To increase bottom end power:
- Increase the compression.
- Advance the timing.
- Use a smaller diameter carburetor.
- Use a long chamber exhaust.
- Use a low pitch impeller.
- Use a larger nozzle bore.
- Use improved reed petals.

To increase top end power:
- Install a larger diameter carburetor.
- Use a short exhaust chamber.
- Go to higher porting specifications.
- Use high-flow reeds.
- Use a higher pitched impeller.
- Use a ride plate that generates lift.

To increase acceleration:
- Increase the compression.
- Use a lighter weight driveshaft.
- Install an aluminum flywheel.
- Check for optimum air flow.

4 MAINTENANCE

4-1 INTRODUCTION

The watercraft being prepared for service probably represents a sizeable investment. In order to protect this investment and for the owner to receive the maximum amount of enjoyment from the craft it must be cared for properly while being used and when it is out of the water. Always store the watercraft with the bow higher than the stern and be sure to remove the inner hull drain plug/s. If you use any type of cover to protect craft, plastic, canvas, whatever, be sure to allow for some movement of air through the hull. Proper ventilation will assure evaporation of any condensation that may form due to changes in temperature and humidity.

GOOD WORDS

The authors estimate 75% of engine repair work can be directly or indirectly attributed to lack of proper care for the engine. This is especially true of care during the off-season period. There is no way on this green earth for a mechanical engine, particularly a marine engine, to be left sitting idle for an extended period of time, say for six months, and then be ready for instant satisfactory service.

Imagine, if you will, leaving your automobile for six months, and then expecting to turn the key, have it roar to life, and be able to drive off in the same manner as a daily occurrence.

It is critical for a marine engine to be run at least once a month, preferably, in the water, but if this is not possible, then a flush attachment **MUST** be connected either directly to the engine block or in the hose line from the jet pump to the engine.

CAUTION

Water must circulate through the jet pump -- to and from the engine, anytime the engine is operating. Circulating water will prevent overheating — which could cause damage to moving engine parts and possible engine seizure.

NEVER, AGAIN NEVER, operate the engine at high speed with a flush device attached. The engine, operating at high speed with such a device attached, would **RUNAWAY** from lack of load on the impeller, causing extensive damage.

At the same time, the shift mechanism, if the unit is so equipped, should be operated through the full range several times. The steering should also be operated from hard-over to hard-over.

Only through a regular maintenance program can the owner expect to receive long life and satisfactory performance at minimum cost.

The material presented in this chapter is divided into four general areas.

1- General information every owner should know.

2- Maintenance tasks that should be performed periodically to keep the craft operating at minimum cost.

After a fun day on salt water, the owner of these personal watercraft had the opportunity to wash them down with fresh water. Such a "maintenance" practice certainly help preserve the paint and wax.

3- Care necessary to maintain the appearance of the craft and to give the owner that "Pride of Ownership" look.

4- Winter storage practices to minimize deterioration during the off-season when the craft is not in use.

In nautical terms, the front of the craft is the **bow;** the rear is the **stern;** the right side, when facing forward, is the **starboard** side; and the left side is the **port** side. All directional references in this manual use this terminology. Therefore, the direction from which an item is viewed is of no consequence, because **starboard** and **port** **NEVER** change no matter where the individual is located or his position -- even standing on his/her head.

After Use Tasks

At the end of a day's use, make a habit of opening the engine compartment to allow fumes to escape and sponging out all the water in the bottom of the hull before trailering the craft. Leave the engine cover off when the craft is stored overnight to allow any moisture in the compartment to evaporate. Slowly open the fuel tank cap to release built up pressure. Pressure in the tank will increase considerably during hot weather. Releasing the pressure reduces the chance of an explosion and ensures smooth fuel flow when the engine is next started.

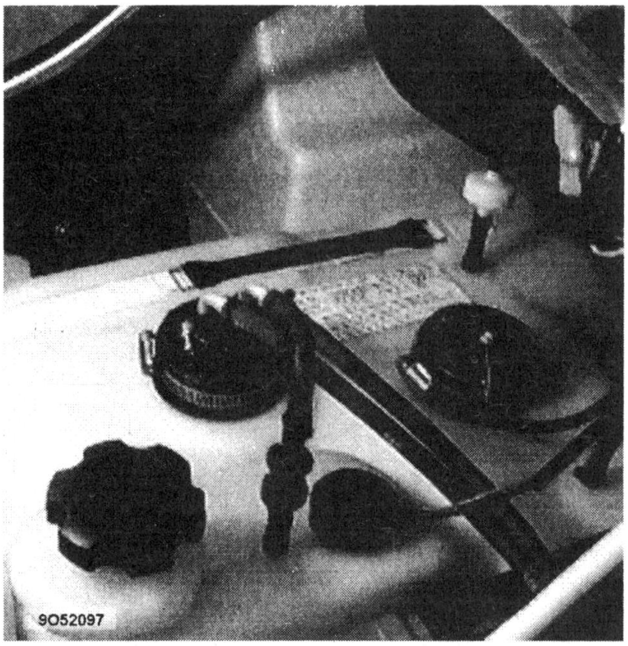

Open the "ON" fuel tank cap slowly during hot weather to release built up pressure in the Tank.

If the craft will remain unused for a week, spray storage oil inside the engine and a light film of lubricant, such as WD-40, Super Lube or Justice Bros. 80, on the engine exterior. Keeping the engine exterior lightly oiled at all times will result in water sliding off the engine and draining away rather than accumulating in casting webs and resulting in corrosion.

Cooling

The engine cooling passages must be flushed with clear water on a regular basis. This is accomplished by simply connecting a "Flushing Kit" per the manufacturer's instructions **OR** by disconnecting the cooling hose from the pump to the engine and connecting a garden hose to the disconnected hose. Such an easy maintenance practice should become a habit and will prevent accumulation of debris which could restrict engine coolant water flow and cause overheating.

Yamaha -- All Models

Only the Yamaha engines covered in this manual are equipped with a thermo-switch

On a Yamaha engine, the cooling hose is attached to the base of the exhaust plate.

Forward cooling water fitting on the cylinder head of a Model 1100 series engine.

engine temperature sensor. This sensor is connected directly to the CDI unit and grounded to the engine kill switch. If the engine temperature exceeds a maximum value specifed by the manufacturer, the ignition will be grounded and the engine shut down to prevent damage through overheating. On a jet pump installation, a functioning engine temperature sensor is an essential early warning device.

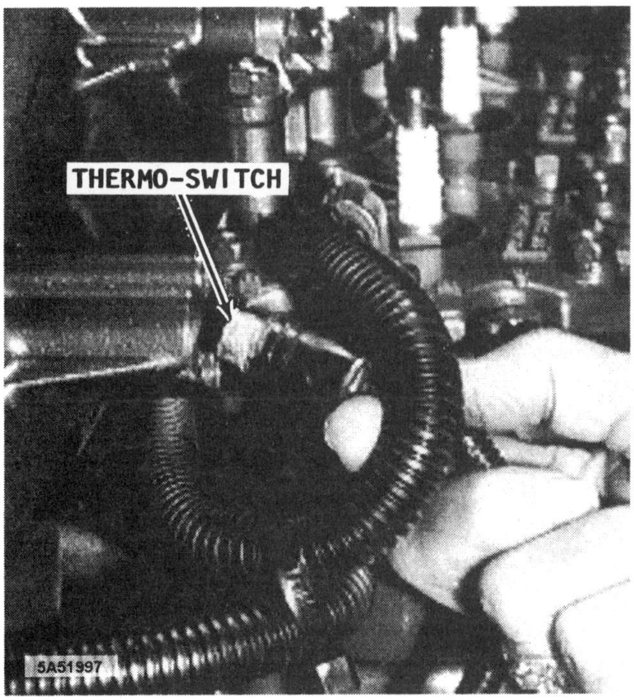

Installing a new thermo-switch into the cylinder head on a Yamaha engine.

On a Yamaha engine, a zinc anode is mounted inside the cooling passage of the block, as indicated.

Controlling Corrosion

Since man first started out on the water, corrosion has been his enemy. The first form was merely rot in the wood and then it was rust, followed by other forms of destructive corrosion in the more modern materials.

The higher the concentration of salt in the water, the worse the corrosion which will take place.

One defense against corrosion is to use similar metals in the manufacture of the parts exposed to the water.

A second defense against corrosion is to insulate dissimilar metals. This can be done by using an exterior coating of Sea Skin or by insulating them with plastic or rubber gaskets.

Some manufacturers use a zinc anode mounted inside the cooling passage of the block, as shown in the accompanying illustration.

Pump Impeller

The pump impeller is a precisely machined and dynamically balanced aluminum spiral. Observe the drilled recesses at exact locations to achieve the delicate balancing.

Excessive vibration of the jet pump may be attributed to an out-of-balance condition caused by the impeller being struck excessively by rocks, gravel or cavitation "burn".

The term cavitation "burn" is a common expression used throughout the world among people working with pumps, impeller blades, and forceful water movement.

The impeller of a jet pump is a precisely machined and dynamically balanced aluminum spiral. Significant damage to a blade will affect the balance.

"Burns" on the impeller blades are caused by cavitation air bubbles exploding with considerable force against the impeller blades. The edges of the blades may develop small "dime size" areas resembling a porous sponge, as the aluminum is actually "eaten" by the condition just described.

Excessive rounding of the impeller edges will reduce efficiency and performance. Therefore, the impeller should be inspected at regular intervals. If rounding is detected, the impeller should be removed from the housing, placed on a work bench and the edges restored to as sharp a condition as possible using a file. Refer to the Jet Pump chapter for detailed procedures on removal and installation of the impeller.

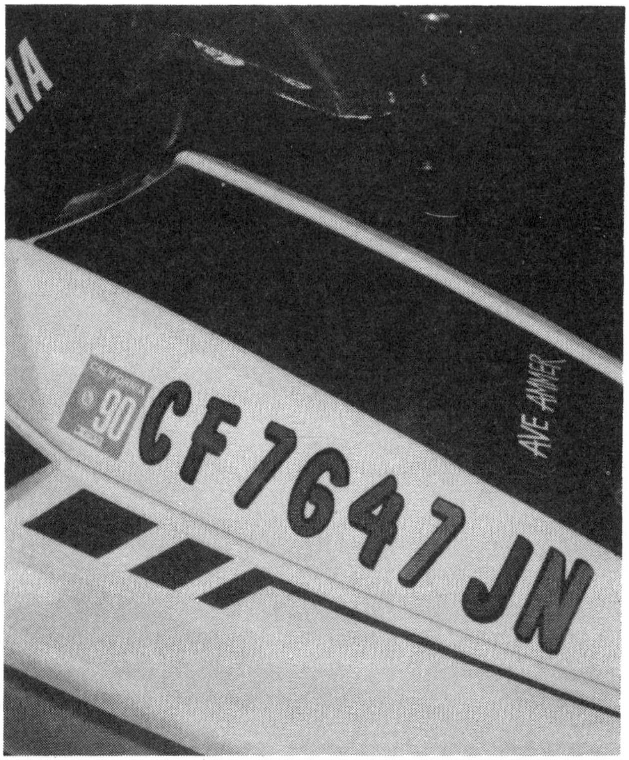

The state license identification number must be prominently displayed on the forward portion of the hull, port and starboard.

On a Yamaha engine, the engine serial number is stamped on a small metal plate permanently attached to the muffler box.

4-2 SERIAL NUMBERS

Most manufacturers use three different identification numbers stamped, embossed or decaled somewhere on the craft.

The engine serial number is the manufacturer's key to engine changes. This number identifies the year of manufacture, the qualified horsepower rating, and the parts book identification. If any correspondence or parts are required, the engine serial number **MUST** be used or proper identification is not possible. A popular location for the engine serial number is on a small metal plate attached to the muffler box, as shown in the accompanying illustration.

Federal regulations require all personal watercraft to have a Hull Identification Number (HIN) permanently attached to the craft in two separate locations: one on the transom on the starboard side, above the

Some manufacturer's have an identification plate permanently attached to the bearing housing, as indicated.

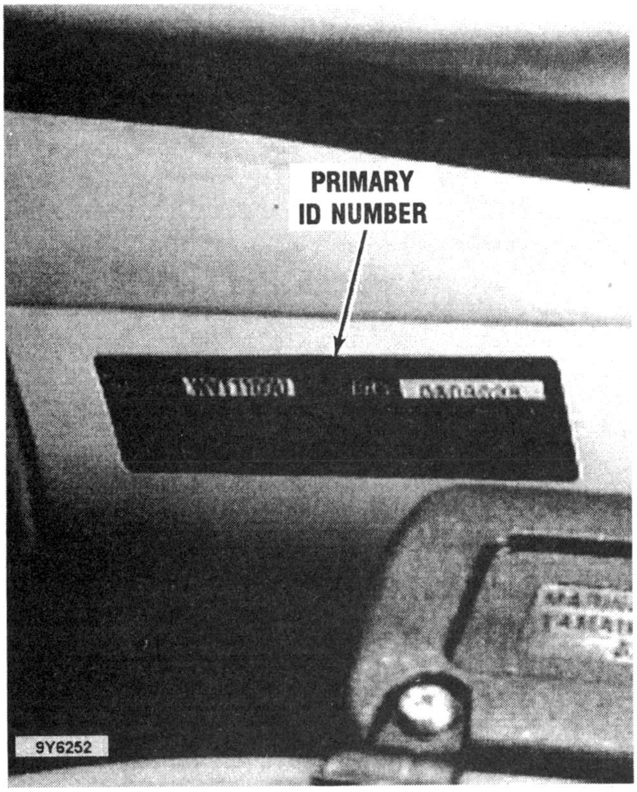

Location of the primary ID number stamped on a label affixed to the inside of the engine compartment.

waterline and the other in an unexposed location, which is usually left to the discretion of the maufacturer. This "HIN" number can be most helpful when attempting to retrieve a stolen craft. The "HIN" number is required in most states in order to properly register the craft.

Some manufacturers also use a Primary I.D. Number stamped on a plate attached to the inside of the engine compartment.

ONE MORE WORD

As a theft prevention measure, all metal plates with any type of identification number are especially made wafer thin. Any attempt to remove these plates will result in cracks across the serial number.

4-3 EMERGENCY TETHER

Yamaha -- All Models

These personal watercraft are equipped with an emergency tether. This tether must be in place behind the "kill" switch or the engine cannot be started. If the engine is operating and the tether is removed, the unit will immediately shut down.

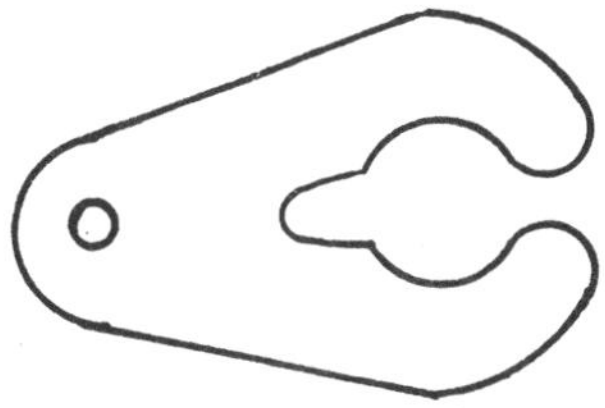

Pattern to be used to fabricate a "homemade" emergency tether, as explained in the text.

Explanation

The plastic tether acts as a spacer, moving the "kill" button out slightly and allowing an internal contact to be closed, permitting the ignition circuit to be completed and the engine to be started.

The "kill" button may now be depressed to shut the engine down with the tether in place. If the tether is pulled free from behind the "kill" button, the button pops inward and the ignition circuit is opened. With the "kill" switch in this position, no amount of cranking will result in engine startup.

The purpose of this tether is two fold.

As a Safety Feature

When this tether is used as intended by the manufacturer, the operater attaches the belt hook onto his/her clothing at any convenient location. Should the operator be thrown from the craft, the tether will be pulled free of the "kill" button, and the engine will shut down.

As a Security Feature

If the craft is left on the beach or dock unattended, the owner may take the entire emergency tether with him/her. Without the tether in place behind the "kill" button, the engine cannot be started. Any attempt to start the engine and steal the craft will be unsuccessful -- unless the thief is familiar with this particular security device.

Temporary Replacement

If the owner loses the emergency tether and is unable to obtain one immediately from the local Yamaha dealer, an emergency substitute tether may be made using only a common knife and a couple pieces of plastic.

First, obtain a piece of plastic from the cover of a container of margarine, whipped topping, or similar product.

Next, using the pattern shown on this page cut out about four shapes, as shown.

Stack the four cutouts together, secure them with a paper clip, or similar object, and then insert them behind the "kill" switch.

SPECIAL WORDS

If the material described is not available, obtain some other pliable material and cut the shape indicated. The thickness of the substitute tether device should be approximately 1/8" (3mm). About 100 pages (50 sheets) of this manual is approximately the proper thickness.

REMEMBER, use this device only in an emergency situation and purchase the proper tether from the local Yamaha dealer at the first opportunity. By substituting this "home made" tether, both the safety and the security features intended by the manufacturer have been lost.

4-4 LUBRICATION - COMPLETE UNIT

As with every type mechanical invention with moving parts, lubrication plays a prominent role in operation, enjoyment, and longevity of the unit.

If a personal watercraft is operated in salt water the frequency of applying lubricant to fittings is usually cut in half as compared with the unit being used in fresh water. The few minutes involved in moving around the craft applying lubricant and at the same time making a visual inspection of its general condition will pay in rich rewards with years of continued service.

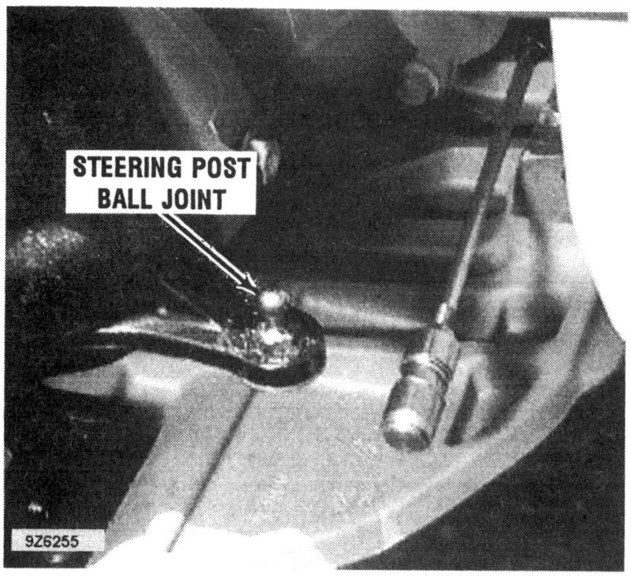

The ball joint indicated, should be lubricated about every 100 hours of operation.

Although the first personal watercraft were seen in this county in the early 1970s, it is not uncommon to see outboard units well over 20 years of age moving a boat through the water as if the unit had recently been purchased from the current line of models. An inquiry with the proud owner will undoubtedly reveal his main credit for its performance to be regular periodic maintenance.

The accompanying chart can be used as a guide to the frequency of maintenance while the craft is being used during the season. Unless otherwise stated use a good brand name multi-purpose water resistant lubricant. Detailed lubrication instructions are given below for locations requiring special attention.

In addition to the normal lubrication listed in the lubrication chart, the prudent owner will inspect and make checks on a regular basis as listed in the accompanying chart.

Throttle Cable Lubrication

Hold the throttle lever in the full open position against the grip. Use a small screwdriver and pry out the small seal from the groove of the throttle stop and a little way along the cable. Spray rust inhibitor along the exposed length of cable. Fill the groove with multi-purpose water resistant lubricant and then pull the seal down along the cable and back into place inside the groove. Wipe away any excess lubricant.

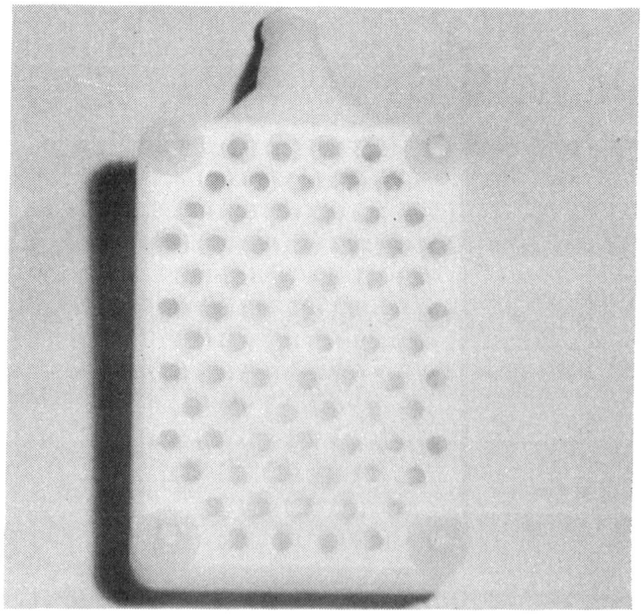

A typical bilge strainer. Such a filtering device is critical to keep the pump and hose clear of debris.

Lubrication Points:	Initially every 10hrs	Initially every 50hrs	Initially every 100hrs	Then every 100hrs	Then every 200hrs
Carburetor throttle shaft			❖	❖	
Throttle cable - engine end			❖	❖	
Throttle cable - handlebar stop			❖	❖	
Choke cable - engine end			❖	❖	
Choke knob shaft			❖	❖	
Steering nozzle pivot shaft			❖	❖	
Steering post arm ball joint			❖	❖	
Reverse gate pivot pins			❖	❖	
Jet pump			❖	❖	
Seat latch (Yamaha WR500)			❖	❖	

Maintenance Tasks:	Initially every 10hrs	Initially every 50hrs	Initially every 100hrs	Then every 100hrs	Then every 200hrs
Check engine alignment					❖
Clean and gap spark plugs	❖	❖	❖	❖	
Adjust carburetor idle	❖		❖	❖	
Adjust carburetor mixture	❖		❖	❖	
Drain and inspect fuel tank					❖
Clean and inspect fuel filter	❖	❖	❖	❖	
Inspect fuel line			❖	❖	
Inspect check valve			❖	❖	
Adjust throttle control			❖	❖	
Adjust choke system			❖	❖	
Adjust steering system			❖	❖	
Inspect impeller		❖	❖	❖	
Check impeller to housing clearance			❖	❖	
Inspect rubber coupling					❖
Inspect electrical connections	❖	❖	❖	❖	
Check battery electrolyte level	❖	❖	❖	❖	
Clean bilge strainer			❖	❖	
Inspect rubber water seal	❖		❖	❖	

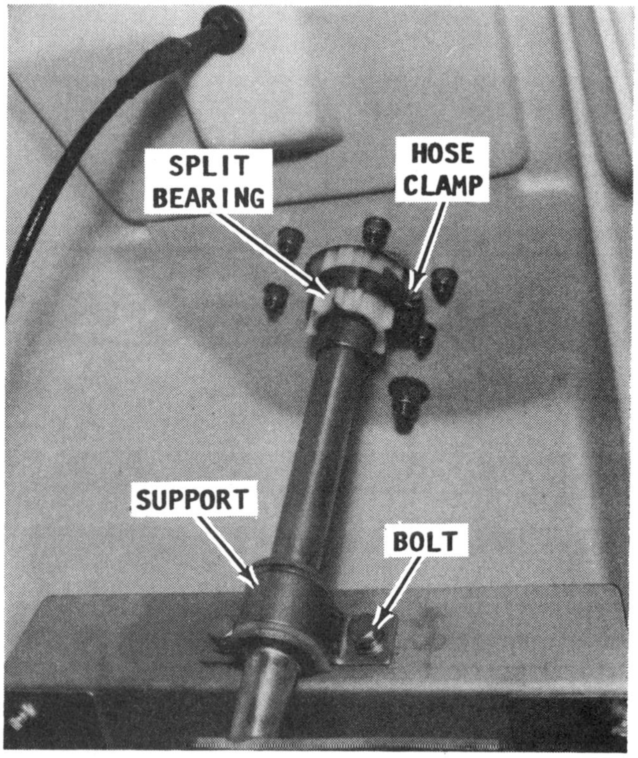

Routine maintenance should include tightening the support bolts and the hose clamp around the split bearing. (The Yamaha WaveRunner 500 is shown here.)

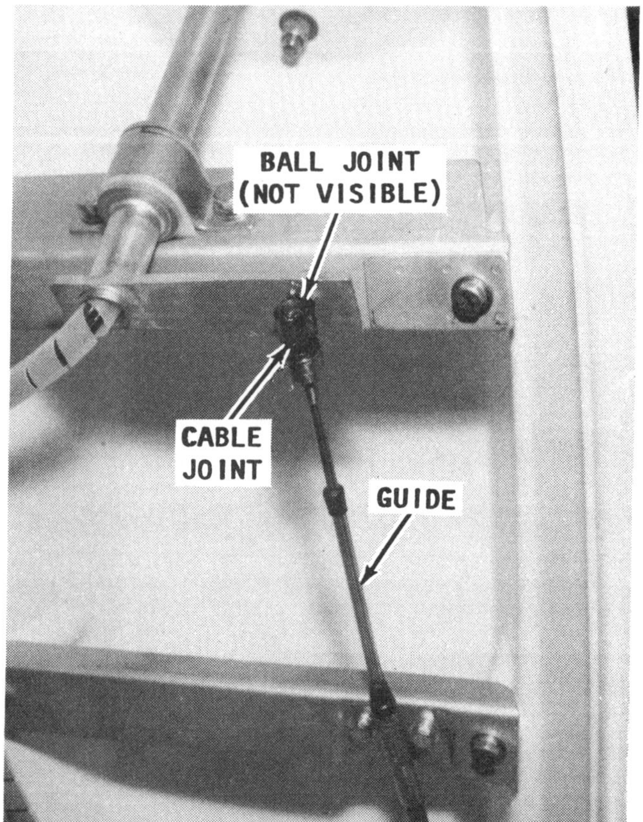

Lubricate the ball joint under the steering cable joint (not visible) and the exposed cable above the guide.

Steering Cable Lubrication

Pry the barrel of the steering cable free of the ball joint on the steering post arm. Coat the ball joint with lubricant and then snap the barrel back onto the ball joint.

Fuel/Oil Mixture
(Units Without Oil Injection)

With very few exceptions, most of the engines covered in this manual are equipped with oil injection. However, for those units requiring oil to be mixed with the gasoline, the following instructions are given and must be followed.

A new or rebuilt engine must be properly broken-in if it is to develop maximum performance. An engine which is incorrectly broken-in will never be able to achieve the maximum rated horsepower. During the initial breaking-in period, the fuel/oil ratio should be very rich, about 20:1 for the first two to four tank fulls. Twenty parts of fuel to one part oil. Two-stroke oil be added to the fuel tank at the ratio of 25:1 for the first ten hours of operation after the unit is brought out of storage. This ratio will **ENSURE** adequate lubrication of moving parts which have been drained of oil during the storage period. Operation of an engine without the proper amount of oil will quickly lead to a significant loss of horsepower.

After the first ten hours of operation, a lower ratio of fuel/oil mixture may be used. In the past, manufacturers of two-stroke engines gave a minimum of 100:1. Yamaha recommends a minimum of 50:1. However, experienced two-stroke mechanics run their own units between 16:1 and 32:1 on the premise it is

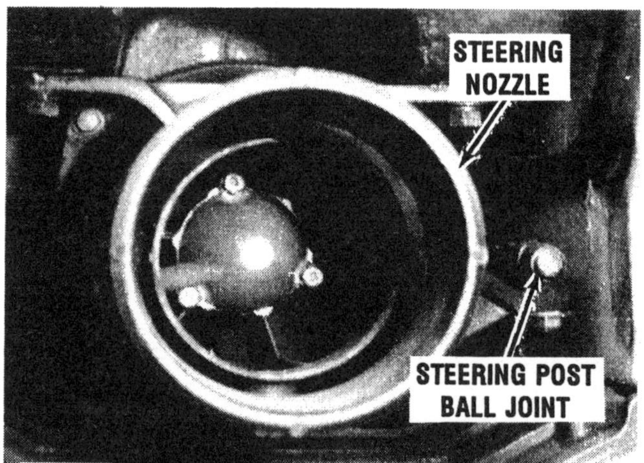

The steering cable is attached to a ball joint on a plate attached to the steering nozzle. Pushing the outer sleeve forward will release the fitting from the ball joint.

cheaper to replace a fouled spark plug then to have a complete engine overhaul with rebored cylinder, oversize pistons and rings. These same mechanics who own oil injected units add an extra ounce of oil per each gallon of fuel. The addition of this extra oil may prevent engine seizure in the event of an oil pump failure or clog in an oil delivery line.

Use only outboard marine oil in the mixture, **NEVER** automotive oils. Four-stroke automotive engine oil is not formulated to burn completely -- only to lubricate. Therefore, auto motive oil, if used in a two-stroke engine will leave an undesirable residue.

Impeller Words

Complete detailed procedures to service the impeller are given in Chapter 10 -- Jet Pump. As the text explains, some damage to the impeller can be corrected, while other more serious damage requires the impeller to be replaced.

The impeller **MUST** remain balanced. Any work on one blade must also be done to the other blades. Out of balance will cause noticeable vibration. Vibration is a terrible enemy, because it can cause expensive damage to the impeller shaft, bearings and seals, besides making a very uncomfortable ride for the operator and her/his passengers.

The blades of an impeller overlap, thus water is trapped and forced through the impeller into the duct and nozzle. The water moving past the impeller resists cavitation because it is under pressure. Blades in the impeller duct are angled exactly opposite to those of the impeller. These duct blades redirect the water to establish a concentrated flow through the nozzle.

Most Jet pumps are provided with a Zerk lubrication fitting. This fitting is accessible through the nozzle opening.

4-5 INSPECTION AND SERVICE

Fuel Check Valve

Before disturbing any hose be sure to have a new hose tie wrap or a small hose clamp to replace the one removed. Original equipment tie wraps must be cut through to remove them from a hose.

Disconnect the ventilation hose from the fitting on the fuel tank. Remove the two tie wraps, one on each end of the check valve. Blow through the check valve in the direction of the arrow embossed on the valve. If the check valve is functioning correctly, air should only be able to flow in the direction indicated by the arrow. If the check valve will not allow air to pass in the direction of the arrow, the fuel will remain in the tank and not be drawn by the fuel pump.

Test the valve again by blowing through the other end. Air should not be able to flow in the opposite direction to the arrow. If the valve allows air to flow in the wrong direction, it will also allow fuel to flow out of the tank, through the valve and spill into the hull as the craft is subjected to violent maneuvers. Therefore, replace the valve if it fails to function correctly.

Install the check valve with new tie wraps or hose clamps with the arrow embossed on the valve pointing **TOWARD THE TANK.**

Fuel Filler Cap

Remove the fuel filler cap and inspect the condition of the rubber seal. Replace

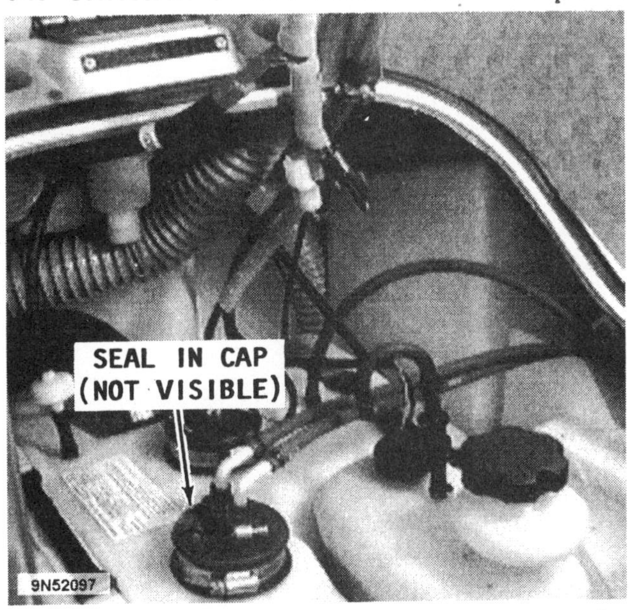

The fuel filler cap seal should be checked at regular intervals to ensure against a leak.

the seal if it is worn or cracked. The small safety chain must be released from the cap to remove the old seal and install the new one. Do not allow the chain to slide down into the tank.

Check the tightness of the large hose clamp around the fuel tube to the tank.

Models Equipped with Oil Injection System Inspection

Remove the oil tank filler cap. Inspect the condition of the seal beneath the cap, and replace the seal if it is worn or cracked. Pull out the oil filter. Rinse the filter in clean solvent and gently blow it dry with compressed air. If the filter is torn it should be replaced.

The oil tank is equipped with a ventilation hose and a check valve similar to the one installed on the fuel tank.

Before disturbing the ventilation hose be sure to have a new hose tie wrap or a small hose clamp to replace the one removed. Original equipment tie wraps must be cut through to remove them from a hose.

Disconnect the ventilation hose from the fitting on the oil tank. Remove the two tie wraps, one on each end of the check valve. Blow through the white end of the check valve. If the check valve is functioning correctly, air should only be able to enter from the white end and out through the green end of the valve. If the check valve will not allow air to pass in this direction, the oil will remain in the tank and not be drawn by the oil pump.

Test the valve again by blowing through the green end. Air should not be able to pass in the opposite direction. If the valve allows air to pass in the wrong direction, it will also allow oil to exit from the tank, through the valve and spill into the hull while the craft is moving through the water. Therefore, replace the valve if it fails to function correctly.

Install the check valve with new tie wraps or hose clamps with the green end **TOWARD THE TANK.**

Water Separator Filter on the Yamaha SuperJet

A water separating fuel filter is installed on the Yamaha SuperJet between the filler nozzle and the fuel check valve. This filter removes water and fuel system contaminants such as dirt, rust and other solids, thus reducing potential problems. This filter should be replaced each season. The bottom screw should be removed after every three or four tankfulls of gas have been used, to allow water to drain from the filter.

Loose Bolts Down the Carburetor!

Periodically remove the flame arrestor and inspect the condition of both the choke and throttle shafts. Most shaft designs incorporate a cutout portion to enable the butterfly valve to lay flat against the shaft. Two small holes are drilled in this cutout portion to accommodate the small screws securing the valve to the shaft. The weakest point of the shaft is at the screw holes. Small cracks form at the holes due to metal fatigue. These cracks elongate the threaded holes and the small screws shake loose. Once loose they are sucked into the carburetor, the intake manifold, the crankcase and eventually find their way into the combustion chamber, where they can cause very expensive damage to pistons, rings, and cylinder walls.

Other bolts in danger of being vibrated loose and sucked down into the carburetor, are the three Phillips head screws securing the lower flame arrestor to the carburetor.

Check the tightness of all bolts likely to be a problem in or above the carburetor, particularily the bolts of the choke and throttle shafts. Should any of these bolts come free, they could cause extensive and expensive damage.

Drain Plug

Remove the drain plug from the transom. Inspect the condition of the O-ring. Replace as necessary. Clean off any dirt or sand from the plug threads. Install the plug and tighten securely.

Impeller Inspection

Inspection of the impeller necessitates placing the craft on its side. Therefore,

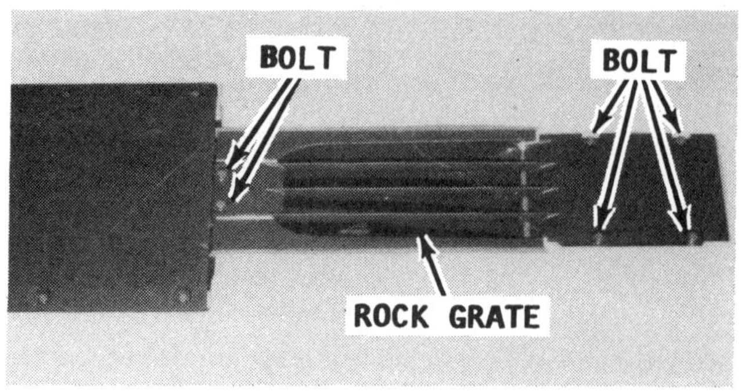

Rock grate attaching bolt location.

before attempting any inspection of the impeller, disconnect and remove the battery from the craft to avoid losing electrolyte through the battery breather hose.

Remove the bolts securing the rock grate to the hull. If the seal between the hull and the pump housing is broken, or the foam packing is damaged, reseal the housing and intake area with silicone sealant to prevent impeller cavitation.

Visually inspect the impeller for damage. If the impeller has sustained considerable damage, large nicks, blades cracked or bent and is no longer fit for service, refer to Chapter 10 -- Jet Pump -- for detailed procedures to remove and replace the impeller.

Using a feeler gauge, measure the clearance between each of the three impeller blades and the housing. Make a note of these clearances. The maximum clearance recommended by the manufacturer for any one of the blades is 0.024" (0.6mm).

The jet pump need not be removed from the craft to perform the procedural steps to bring the jet impeller closer to the casting wall.

See the appropriate section in the jet pump chapter to change the number of shim material pieces. Increasing the amount of shim material will shift the impeller further into the tapered part of the housing and reduce the clearance.

If the clearance is not kept to a minimum, the jet pump will lose efficiency by allowing excess water to pass between the blades and the housing. This water has no thrust and will actually slow the stream of water under pressure from the impeller.

Install the rock grate and tighten the attaching bolts securely.

A new pump impeller, ready for service. If the internal threads are even slightly damaged, or any of the blades are seriously nicked, chipped, or cracked, the impeller should be replaced.

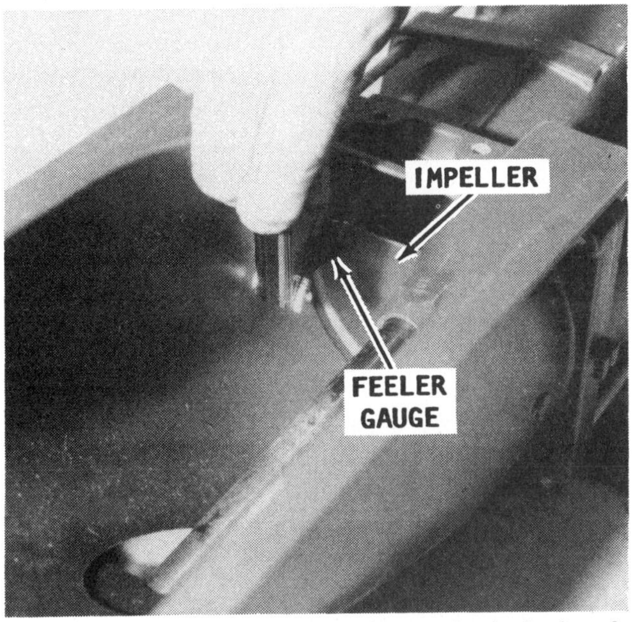

Using a blade type feeler gauge to check the impeller-to-housing clearance on a Yamaha mixed flow pump. Shim material may be used to obtain correct clearance.

Rubber Coupler Inspection

If the engine and jet pump are correctly aligned, the rubber coupler will show little wear for many seasons. If the alignment is incorrect, the rubber coupler will wear quickly and possibly even fail. If the rubber coupler requires replacement, the engine must be removed. The task of engine alignment -- both horizontal and vertical -- must always be the final step of coupler replacement. Refer to the Engine chapter for engine removal, installation and alignment.

However, if the rubber coupler is only slightly worn, then engine alignment procedures may be performed to reduce further coupler wear. Refer to the Engine chapter for detailed engine alignment procedures.

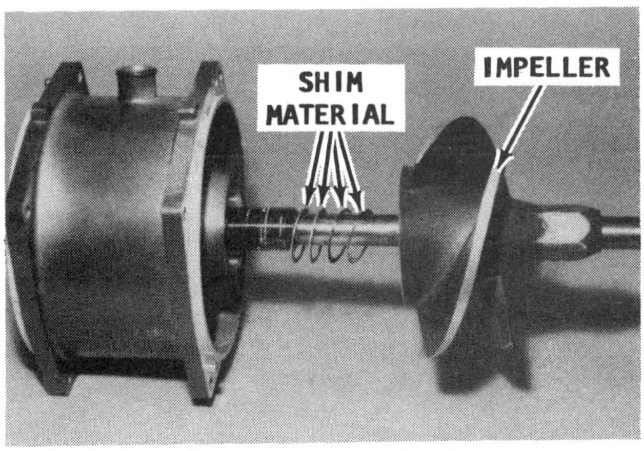

On a Yamaha mixed flow pump, shim material is used on the shaft inside the housing to provide correct impeller-to-housing clearance.

The rubber coupler must remain in good condition to ensure correct engine alignment.

4-6 PRE-SEASON PREPARATION

Satisfactory performance and maximum enjoyment can be realized if a little time is spent in preparing the unit for service at the beginning of the season. Assuming the unit has been properly stored, as outlined in Section 4-10, a minimum amount of work is required to prepare the unit for use.

EXTERIOR

After the cover protecting the craft from the weather, dust and dirt has been removed, a thorough washing of the hull is certainly in order. As explained later in this chapter, a good waxing and polishing will give the owner a "pride of ownership" when using the unit in a crowded waterway and especially during a competition of any kind.

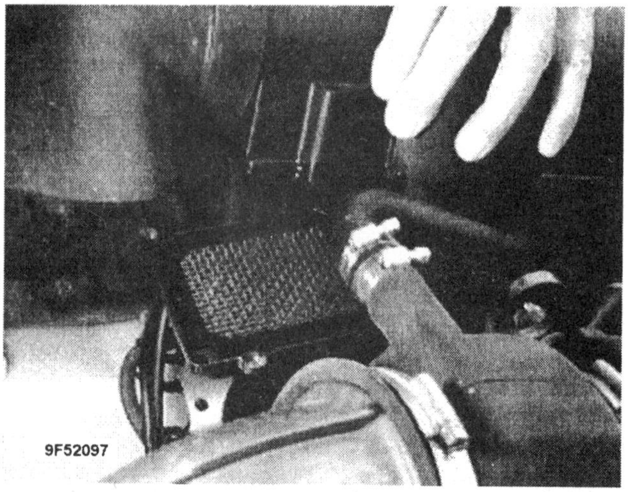

Just a little preparation time spent at the beginning of each season will reward the owner with satisfactory performance and maximum enjoyment.

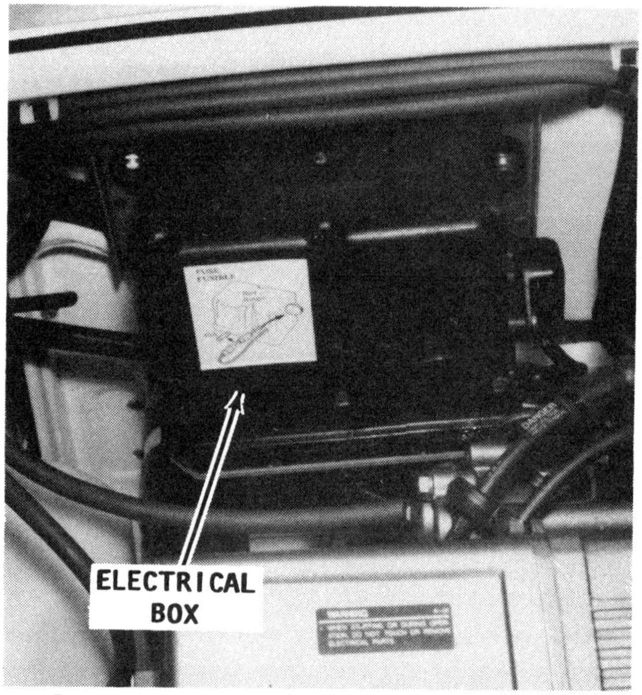

Location of the electrical box on a Yamaha personal watercraft.

INTERIOR

Removing the seat and lifting the engine cover exposes the interior of the engine compartment and other areas to inspection and possible "pre-season" tasks as outlined in this section.

The following steps outline an adequate and logical sequence of tasks to be performed before using the craft the first time in a new season.

The opened electrical box shown contains most of the ignition and electrical components installed on the craft covered in the manual.

When the flywheel cover is removed, ***TAKE CARE*** *not to lose the spring and two washers from the recess for the idler gear shaft.*

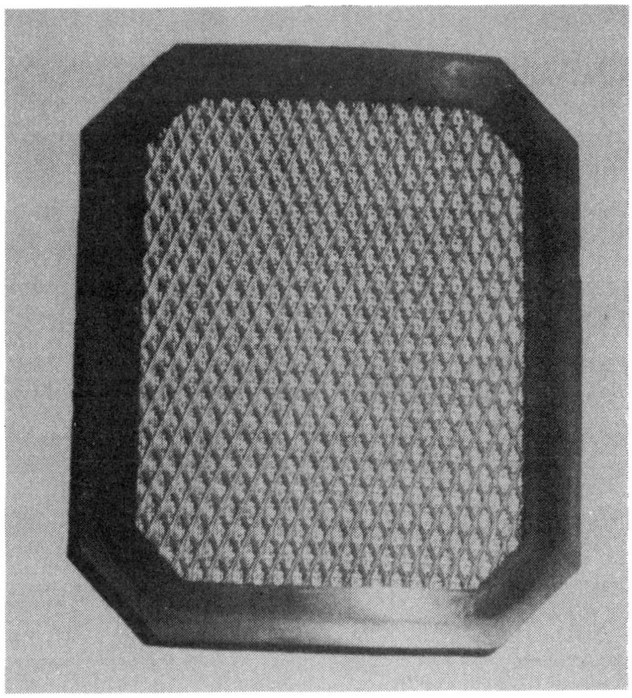

On a Yamaha, the condition of the rubber gasket around the flame arrestor screen must remain in good condition.

GOOD WORDS

All manufacturers recommend the fuel filter be replaced at the start of each season or at least once a year. There may be as many as three fuel filters on any engine. One at the main fuel tank pickup, another at the reserve tank pickup, and a third in-line filter, mounted between the tank and the fuel pump. Some model carburetors may have an internal filter which can only be serviced by partially dismantling the carburetor.

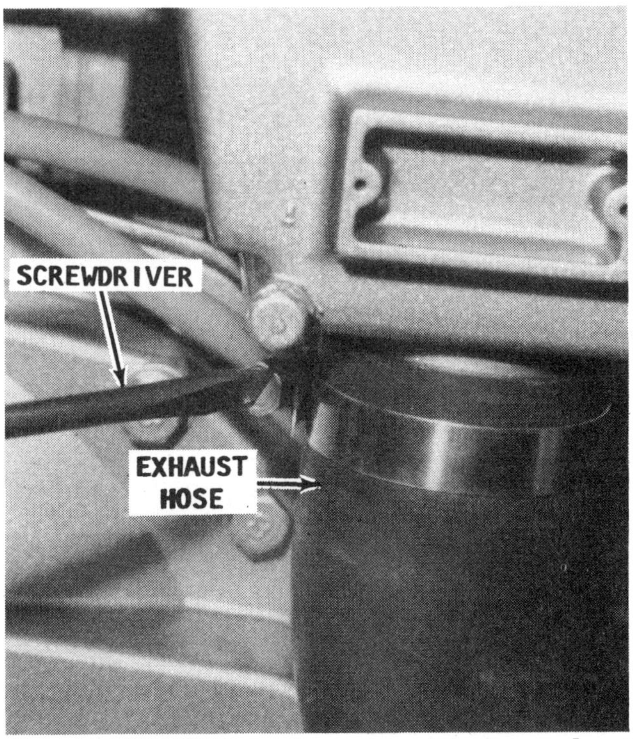

Tightening the hose clamp around the large exhaust hose at the muffler.

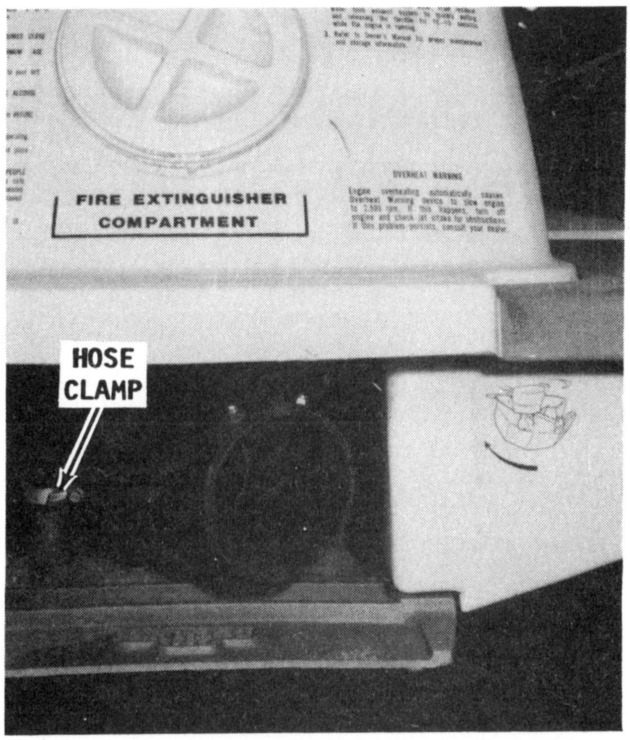

Check the engine cooling hose and bilge hose connections on the jet pump, to ensure they are tight.

1- Lubricate the craft according to the manufacturer's recommendations. Refer to the lubrication chart. Remove, clean, inspect, adjust, and install the spark plugs with new gaskets (if they require gaskets). Make a thorough check of the ignition system. This check should include: the ignition coil, stator assembly, condition of the wiring, and the battery electrolyte level and charge.

If the exhaust outlet was plugged at the end of the last season, remove the plug.

2- Take time to check the gasoline tank and all fuel lines, fittings, couplings, valves, including the flexible tank fill and vent. Turn on the fuel supply valve at the tank. If the fuel was not drained at the end of the previous season, make a careful inspection for gum formation. When gasoline is allowed to stand for long periods of time, gummy deposits form. This gum can clog the filters, lines, and passageways in the carburetor.

3- Close all water drains. Check and replace any defective water hoses. Check to be sure the connections do not leak. Replace any spring-type hose clamps, if they have lost their tension, or if they have distorted the water hose, with band-type clamps.

Check the electrolyte level in the battery as part of the pre-season maintenance tasks.

4- The engine can be run with the jet pump in water to flush it. If this is not practical, a flush attachment may be used. This device is attached to the engine water supply hose, between the engine and the pump. Attach a garden hose, turn on the water, allow the water to flow into the engine for awhile, and then start the engine.

CAUTION

Water must circulate through the jet pump -- to and from the engine, anytime the engine is operating. Circulating water will prevent overheating -- which could cause damage to moving engine parts and possible engine seizure.

Check the exhaust outlet for water discharge. Check for leaks. Check operation of the thermostat, if so equipped.

5- Check the electrolyte level in the battery and the voltage for a full charge. Clean and inspect the battery terminals and cable connections. **TAKE TIME** to check the polarity, if a new battery is being installed. Cover the cable connections with grease or special protective compound as a prevention to corrosion formation. Check all electrical wiring and grounding circuits.

6- Check all electrical parts on the engine and lower portions of the hull to be sure they are not of a type that could cause ignition of an explosive atmosphere. Rubber caps help keep spark insulators clean and reduce the possibility of arcing. Electric cranking motors and high-tension wiring harnesses should be of a marine type to prevent an explosive mixture from igniting.

4-7 SEALANTS, ADHESIVES, LUBRICANTS, AND FUEL STABILIZERS

It is common practice for the larger manufacturers of personal watercraft to market their own line of products for use on their craft. Yamaha chemical engineers have developed such a line including sealants, adhesives, and lubricants, available for use with Yamaha outboard units, stern drives, personal watercraft, snowmobiles, and motorcycles. Throughout this manual, the authors recommend the application of the manufacturer's products as a first choice. All products listed are alternatives of equal value, and may be used with confidence if the manufacturer's line is not available.

Sealants and Adhesives

Four sealants are recommended and they are **NOT** interchangeable. Each is designed to perform under a different set of conditions.

VHT^{r} (very high temperature) Quick Gasket compound is a silicone rubber based adhesive recommended for use where rubber gaskets are required next to a metal surface at high temperature. This sealant is used on the exhaust manifold cover gaskets. The substance has a milky white color.

Permatex #27, a product of the Loctite Corporation, is a high temperature sealant and is usually applied to gaskets.

Yamabond #4 is a non-hardening material and is recommended for metal to metal joints such as the crankcase halves and the lower crankshaft oil seal housing. This substance is highly resistant to oil and gasoline.

Loctite or Lock N' Seal is a non-hardening adhesive. This material is recommended for application to the threads of load bearing fasteners. Loctite helps prevent loosening of the bolt due to vibration, thread wear, and corrosion. Loctite **MUST** be applied **ONLY** to clean and dry parts.

Lubricants

Four different lubricants are recommended in the lubrication procedures presented in this manual. These lubricants are **NOT** interchangeable, each is designed to perform under varying conditions.

Yamaha or Yamalube All-Purpose Marine Grease is a general marine lubricant, chemically formulated to resist salt water. This lubricant is recommended for application to bearings, bushings, and oil seals.

Yamalube Lubricant is a two-stroke engine oil. It has a petroleum base, and is considered a clean burning lubricant. Yamalube reduces carbon deposits and ensures maximum protection against engine wear. This lubricant also contains an ashless detergent to keep piston rings "free". Oil additives are usually not recommended by the manufacturer, and in some cases the use of such a substance may invalidate the warranty.

Fuel Stabilizer

Yamaha Fuel Conditioner and Stabilizer or "Sta-Bil" is recommended during engine operation and during the storage period. The material absorbs water in the fuel system and protects against corrosion.

If used during operation, this fuel additive will prevent the formation of gum and varnish deposits and greatly extend the period between required carburetor overhauls.

When added to the fuel during storage, the additive will prevent the fuel from "souring" for up to twelve full months.

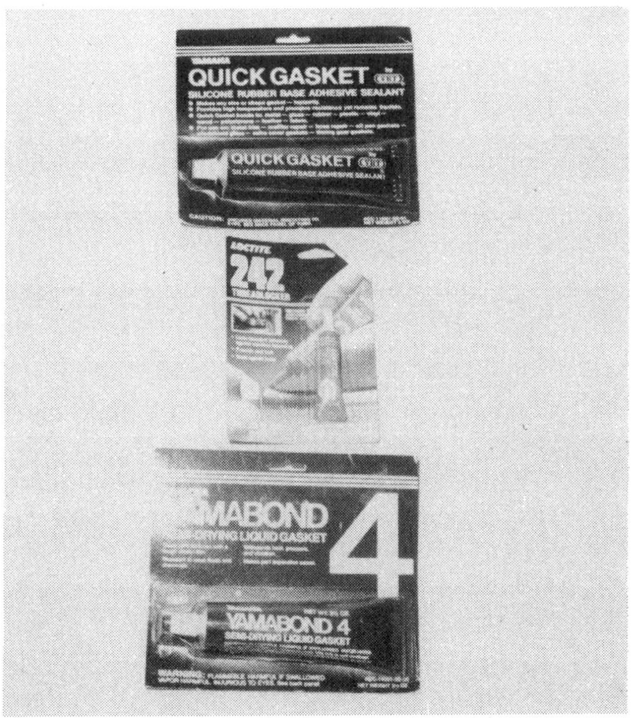

Manufacturer recommended sealants.

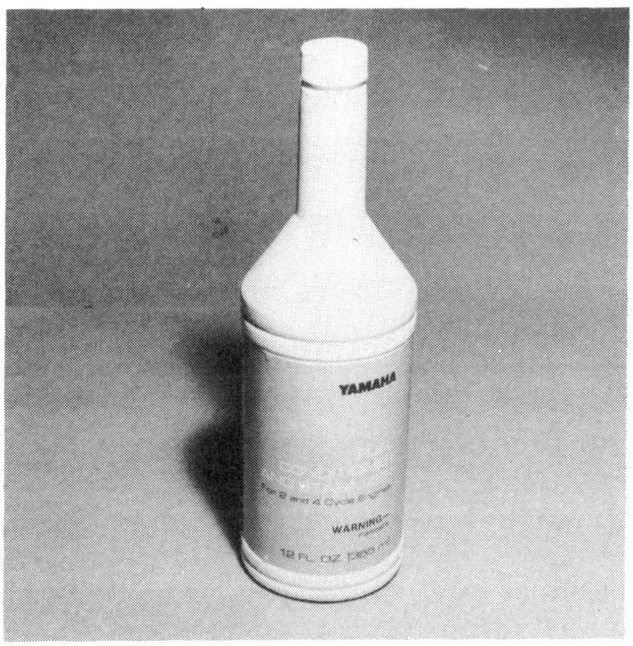

Yamaha Fuel Conditioner and Stabilizer may be used to keep the gasoline in the fuel from "souring". Such an additive will prevent the fuel from "souring" for up to twelve full months.

4-8 FIBERGLASS HULLS

Fiberglass reinforced plastic hulls are tough, durable, and highly resistant to impact. However, like any other material they can be damaged. One of the advantages of this type of construction is the relative ease with which it may be repaired. Because of its break characteristics, and the simple techniques used in restoration, these hulls have gained popularity throughout the world.

A fiberglass hull has almost no internal stresses. Therefore, when the hull is broken or stove-in, it retains its true form. It will not dent to take an out-of-shape set. When the hull sustains a severe blow, the impact will be either absorbed by deflection of the laminated panel or the blow will result in a definite, localized break. Repairs are usually confined to the general area of the rupture.

Cleaning, Waxing, and Polishing

Any craft should be washed with clear water after each use to remove surface dirt and any salt deposits from use in salt water. Regular rinsing will extend the time between waxing and polishing. It will also give "pride of ownership", by having a sharp looking piece of equipment. Elbow grease, a mild detergent, and a brush will be required to remove stubborn dirt, oil, and other unsightly deposits.

Avoid harsh abrasives or strong chemical cleaners. A white buffing compound can be used to restore the original gloss to a scratched, dull, or faded area. The finish should be thoroughly cleaned, buffed, and polished at least once each season. Take care when buffing or polishing with a marine cleaner not to overheat the surface being worked, because the area will become "burned".

4-9 SUBMERGED ENGINE SERVICE

A submerged engine is always the result of an unforeseen accident. Once the craft is recovered, special care and service procedures **MUST** be closely followed in order to return the unit to satisfactory performance.

NEVER, again we say **NEVER** allow an engine that has been submerged to stand more than a couple hours before following the procedures outlined in this section and making every effort to get it running. Such delay will result in serious internal damage. If all efforts fail and the engine cannot be started after the following procedures have been performed, the engine should be disassembled, cleaned, assembled, using new gas-

A regular maintenance program certainly helps keep the watercraft in "useable" condition and the unit operating with peak performance. Here several watercraft maneuver in an inner harbor area before moving to open water at sea for a fun day on the waves.

kets, seals, and O-rings, and then started as soon as possible.

Submerged engine treatment is divided into three unique problem areas: submersion in salt water; submerged while powerhead was running; and a submerged unit in fresh water.

The most critical of these three circumstances is the engine submerged in salt water, with submersion while running, a close second.

Salt Water Submersion

NEVER attempt to start the engine after it has been recovered. This action will only result in additional parts being damaged and the cost of restoring the engine increased considerably. If the engine was submerged in salt water the complete unit **MUST** be disassembled, cleaned, and assembled with new gaskets, O-rings, and seals. The corrosive effect of salt water can only be eliminated by the complete job being properly performed.

Submerged While Running
Special Instructions

If the engine was running when it was submerged, the chances of internal engine damage is greatly increased. Remove the spark plugs to prevent compression in the cylinders. Use a socket wrench on the flywheel nut to rotate the crankshaft. If the attempt fails, the chances of serious internal damage, such as: bent connecting rod, bent crankshaft, or damaged cylinder, is greatly increased. If the crankshaft cannot be rotated, the engine must be completely disassembled.

CRITICAL WORDS

Never attempt to start an engine that has been submerged. If there is water in the cylinder, the piston will not be able to compress the liquid. The result will most likely be a bent connecting rod.

Submerged Engine — Fresh Water
SPECIAL WORDS

As an aid to performing the restoration work, the following steps are numbered and should be followed in sequence. However, illustrations are not included with the procedural steps because the work involved is general in nature.

1- Recover the craft as quickly as possible.

2- Remove the engine cover and the spark plugs.

3- Remove the carburetor float bowl cover, or the bowl.

4- Flush the outside of the engine with fresh water to remove silt, mud, sand, weeds, and other debris. **DO NOT** attempt to start the engine if sand has entered any part of the engine. Such action will only result in serious damage to engine components. Sand in the engine means the unit must be disassembled.

CRITICAL WORDS

Never attempt to start an engine that has been submerged. If there is water in the cylinder, the piston will not be able to compress the liquid. The result will most likely be a bent connecting rod.

5- Remove as much water as possible from the engine. Most of the water can be eliminated by first holding the engine in a horizontal position with the spark plug holes **DOWN**, and then the flywheel with a socket wrench on the flywheel nut. Rotate the crankshaft through at least 10 complete revolutions. If you are satisfied there is no water in the cylinders, proceed with Step 6 to remove moisture.

6- Alcohol will absorb moisture. Therefore, pour alcohol into the carburetor throat and again rotate the crankshaft.

7- Pour alcohol into the spark plug openings and again rotate the crankshaft.

8- With assistance, rotate the craft into the horizontal position until the spark plug openings are facing **DOWN**. Pour engine oil into the carburetor throat and, at the same time, rotate the crankshaft to distribute oil throughout the crankcase.

9- With the craft upright, pour approximately one teaspoon of engine oil into each spark plug opening. Rotate the crankshaft to distribute the oil in the cylinders.

10- Install and connect the spark plugs.

11- Install the carburetor float bowl cover, or the bowl.

12- Obtain **FRESH** fuel and attempt to start the engine. If the engine starts, allow it to run for approximately an hour to eliminate any unwanted moisture remaining in the engine.

CAUTION

Water must circulate through the jet pump — to and from the engine, anytime the

engine is operating. Circulating water will prevent overheating — which could cause damage to moving engine parts and possible engine seizure.

13- If the engine fails to start, determine the cause, electrical or fuel, correct the problem, and again attempt to get it running. **NEVER** allow an engine to remain unstarted for more than a couple hours without following the procedures in this section and attempting to start it. If attempts to start the engine fail, the unit should be disassembled, cleaned, assembled, using new gaskets, seals, and O-rings, as **SOON** as possible.

4-10 WINTER STORAGE

Taking extra time to store the craft properly at the end of each season, will increase the chances of satisfactory service at the next season. **REMEMBER,** idleness is the greatest enemy of a marine engine. The unit should be run on a monthly basis. The steering and shifting mechanism should also be worked through complete cycles several times each month. The owner who spends a small amount of time involved in such maintenance will be rewarded by satisfactory performance, and greatly reduced maintenance expense for parts and labor.

Proper storage involves adequate protection of the unit from physical damage, rust, corrosion, and dirt.

Lubricate the ball joint on the steering post with Yamalube, or equivalent, as part of the winter storage program.

The following steps provide an adequate maintenance program for storing the unit at the end of a season.

1- Empty all fuel from the carburetor.

For many years there has been the widespread belief simply shutting off the fuel at the tank and then running the engine until it stops is the proper procedure before storing the engine for any length of time. Right? **WRONG!**

First, it is **NOT** possible to remove all fuel in the carburetor by operating the engine until it stops. Considerable fuel is trapped in the float chamber and other passages and in the line leading to the carburetor. The **ONLY** guaranteed method of removing **ALL** fuel is to take the time to remove the carburetor, and drain the fuel.

Secondly, if the engine is operated with the fuel supply shut off until it stops, the fuel and oil mixture inside the block is removed, leaving bearings, pistons, rings, and other parts without any protective lubricant.

Remove the spark plugs and pour about one ounce of two-cycle engine oil into each spark plug hole. Wait a minute or two and then slowly rotate the flywheel/crankshaft through two complete revolutions to evenly distribute the oil. Install the spark plugs.

2- Drain the fuel tank and the fuel lines. Pour approximately one quart (0.96 liters) of benzol (benzine) into the fuel tank, and then rinse the tank and pickup filter with the benzol. Drain the tank. Store the craft with the engine compartment door open to allow air to circulate around the tank and with the fuel vent **OPEN** to allow air to circulate through the tank.

3- Clean the in-line fuel filter with benzol, see the Fuel chapter.

4- Lubricate the throttle and shift linkage. Lubricate the steering pivot shaft with Yamalube or equivalent.

5- Plug the exhaust outlet with a shop towel or similar item to prevent any type of contaminant from entering the exhaust system.

Battery Storage

Remove the battery from the craft and keep it charged during the storage period. Clean the battery thoroughly of any dirt or corrosion, and then charge the battery to the full specific gravity reading. After charging, store the battery in a clean cool dry place where it will not be damaged or knocked over.

NEVER store the battery with anything on top of it or cover the battery in such a manner as to prevent air from circulating around the filler caps. All batteries, both new and old, will discharge during periods of storage, more so if they are hot than if they remain cool. Therefore, the electrolyte level and the specific gravity should be checked at regular intervals. A drop in the specific gravity reading is cause to charge the battery back to a full reading.

One of the largest personal watercraft battery manufacturers recommends that a battery in storage should be checked every two weeks and charged if necessary. The electrolyte level can also be replenished at this time to prevent sulfation occurring.

In cold climates, **EXERCISE CARE** in selecting the battery storage area. A fully-charged battery will freeze at about 60° below zero. A discharged battery, almost dead, will have ice forming at about 19° above zero.

4-11 PRE-SEASON CHECK

Before attempting to start the craft after winter storage, check the steering and throttle action for smooth operation, without binding. If the battery was removed for storage, check to make sure it has a full charge.

Filling the Battery

Remove each filler cap using a pair of pliers. Fill each cell to the proper level with distilled water. The level of electrolyte should be between the upper and lower level marks during operation. When filling the battery, fill to the upper line and allow the battery to stand for twenty minutes. Check the level again and replenish as necessary.

Use a temperature corrected hydrometer to test the specific gravity of the electrolyte. At 20°C (68°F) the hydrometer reading should be 1.26 on the scale. If it is necessary to charge the battery, leave the filler caps lightly resting on the cell openings to allow the gases to escape. The charging current should not exceed 1.9 amps for 10 hours.

After charging, push each filler cap into place and wipe the top of the battery clean before installation.

Clean the battery posts and battery cable ends with a wire brush to ensure good, clean connections. Clean the top surface of the battery and identify the "POS" or "+" and "NEG" or "-" embossed symbols. Correctly connect the battery cables to the battery observing polarity. If the cables are connected backwards, the ignition system **WILL** be destroyed the first time the engine is started.

Make sure the breather pipe is in place on the battery and the pipe is not pinched when the battery is installed.

First Time Start

If the proper maintenance was observed at the end of the previous season, both the carburetor and fuel tank should be completely empty. Fill the gas tank with the proper mixture and open the fuel valve, if equipped. Open the choke. **DO NOT** attempt to crank the engine until it starts, **AT THIS TIME.** Considerable cranking time will be spent before the oil/fuel mixture reaches engine bearings and other moving parts. Expensive parts may be damaged due to lack of lubrication and the cranking motor will become excessively hot, which is also **BAD NEWS.**

CAUTION

Water must circulate through the jet pump -- to and from the engine, anytime the engine is operating. Circulating water will prevent overheating -- which could cause damage to moving engine parts and possible engine seizure.

Battery life may be extended considerably if it is removed from the craft for storage during the winter months. Proper maintenance or securing it without possibility of movement will also prolong battery life.

A realistic maintenance program for the hull, powerplant, and jet pump can keep the craft performing in fine form, even with a skier in tow.

The correct procedure for starting is to obtain an **AEROSOL** can of WD-40. It must be an aerosol canister because the liquid must be atomized, a squirt can will not do the job. **DO NOT** use ether or a commercial starting fluid because they will evaporate almost instantly. These products work well with four-stroke engines equipped with an oil pump, but they do not contain a lubricant essential for a two-stroke engine. WD-40 is an extremely flammable oil.

Make sure both spark plugs are tight, so the mist from the canister will not ignite. Spray the WD-40 through the flame arrestor and continue spraying with **NO** throttle until the engine starts. As soon as the engine is operating, cease spraying the WD-40. The engine may emit some smoke for a few seconds after it starts. Watch the sediment bowl (if so equipped). As soon as it fills, the engine should operate on the regular oil/fuel mixture. Work the throttle to keep the engine at idle speed until it reaches operating temperature, then close the choke. Advance the throttle a few times and the engine should then idle smoothly.

5
TROUBLESHOOTING

5-1 INTRODUCTION

This chapter is divided into five main sections as follows:

5-2 Mechanical engine problems.
5-3 Fuel system problems.
5-4 Ignition system faults.
5-5 Cranking system failures.
5-6 Charging system malfunctions.
5-7 Troubleshooting Charts

If a change in engine rpm is experienced at normal operating speed, such a change is usually a symptom of an engine problem or trouble in the jet pump. An increase or a decrease in rpm may be an indication of the area to be checked. The following generalizations may be helpful in isolating the problem.

A noticeable change in craft performance, as evidenced by one of the following symptoms, may be attributed to one or more of the areas listed:

Lower than Normal Engine Rpm

Mechanical problems in the engine:
- Plugged flame arrestor.
- Fouled spark plug/s, incorrect heat range or gap.
- Shorted or weak ignition coil.
- Contaminated fuel.
- Restricted exhaust system.
- Inadequate fuel pump pressure.
- Loss of compression due to blown head gasket.

Mechanical problems in the jet drive:
- Worn or damaged impeller.
- Main bearing failure.
- Rubber coupler failure.

Higher than Normal Engine Rpm

Mechanical problem in the engine:
- None.

Mechanical problems in the jet drive:
- Clogged intake grate -- possibly plastic bag or other debris.
- Line, sea weed, etc. entangled in impeller.
- Ingested sand.

If a reduction in speed is experienced, accompanied with no loss or gain of engine rpm, the loss of performance can fairly accurately be attributed to some type of drag on the craft or restriction of the water ejected from the jet pump.

Drag on the hull is usually caused by damage to the craft.

Many times, drag from the jet pump is caused by a partially lowered reverse gate, if so equipped, or from dragging debris caught in the intake grate.

A partially lowered reverse gate may be caused by incorrect cable adjustment or by binding around the gate pivot pins.

Engine Troubleshooting

Troubleshooting must be a well thought-out procedure. Always attempt to proceed

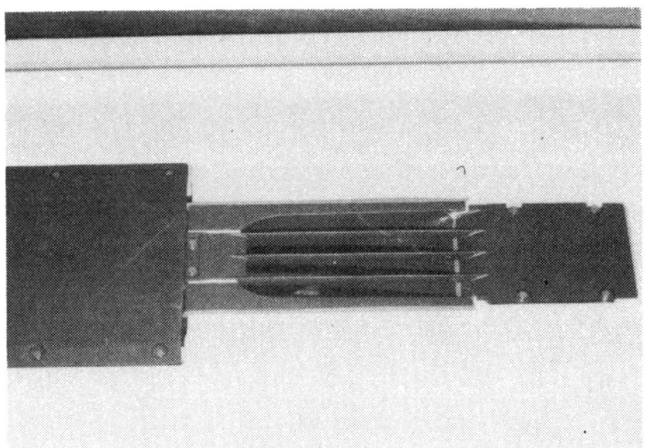

An intake grate clogged with seaweed, line, or the most dangerous debris of all -- plastic bag or wrapping -- will cause serious problems to the engine and jet pump.

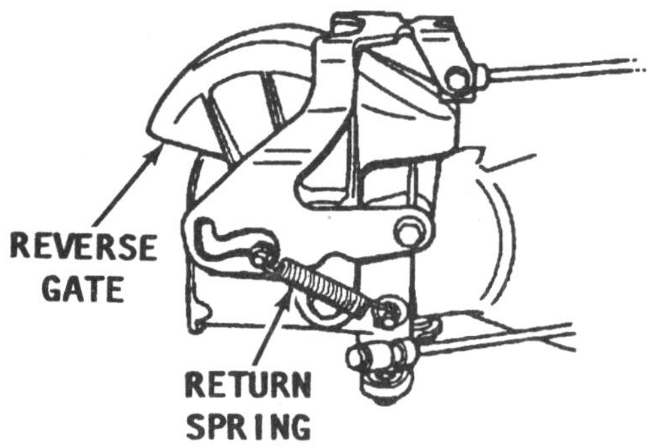

A weak return spring may be the cause of a partially lowered reverse gate — restricting forward speed.

with the troubleshooting in an orderly manner. The "shot in the dark" approach will only result in wasted time, incorrect diagnosis, replacement of unnecessary parts, and frustration.

Obviously, if the instructions are to be of maximum benefit as a guide, they must be fully understood and followed in the proper sequence.

When an engine fails to start, the trouble must be localized to one of four general areas: cranking system; ignition system; fuel system; or compression. Each of these areas must be systematically inspected until the trouble is isolated. At that time, detailed tests of the system or area must be made to determine the part causing the problem. The last section of this chapter describes charging system troubleshooting.

Troubleshooting Check

When using this Troubleshooting Check, proceed sequentially through each test until the defect is uncovered. Then skip to the detailed testing procedure and check for that system. For example, if, when using the Troubleshooting Check procedure, the first two systems, cranking and ignition tests OK, but the third test shows there is trouble in the fuel system, then proceed to the detailed test under the Fuel System Troubleshooting Check in Section 5-3.

Cranking System Test

1- Turn the key switch to the **START** position or press the ignition button. The cranking motor should crank the engine at a normal rate of speed.

If the cranking motor cranks the engine slowly or fails to crank it at all, the trouble is either in the battery or in the cranking system. Test the battery first, then if the battery checks out, proceed directly to Troubleshooting the Cranking System in Section 5-7 for detailed testing procedure to isolate the problem.

Ignition System Test

2- Connect a standard spark tester (available at almost any automotive parts store at very nominal cost), between the spark plug and the spark plug lead. Hold the spark plug lead with an insulated holder (to avoid receiving a "shock" when the current

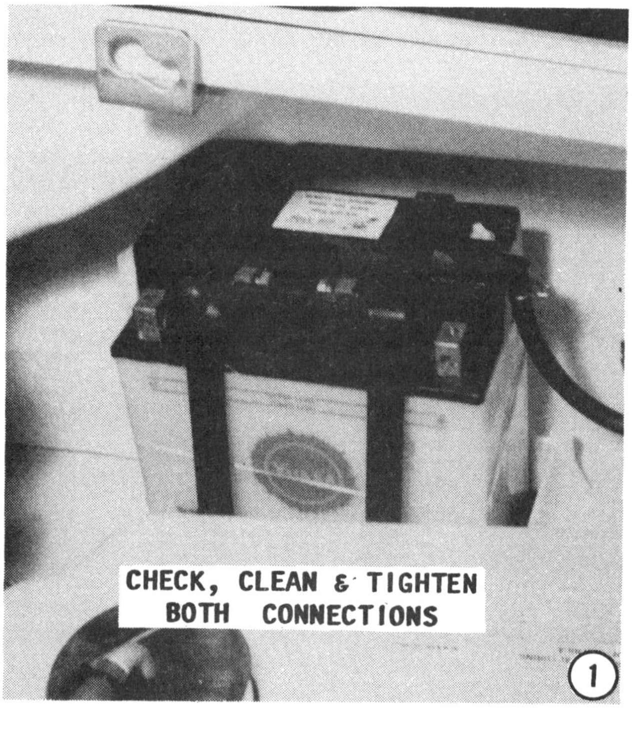

passes through). Crank the engine with the cranking motor. If there is **NO** spark, or if the spark is very weak, the trouble is in the ignition system. Proceed directly to the Ignition Troubleshooting in Section 5-4 for detailed testing procedures to uncover the problem.

3- Remove the flame arrestor. Look down into the throat of the carburetor and at the same time open and close the throttle several times. Observe the throttle valve to verify it moves from the fully closed to the fully open position. Perform the same check with the choke valve.

Attempt to determine the age of the fuel in the fuel tank. Many fuels tend to "sour" in three to four months, especially if an additive such as Sta-Bil has not been added. Other fuels take longer to "sour". In no case should an attempt be made to start the engine if the fuel in the tank is more than 12 months old.

Compression Test

4- Good compression is the key to proper engine performance. An engine with worn piston rings or a blown gasket cannot be made to perform satisfactorily until the mechanical defects contributing to low compression are corrected. Generally, a compression gauge is used to determine the cranking pressure within each cylinder.

To make a compression test, remove both spark plugs and remember or identify

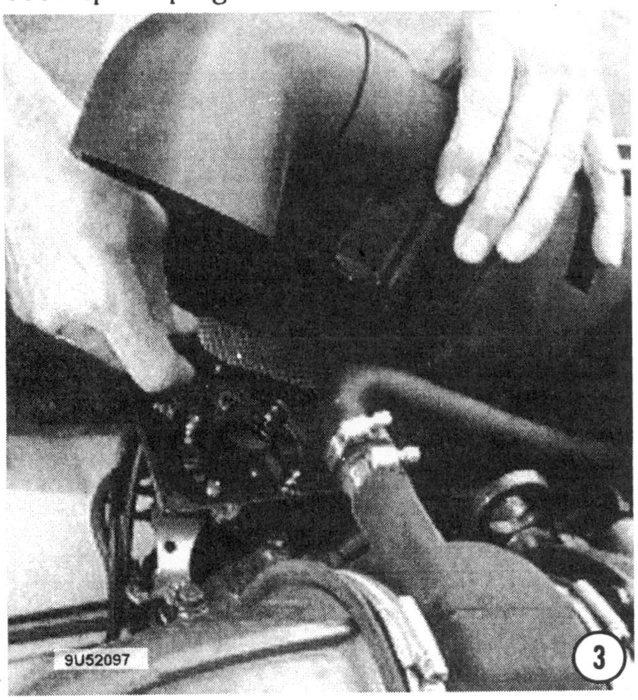

from which cylinder they were taken. Evaluation of the spark plug firing end can be most useful in determining how the cylinder is functioning. After the spark plugs have been removed, install a compression gauge into one cylinder and crank the engine.

The throttle valve and choke **MUST** be in the **WIDE OPEN** position in order to obtain maximum readings. Crank the engine through several revolutions and observe the highest reading on the compression gauge.

The cranking compression for a new engine is 142 psi. The significance in a compression test is the variation in pressure readings between the cylinders. As long as this variation is between 20-30 psi, cylinder compression is considered as "satisfactory". If a greater variation exists, then the lower reading cylinder should be checked by making a cylinder leak test. A simple leak test can be made by first inserting a teaspoonful of oil into the spark plug opening of the lower reading cylinder, and then cranking the engine a few times to distribute the oil.

Check the compression again to see if inserting the oil caused a change. The oil helps make a temporary seal around the

A gasoline stabilizer and conditioner may be used to prevent fuel from "souring" for up to twelve full months.

rings and increases the compression. If the reading increased, the compression loss was probably due to worn rings. If the reading did not change appreciably, the loss may be due to a blown head gasket.

5-2 MECHANICAL ENGINE PROBLEMS

Jumping Waves

Even though "jumping waves" with a personal watercraft may be considered **GREAT** sport, consider the extensive internal engine damage which will surely occur if this type action is consistently practiced. When airborne, the engine rpm rapidly increases to probably 12,000 or more. As soon as the craft is back in the water, the engine rpm instantly decreases to about 6,000. This sudden increase and decrease in engine speed dramatically shortens engine life. Bent crankshafts and broken connecting rods can usually be directly attributed to this type of "fun play".

Easy Check for Twisted Crankshaft

A twisted crankshaft may be detected by first removing the spark plugs and setting up a dial indicator in one of the spark plug openings. If a dial indicator is not available, a pencil, straw, or other small diameter straight object may be used.

With the indicator, or other device, in place, determine the TDC (top dead center) of the No. 1 piston. Now, make two matching marks -- one on the flywheel and the other adjacent on the stator. Next, rotate the flywheel **EXACTLY** 180° -- preferably using a degree wheel on the flywheel. Make a second mark on the stator adjacent to the mark on the flywheel.

NOW, check for TDC of the other piston. The dial indicator should indicate the same reading as for the first piston **AND** the two marks on the stator should be **EXACTLY** opposite each other through the center of the crankshaft. If the indicator is off or if the marks on the stator are not aligned, as described -- the crankshaft is twisted and **MUST** be replaced.

Engine Noises

Engine noises can be generally classified as knocks, slaps, clicks, or squeaks. These noises are usually caused by loose bearings, sloppy pistons, or other moving parts of the engine.

A main bearing knock is usually identified by a dull thud which is noticeable under engine load. Attempting to move the craft under power with it tied to the dock will bring out a main bearing knock. If you pull

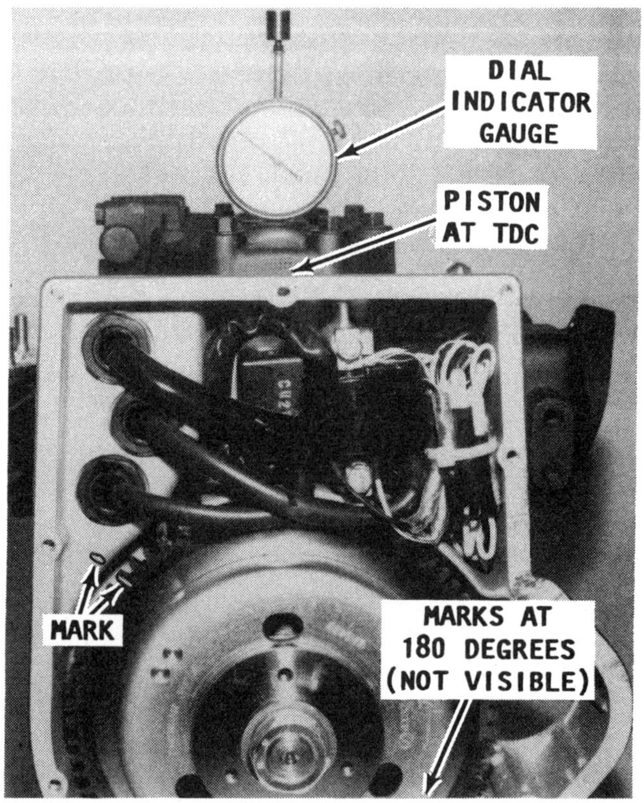

Making a simple easy check for a twisted crankshaft, as explained in the text.

the spark plug wire from one plug at a time and the noise disappears when one of the wires is removed, then the noise is probably coming from that cylinder. The cause may be either the rod bearing, piston pin, or the piston, which has quieted down because the load has been removed from the part. If a rod bearing has failed, the noise will be loudest when the engine is decelerating. Piston pin noise and piston pin slap are generally louder when a cold engine is first started.

Carbon build up in the combustion chamber can cause interference with a piston.

Many times the source of an unusual sound may be isolated by using a stethoscope or other listening device. One such device is a long shank screwdriver. Allow your hand to extend over the end of the handle, press an ear to your hand, and then probe with the other end of the screwdriver by touching it firmly against the block at each cylinder or noise area. Take care and use good judgment when using this method of attempting to detect the cause of a problem because the noise will travel through other metallic parts of the engine and could lead to a false interpretation of what you are hearing.

The tiniest pin hole or tear in the carburetor diaphragm will seriously affect carburetor performance.

5-3 FUEL SYSTEM PROBLEMS

The following paragraphs provide an orderly sequence of tests to pinpoint problems in the system. It is very rare for the carburetor by itself to cause failure of the engine to start.

Many times fuel system troubles are caused by a plugged fuel filter, a defective fuel pump, or by a leak in the fuel line from the fuel tank to the fuel pump or by a

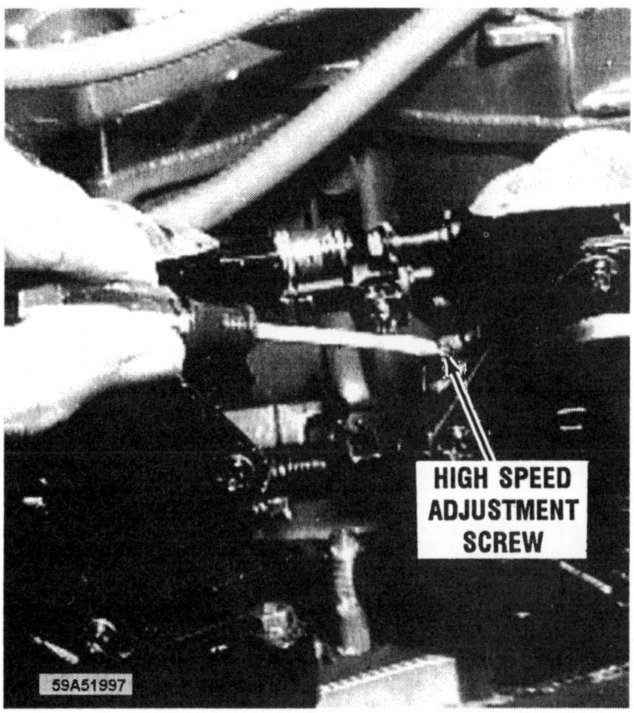

An air/fuel mixture problem in the carburetor will prevent the engine from operating smoothly at idle speed.

A small leak between the carburetor and the intake manifold will cause rough engine performance at idle rpm.

vacuum leak in the line between the pump and the crankcase.

Fuel will begin to sour in three to four months and will cause engine starting problems. A fuel additive such as Sta-Bil may be used to prevent gum from forming during storage or prolonged idle periods.

When the engine is hot, the fuel system can cause starting problems. After a hot engine is shut down, the temperature inside the fuel bowl may rise to 200°F and cause the fuel to actually boil. All carburetors are vented to allow this pressure to escape to the atmosphere. However, some of the fuel may percolate over the high-speed nozzle and overflow into the intake manifold.

In order for this raw fuel to vaporize enough to burn, considerable air must be added to lean out the mixture. Therefore, the only remedy is to open the throttle as wide as possible and to crank the engine until enough air is drawn in to provide the proper mixture for the engine to start. **NEVER** move the throttle lever back-and-forth in an attempt to start a hot engine. This action will only compound the problem by adding more fuel to an already too-rich mixture.

A leak between the fuel tank and the pump many times will not appear when the engine is operating because the suction created by the pump sucking fuel will not allow the fuel to leak. Once the engine is turned off and the suction no longer exists, fuel may begin to leak.

1

Engine Surge

If the engine operates as if the load on the craft was being constantly increased and decreased, even though the operator attempts to maintain a constant engine speed, the problem can most likely be attributed to the fuel pump.

Rough Engine Idle

Problems preventing an engine from running smoothly include: a fouled spark plug; an air leak in the intake manifold; and uneven compression between the cylinders.

Of course any problem in the carburetor affecting the air/fuel mixture will also prevent the engine from operating smoothly at idle speed. These problems usually include: leaking needle valve and seat; a dirty flame arrestor; defective choke; and improper adjustments for idle mixture or idle speed.

5-4 IGNITION SYSTEM FAULTS

WARNING

Check to be sure the engine compartment is well ventilated and free of any gasoline vapors before starting any of the following tests. A spark will be generated creating a potential fire hazard if fuel vapors are present.

1- Check to be sure the battery has a full charge. If not, correct the condition by charging the battery or making a substitution.

2- Check all the terminal connections inside the electrical box. Check all primary

2

and secondary ignition wiring, the engine "kill" switch and the ignition switch.

3- Use a spark tester and check for spark. If a spark tester is not available, hold the plug wire about 1/4" (6.4mm) from the engine. Crank the engine through a few revolutions using the cranking motor and check for spark. A strong spark over a wide gap must be observed when testing in this manner, because under compression a strong spark is necessary in order to ignite the air/fuel mixture in the cylinder. This means it is possible to think a strong spark is present, when in reality the spark will be too weak when the plug is installed. If there is no spark, or if the spark is weak, the trouble is most likely under the flywheel in the stator assembly.

4- Perform the resistance test procedures given in the Ignition chapter to identify the faulty component.

Intermittent or Multiple Problems

Many ignition problems occur only during engine operation, when the component is subject to vibration and/or an increase in temperature. Many of these defective components return to normal once the engine is shut down and allowed to cool.

There is also the possibility of more than one defective component in the ignition system. One component failure may have caused a surge of power and "fried" another component.

Make every attempt to avoid the **BUY** and **TRY** method of troubleshooting. In **MOST** cases electrical components are not returnable, once the item leaves the store.

SPARK PLUG EVALUATION

Removal: Remove the spark plug wires by pulling and twisting on only the molded cap. **NEVER** pull on the wire or the connection inside the cap may become separated or the boot damaged. Remove the spark plugs and identify from which cylinder they were taken. **TAKE CARE** not to tilt the socket as you remove the plug or the insulator may be cracked.

Examine: Carefully examine the firing end to determine the firing condition in each cylinder.

Correct Color: A proper firing plug should be dry and powdery. Hard deposits inside the shell indicate the engine is starting to use some oil, but not enough to cause concern. The most important evidence is

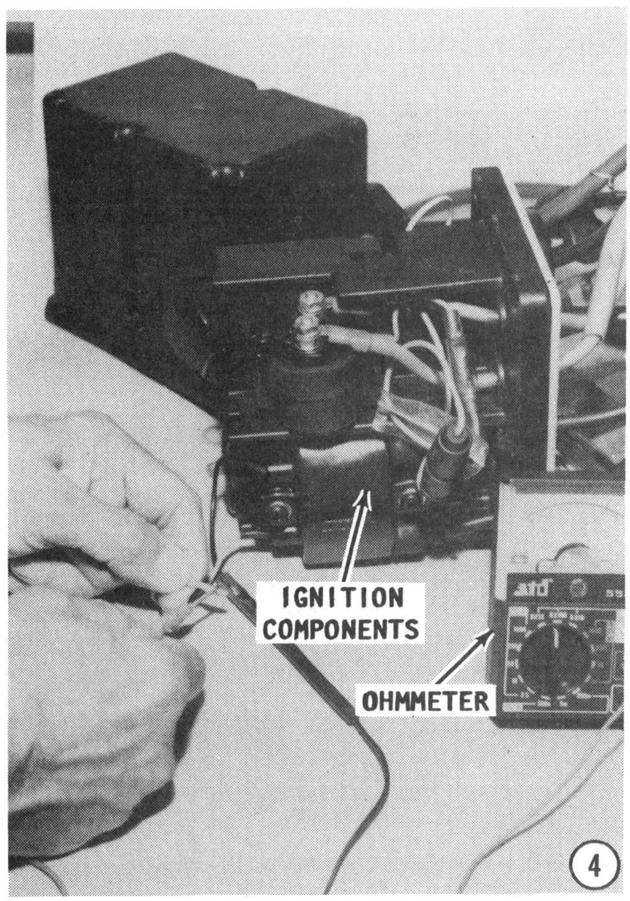

Excessive overheating, heavy load. Use a spark plug with a lower heat rating.

Spark plug fouled by oil. The engine may need an overhaul.

Powdery deposits have melted and shorted-out this spark plug.

the light gray color of the porcelain, which is an indication this plug has been running at the correct temperature. This means the plug is one with the correct heat range and also that the air/fuel mixture is correct.

Overheating: A dead white or gray insulator, which is generally blistered, is an indication of overheating and pre-ignition. The electrode gap wear rate will be more than normal and in the case of pre-ignition, will actually cause the electrodes to melt. Overheating and pre-ignition are usually caused by overadvanced timing, detonation from using too-low an octane rating fuel, an excessively lean air/fuel mixture, or problems in the cooling system.

Rich Mixture: A black, sooty condition on both the spark plug shell and the porcelain is caused by an excessively rich air/fuel mixture, both at low and high speeds. The rich mixture lowers the combustion temperature so the spark plug does not run hot enough to burn off the deposits.

Deposits formed only on the shell is an indication the low-speed air/fuel mixture is too rich. At high speeds with the correct mixture, the temperature in the combustion chamber is high enough to burn off the deposits on the insulator.

Too Cool: A dark insulator, with very few deposits, indicates the plug is running too cool. This condition can be caused by low compression or by using a spark plug of an incorrect heat range. If this condition shows on only one plug it is most usually

Red, brown, or yellow deposits, are by-products of combustion from fuel and lubricating oil.

caused by low compression in that cylinder. If both plugs have this appearance, then it is probably due to the plugs having a too-low heat range.

Fouled: A fouled spark plug may be caused by the wet oily deposits on the insulator shorting the high-tension current to ground inside the shell. The condition may also be caused by ignition problems which prevent a high-tension pulse to be delivered to the spark plug.

Carbon Deposits: Heavy carbon-like deposits are an indication of excessive oil consumption. This condition may be the result of worn piston rings.

Electrode Wear: Electrode wear results in a wide gap and if the electrode becomes carbonized it will form a high-resistance path for the spark to jump across. Such a condition will cause the engine to misfire during acceleration. If both plugs are in this condition, it can cause an increase in fuel consumption and very poor performance at high-speed operation. The solution is to replace the spark plugs with a rating in the proper heat range and gapped to specification.

Red rust-colored deposits on the entire firing end of a spark plug can be caused by water in the cylinder combustion chamber. This can be the first evidence of water entering the cylinders through the exhaust manifold. This condition **MUST** be corrected at the first opportunity.

5-5 CRANKING SYSTEM FAILURES

Regardless of how or where the solenoid is mounted, the basic circuits of the starting system on all makes of cranking motors are the same and similar tests apply. In the following testing and troubleshooting procedures, the differences are noted.

WARNING

ALWAYS TAKE TIME TO VENT THE BILGE WHEN MAKING ANY OF THE TESTS AS A PREVENTION AGAINST IGNITING ANY FUMES ACCUMULATED IN THAT AREA.

All engine cranking problems fall into one of three problem areas:

1- The cranking motor fails to turn.

2- The cranking motor spins rapidly, but does not crank the engine.

3- The cranking motor cranks the engine, but too slowly.

The following paragraphs provide a logical sequence of tests designed to isolate a problem in the cranking system.

Battery Test

1- If the starter relay clicks, the battery charge is too low to keep the starting relay engaged when the starter load is brought into the circuit.

If the cranking motor spins without cranking the engine, the drive is broken. The cranking motor will have to be removed for repairs.

Cable Connection Test

2- Check the connections at the battery, starter relay, starter, ignition switch, and the "kill" switch.

Starter Relay Test (or Solenoid Test)

3- Operate the bilge blower for at least five minutes to clear any fumes accumulated in the bilge.

TAKE EVERY PRECAUTION TO ENSURE THERE ARE NO GASOLINE FUMES IN THE BILGE BEFORE MAKING THESE TESTS.

Select the Rx1000 ohm scale. Calibrate the meter by making contact with the meter leads to each other, and then rotating the calibration knob on the meter until the needle indicates zero ohms. Separate the meter leads.

Make contact with the Red meter lead to one of the large terminals on the solenoid. Make contact with the Black meter lead to the other large solenoid terminal. **NEVER** connect the battery leads to the large terminals of the solenoid, or the meter will be damaged.

Using battery jumper leads, connect the positive lead from the positive terminal of the battery to the small terminal of the solenoid which had the Brown lead attached. Connect the negative lead to the negative battery terminal and the other small terminal of the solenoid which had the Black lead attached. If the meter needle indicates continuity, the solenoid is serviceable. If the meter fails to indicate continuity, the solenoid is defective and **MUST** be replaced.

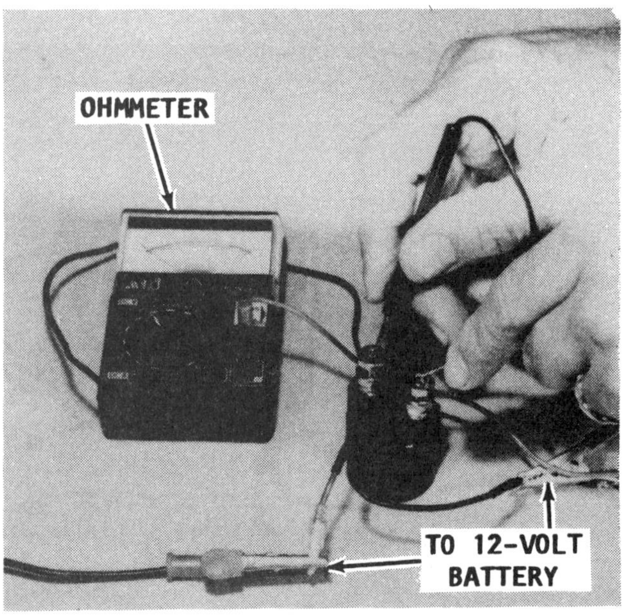

Hookup to test a cranking motor relay using an ohmmeter and a 12-volt battery.

Checking Cranking Circuit Resistance

If the cranking motor turns very slowly or not at all, or if the solenoid fails to engage the gear with the flywheel, the cause may be excessive resistance in the cranking circuit.

The following checks can be performed with the cranking motor installed on the engine.

1- Test the battery and bring it up to a full charge, if necessary.

GROUND the ignition coil primary lead to prevent the engine from firing during the following checks.

2- Measure the voltage drop during cranking between the positive battery post and the battery lead terminal of the solenoid.

3- Measure the voltage drop during cranking between the battery lead terminal of the solenoid and the motor lead terminal of the solenoid.

4- Measure the voltage drop during cranking between the negative battery post and the starter motor frame.

If the voltage drop during any of the previous three tests is more than 0.2 volt, excessive resistance is indicated in the circuit being checked. Trace and correct the cause of the resistance.

If the solenoid fails to activate, the problem may be due to excessive high voltage drop in the solenoid circuit. To check voltage drop in this circuit, measure the voltage drop during cranking, between the battery terminal of the solenoid and the switch terminal of the solenoid. If the voltage drop is more than 2.5 volts, the resistance is excessive in the solenoid circuit.

If the voltage drop is not more than 2.5 volts and the solenoid does not activate, measure the voltage available at the switch terminal of the solenoid. The solenoid should activate with 8.0 volts at temperatures up to 200°F. If it does not activate, remove the cranking motor and test the solenoid.

Cranking System Voltage Tests

Even though the cranking motor cannot be tested accurately while it is mounted on the engine, several tests can be made for excessive resistance in the cranking system

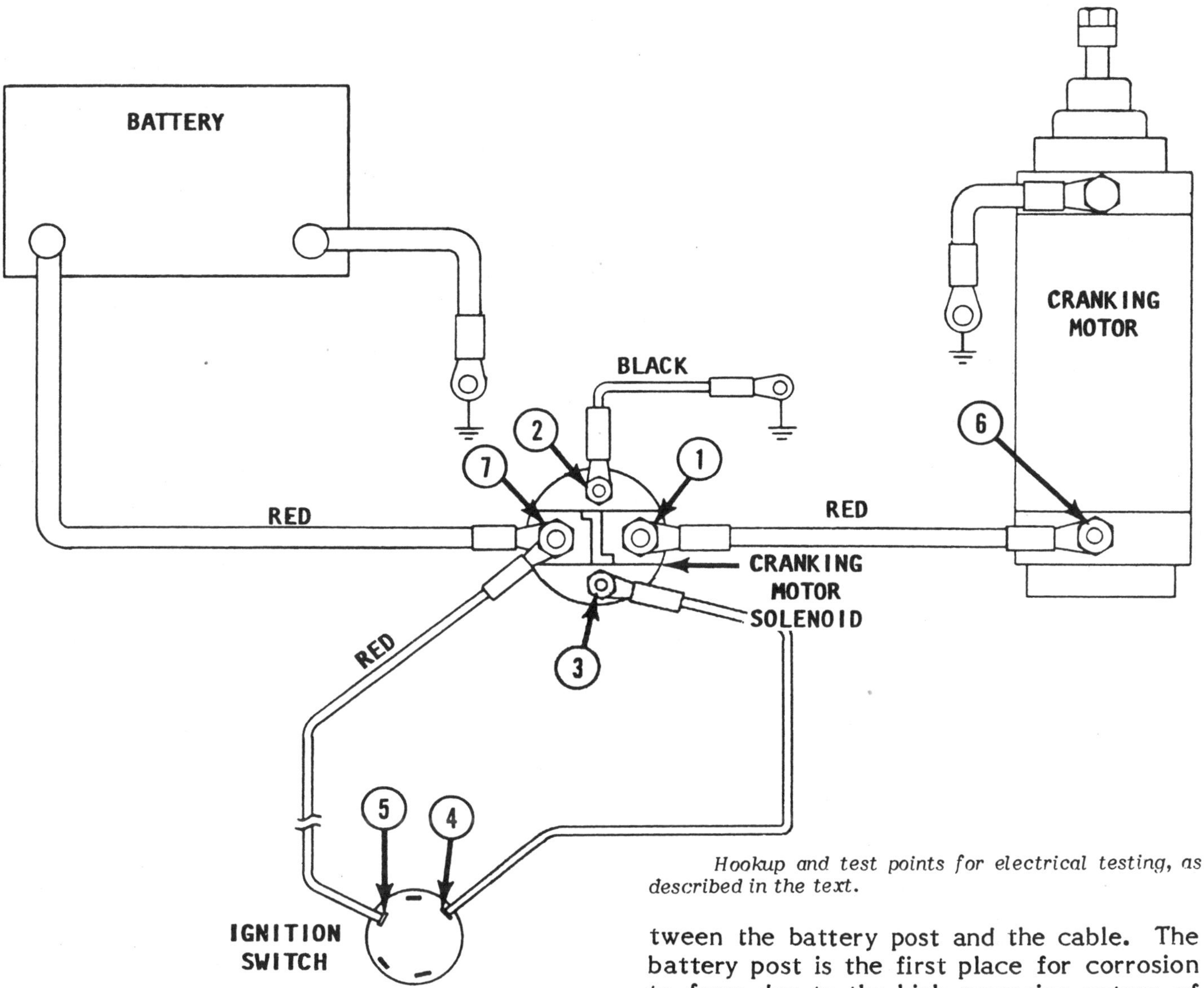

Hookup and test points for electrical testing, as described in the text.

circuits. The following four tests are designed to isolate excessive resistance with the system under load.

GROUND the ignition coil primary lead to prevent the engine from firing during the following checks.

The circled numbers on the accompanying illustration are keyed to the tests and indicate the connection for the voltmeter leads.

Test 1 Voltage Drop Across the Battery Terminal Cable and Post:

Connect the positive lead of the voltmeter to the positive post of the battery and the negative lead of the voltmeter to the battery terminal of the cranking motor. Turn the ignition switch to **START** and note the reading of the voltmeter.

If the reading is more than 0.5 volt, there is a high-resistance connection between the battery post and the cable. The battery post is the first place for corrosion to form due to the high corrosive nature of the battery electrolyte (acid).

Remove both battery cable connectors; clean the connectors and the battery posts thoroughly; replace the connectors; and tighten them securely.

Test 2 Voltage Drop In the Battery Cable to Starter Relay:

Leave the positive lead of the voltmeter connected to the positive post of the battery. Connect the negative lead of the voltmeter to the battery terminal of the cranking motor relay. Do not connect it to the cable, but directly to the terminal.

Attempt to crank the engine as described in Test 1, and note the voltage drop. If the voltage drops more than 0.1 volt, the starter is drawing too much current because the cable is too thin, or the connection at the relay is corroded. Clean and tighten the connection or replace the cable.

Test 3 Voltage Drop Across the Contacts Inside the Starter Relay:

Leave the positive lead of the voltmeter connected to the positive battery post. Connect the negative lead of the voltmeter to the cranking motor terminal of the relay, as shown. Attempt to crank the engine as described in Test 1 and note the voltage drop. If the voltage drop is more than 0.3 volt, the starter relay must be replaced because the contacts are burned.

Test 4 Voltage Drop Between the Negative Battery Post and the Engine Ground:

Connect the positive lead of the voltmeter to a **GOOD** engine ground. Do not attempt to obtain a good ground on a painted surface. Connect the negative lead of the voltmeter to the negative battery post. Attempt to crank the engine as described in Test 1 and note the voltage drop. If the voltage drop is more than 0.1 volt, the negative battery post or the cable connector is corroded and must be cleaned and the connector tightened securely. One other possibility is paint between the engine and the cable. Remove the cable, scrape the paint away to bare metal, connect the cable again and repeat the test.

5-6 CHARGING SYSTEM MALFUNCTIONS

The lighting coil, rectifier/regulator, battery, and the necessary wiring to connect

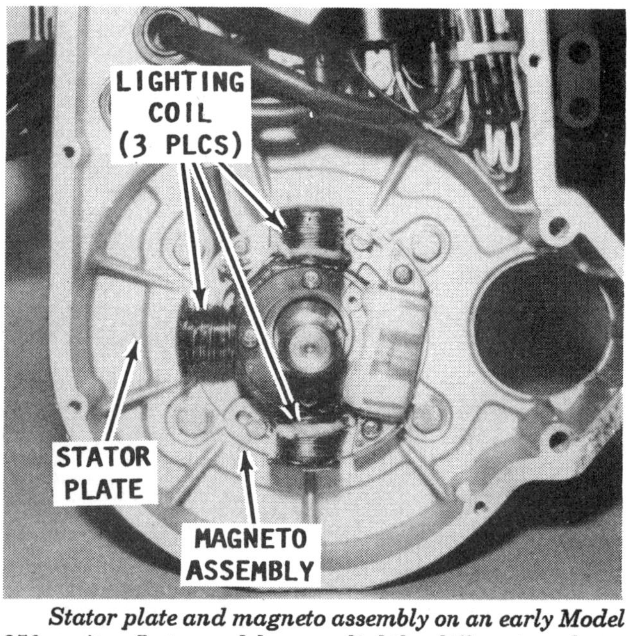

Stator plate and magneto assembly on an early Model 650 unit. Late models are slightly different and are secured with only two bolts instead of four, as shown.

it all together comprise the charging system.

Before the charging system is blamed for battery problems, consider other areas which may be the cause:

1- Operating at low speed for short periods.

2- Voltage losses due to high resistance.

3- Corroded battery cables, connectors, and terminals.

4- Low electrolyte level in the battery cells.

5- Prolonged disuse of the battery causing a self-discharged condition.

Service the battery, refer to Section 5-3. If, after charging, the battery fails to give the required specific gravity reading, then the battery will never hold a charge and must be replaced. This problem may have originated with the battery, a shorted cell perhaps, or may be attributed to the failure of the rectifier/regulator or lighting coil. Refer to the Ignition chapter for resistance tests on these two components.

5-7 TROUBLESHOOTING CHARTS

The following six charts are presented as an aid to troubleshooting the engine and jet pump. Refer to the heading in the uppermost box which most closely identifies the problem, and then work downward from there. The probable causes are listed in columns under a specific system, for example: Fuel system, or Electrical system. Once a possible cause is identified, refer to the specific chapter for procedures on testing and service.

When using the charts -- proceed step-by-step through each of the tests or checks until the defect or cause of the problem is uncovered.

FIRST CHART -- Page 5-13 -- sets up the condition of the engine failing to start.

SECOND CHART -- Page 5-14 -- covers situation of engine starting, then stopping, without cause.

THIRD CHART -- Page 5-15 -- deals with an engine misfiring.

FOURTH CHART -- Page 5-16 -- most involved chart of the set -- covers loss of engine power.

FIFTH CHART -- Page 5-17 -- checks out strange unexplained engine noises.

SIXTH CHART -- Page 5-18 -- covers problems involving the jet pump.

CHART ONE

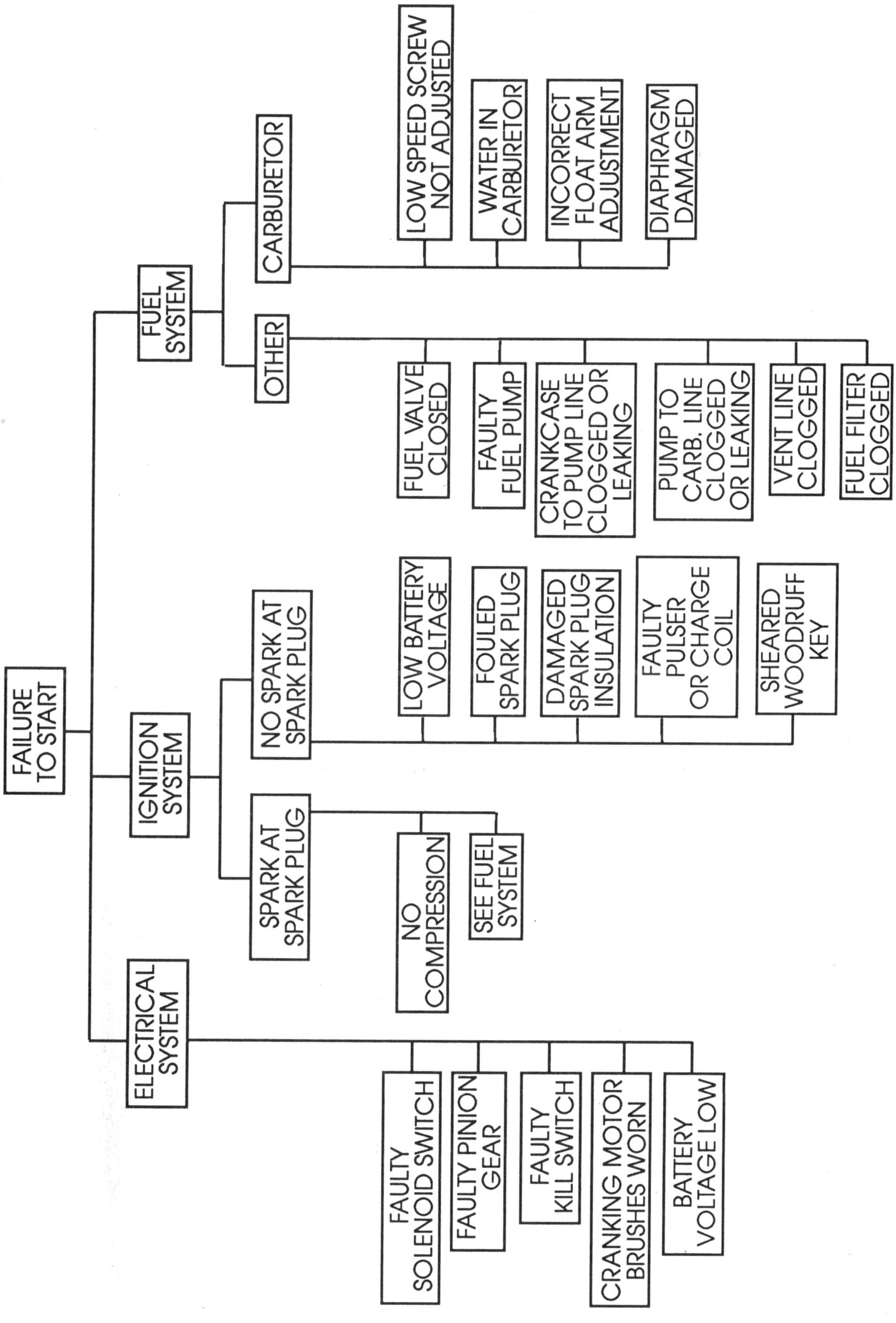
FAILURE TO START
FUEL SYSTEM
CARBURETOR
LOW SPEED SCREW NOT ADJUSTED
WATER IN CARBURETOR
INCORRECT FLOAT ARM ADJUSTMENT
DIAPHRAGM DAMAGED
OTHER
FUEL VALVE CLOSED
FAULTY FUEL PUMP
CRANKCASE TO PUMP LINE CLOGGED OR LEAKING
PUMP TO CARB. LINE CLOGGED OR LEAKING
VENT LINE CLOGGED
FUEL FILTER CLOGGED
IGNITION SYSTEM
NO SPARK AT SPARK PLUG
LOW BATTERY VOLTAGE
FOULED SPARK PLUG
DAMAGED SPARK PLUG INSULATION
FAULTY PULSER OR CHARGE COIL
SHEARED WOODRUFF KEY
SPARK AT SPARK PLUG
NO COMPRESSION
SEE FUEL SYSTEM
ELECTRICAL SYSTEM
FAULTY SOLENOID SWITCH
FAULTY PINION GEAR
FAULTY KILL SWITCH
CRANKING MOTOR BRUSHES WORN
BATTERY VOLTAGE LOW

CHART TWO

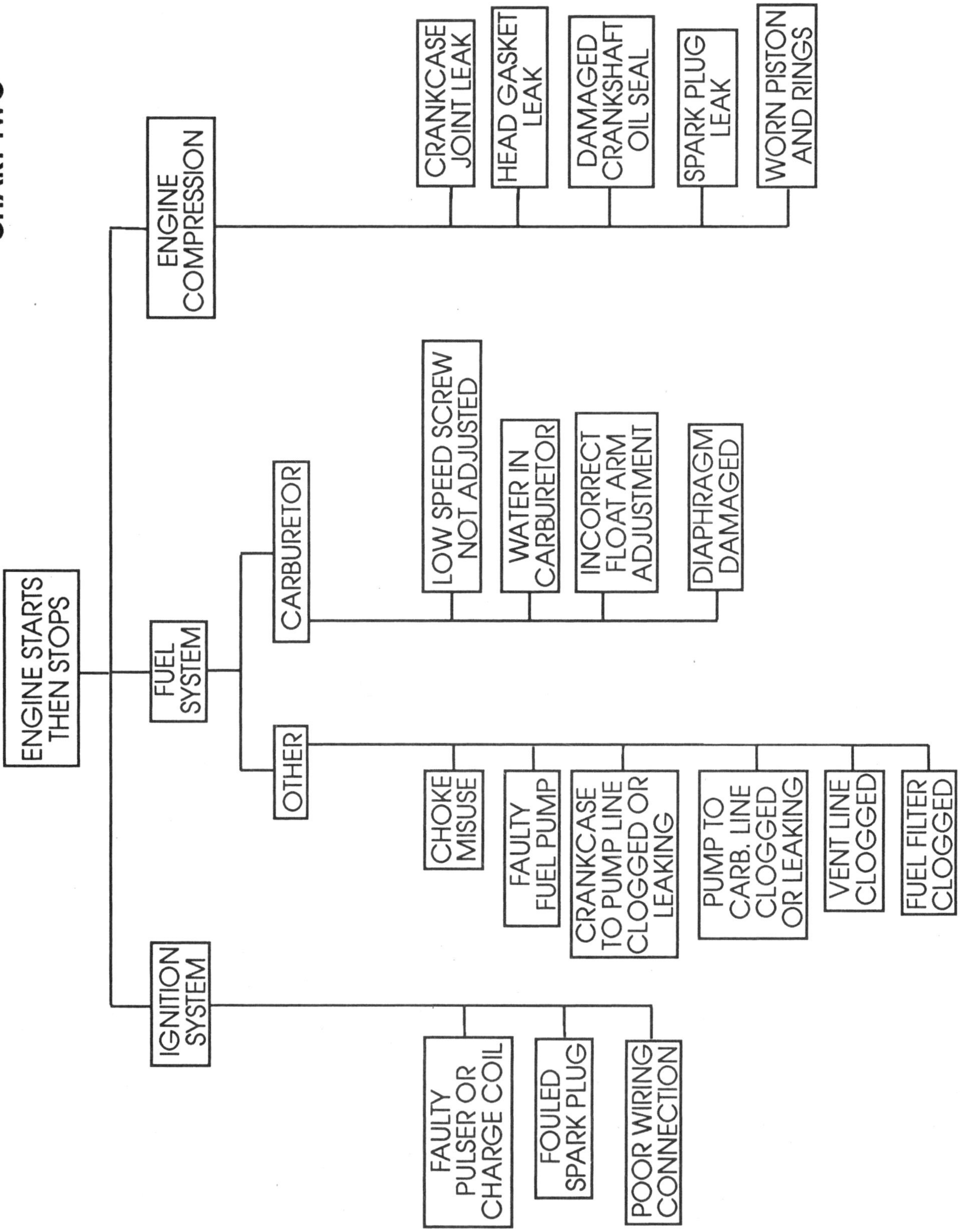
ENGINE STARTS THEN STOPS
ENGINE COMPRESSION
CRANKCASE JOINT LEAK
HEAD GASKET LEAK
DAMAGED CRANKSHAFT OIL SEAL
SPARK PLUG LEAK
WORN PISTON AND RINGS
FUEL SYSTEM
CARBURETOR
LOW SPEED SCREW NOT ADJUSTED
WATER IN CARBURETOR
INCORRECT FLOAT ARM ADJUSTMENT
DIAPHRAGM DAMAGED
OTHER
CHOKE MISUSE
FAULTY FUEL PUMP
CRANKCASE TO PUMP LINE CLOGGED OR LEAKING
PUMP TO CARB. LINE CLOGGED OR LEAKING
VENT LINE CLOGGED
FUEL FILTER CLOGGED
IGNITION SYSTEM
FAULTY PULSER OR CHARGE COIL
FOULED SPARK PLUG
POOR WIRING CONNECTION

CHART THREE

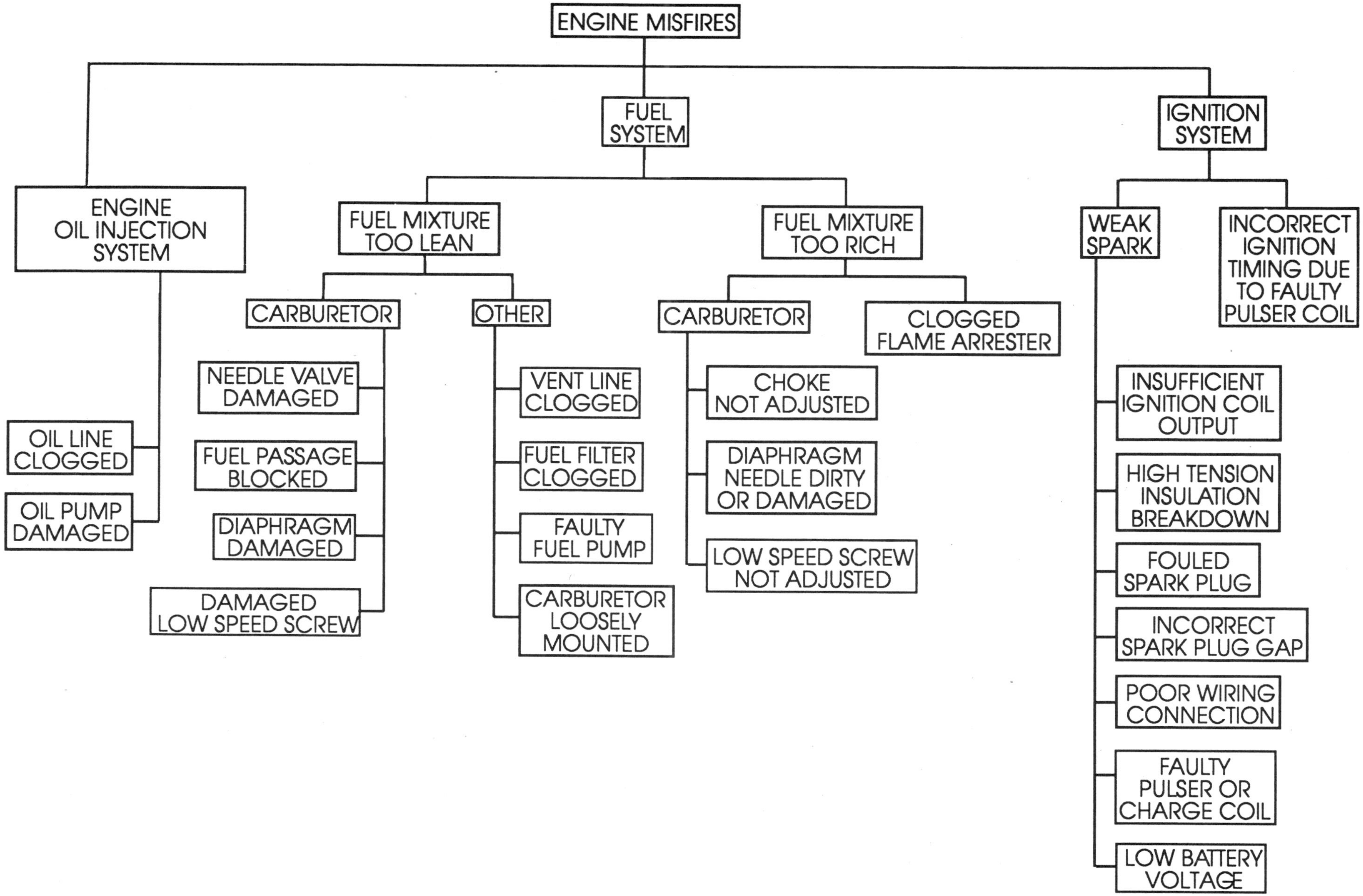
ENGINE MISFIRES
ENGINE OIL INJECTION SYSTEM
OIL LINE CLOGGED
OIL PUMP DAMAGED
FUEL SYSTEM
FUEL MIXTURE TOO LEAN
CARBURETOR
NEEDLE VALVE DAMAGED
FUEL PASSAGE BLOCKED
DIAPHRAGM DAMAGED
DAMAGED LOW SPEED SCREW
OTHER
VENT LINE CLOGGED
FUEL FILTER CLOGGED
FAULTY FUEL PUMP
CARBURETOR LOOSELY MOUNTED
FUEL MIXTURE TOO RICH
CARBURETOR
CHOKE NOT ADJUSTED
DIAPHRAGM NEEDLE DIRTY OR DAMAGED
LOW SPEED SCREW NOT ADJUSTED
CLOGGED FLAME ARRESTER
IGNITION SYSTEM
WEAK SPARK
INSUFFICIENT IGNITION COIL OUTPUT
HIGH TENSION INSULATION BREAKDOWN
FOULED SPARK PLUG
INCORRECT SPARK PLUG GAP
POOR WIRING CONNECTION
FAULTY PULSER OR CHARGE COIL
LOW BATTERY VOLTAGE
INCORRECT IGNITION TIMING DUE TO FAULTY PULSER COIL

CHART FOUR

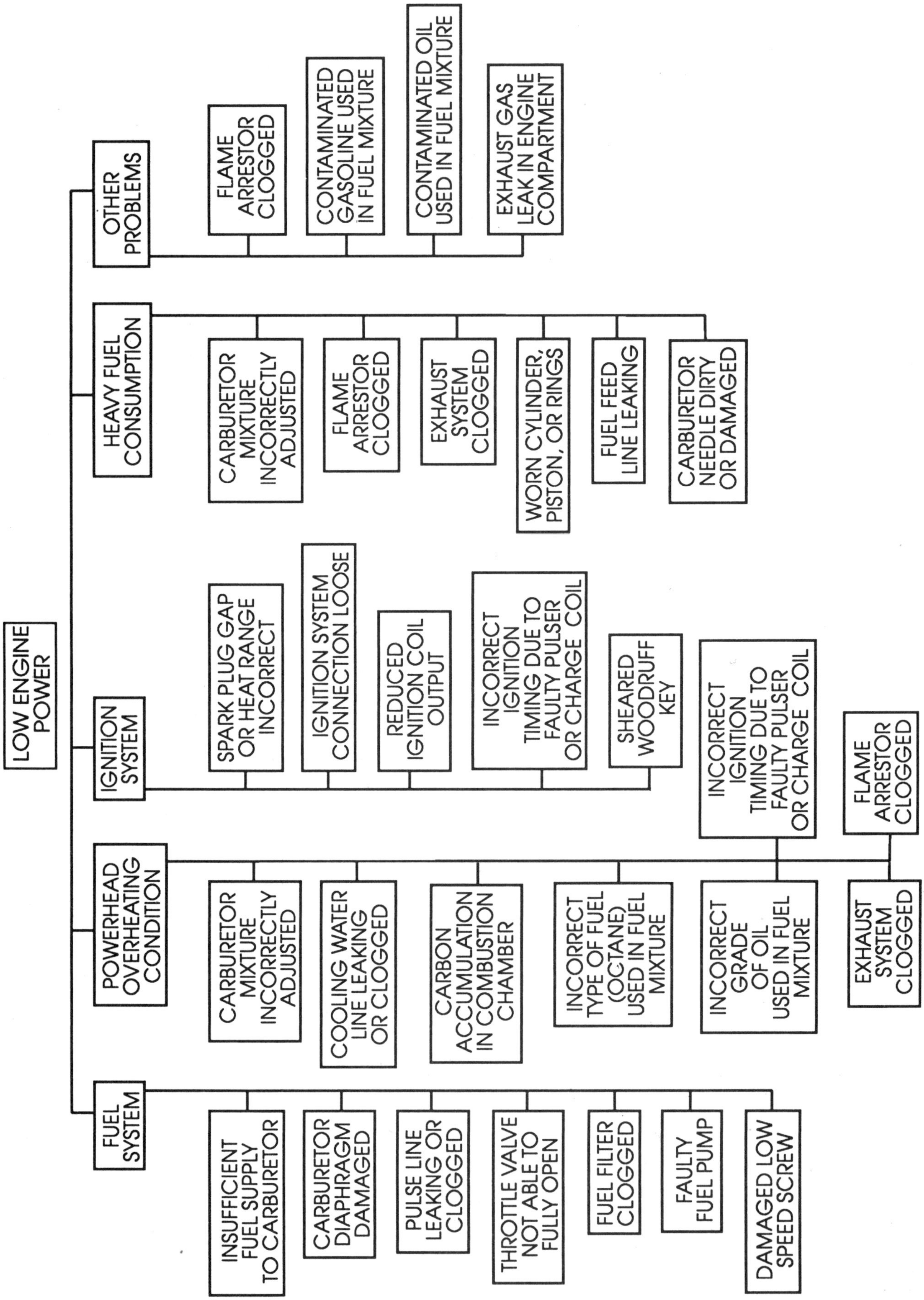
LOW ENGINE POWER
FUEL SYSTEM
INSUFFICIENT FUEL SUPPLY TO CARBURETOR
CARBURETOR DIAPHRAGM DAMAGED
PULSE LINE LEAKING OR CLOGGED
THROTTLE VALVE NOT ABLE TO FULLY OPEN
FUEL FILTER CLOGGED
FAULTY FUEL PUMP
DAMAGED LOW SPEED SCREW
POWERHEAD OVERHEATING CONDITION
CARBURETOR MIXTURE INCORRECTLY ADJUSTED
COOLING WATER LINE LEAKING OR CLOGGED
CARBON ACCUMULATION IN COMBUSTION CHAMBER
INCORRECT TYPE OF FUEL (OCTANE) USED IN FUEL MIXTURE
INCORRECT GRADE OF OIL USED IN FUEL MIXTURE
INCORRECT IGNITION TIMING DUE TO FAULTY PULSER OR CHARGE COIL
EXHAUST SYSTEM CLOGGED
FLAME ARRESTOR CLOGGED
IGNITION SYSTEM
SPARK PLUG GAP OR HEAT RANGE INCORRECT
IGNITION SYSTEM CONNECTION LOOSE
REDUCED IGNITION COIL OUTPUT
INCORRECT IGNITION TIMING DUE TO FAULTY PULSER OR CHARGE COIL
SHEARED WOODRUFF KEY
HEAVY FUEL CONSUMPTION
CARBURETOR MIXTURE INCORRECTLY ADJUSTED
FLAME ARRESTOR CLOGGED
EXHAUST SYSTEM CLOGGED
WORN CYLINDER, PISTON, OR RINGS
FUEL FEED LINE LEAKING
CARBURETOR NEEDLE DIRTY OR DAMAGED
OTHER PROBLEMS
FLAME ARRESTOR CLOGGED
CONTAMINATED GASOLINE USED IN FUEL MIXTURE
CONTAMINATED OIL USED IN FUEL MIXTURE
EXHAUST GAS LEAK IN ENGINE COMPARTMENT

CHART FIVE

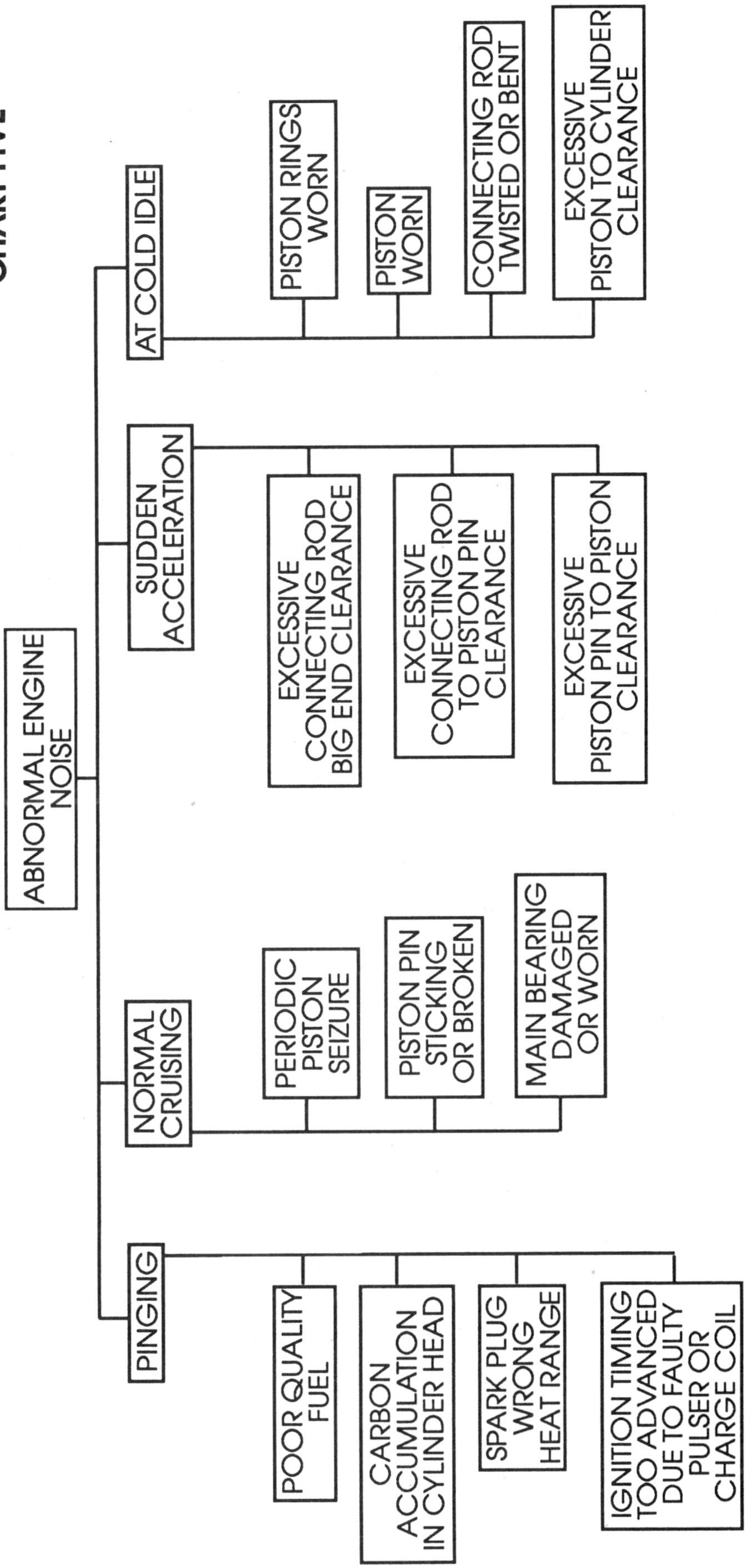

ABNORMAL ENGINE NOISE
PINGING
POOR QUALITY FUEL
CARBON ACCUMULATION IN CYLINDER HEAD
SPARK PLUG WRONG HEAT RANGE
IGNITION TIMING TOO ADVANCED DUE TO FAULTY PULSER OR CHARGE COIL
NORMAL CRUISING
PERIODIC PISTON SEIZURE
PISTON PIN STICKING OR BROKEN
MAIN BEARING DAMAGED OR WORN
SUDDEN ACCELERATION
EXCESSIVE CONNECTING ROD BIG END CLEARANCE
EXCESSIVE CONNECTING ROD TO PISTON PIN CLEARANCE
EXCESSIVE PISTON PIN TO PISTON CLEARANCE
AT COLD IDLE
PISTON RINGS WORN
PISTON WORN
CONNECTING ROD TWISTED OR BENT
EXCESSIVE PISTON TO CYLINDER CLEARANCE

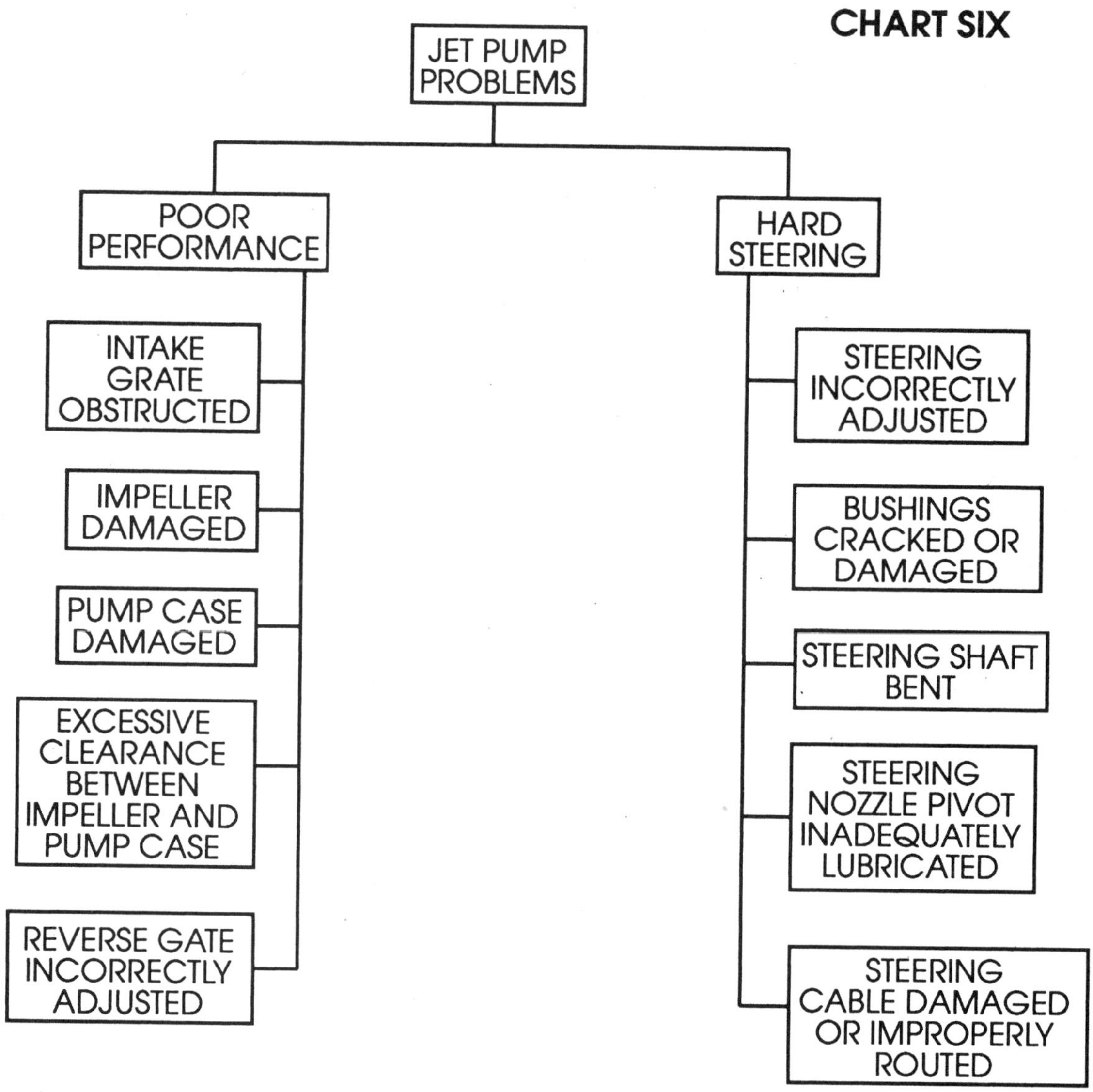
CHART SIX
JET PUMP PROBLEMS
POOR PERFORMANCE
INTAKE GRATE OBSTRUCTED
IMPELLER DAMAGED
PUMP CASE DAMAGED
EXCESSIVE CLEARANCE BETWEEN IMPELLER AND PUMP CASE
REVERSE GATE INCORRECTLY ADJUSTED
HARD STEERING
STEERING INCORRECTLY ADJUSTED
BUSHINGS CRACKED OR DAMAGED
STEERING SHAFT BENT
STEERING NOZZLE PIVOT INADEQUATELY LUBRICATED
STEERING CABLE DAMAGED OR IMPROPERLY ROUTED

6
FUEL AND OIL

6-1 INTRODUCTION

The carburetion and ignition principles of two-cycle engine operation **MUST** be understood in order to perform a proper tune-up on a marine engine.

If you have any doubts concerning your understanding of two-cycle engine operation, it would be best to study the Introduction section in the first portion of Chapter 8, before tackling any work on the fuel system.

The fuel system includes the fuel tank, fuel pump, fuel filters, carburetor, and the associated parts to connect it all together. Regular maintenance of the fuel system to obtain maximum performance, is limited to changing the fuel filters at regular intervals and using fresh fuel.

If a sudden increase in gas consumption is noticed, or if the engine does not perform properly, a carburetor overhaul, including boil-out, or replacement of the fuel pump may be required.

6-2 GENERAL CARBURETION INFORMATION

The carburetor is merely a metering device for mixing fuel and air in the proper proportions for efficient engine operation. At idle speed, a marine engine requires a mixture of about 8 parts air to 1 part fuel. At high speed or under heavy duty service, the mixture may change to as much as 12 parts air to 1 part fuel.

DIAPHRAGM CARBURETORS

Description

The two carburetors used on the Yamaha engines powering the personal watercraft covered in this manual are the Mikuni BN38 and the Mikuni BN 44. Both are diaphragm type units. Both have an integral fuel pump and operate on the same principle even though they differ in design. However, on a triple carburetor installation, only the No. 1 and No. 2 carburetors have the fuel pump -- the third does not.

Operation

Following the fuel through its course, from the fuel tank to the combustion cham-

Regular maintenance of the fuel system is limited to changing the fuel filters at regular intervals and using fresh fuel. Illustration shows two of the three carburetors installed on a Model 1100 Series engine.

ber of the cylinder, will provide an appreciation of exactly what is taking place.

After the engine starts, the fuel passes through the pump to the carburetor. All systems have some type of filter installed somewhere in the line between the tank and the carburetor.

Fuel is delivered to an inlet valve under pressure from the integral fuel pump. When the piston is on its upward stroke, the pressure in the carburetor throat orifice and the crankcase is less than atmospheric. The fuel chamber above the diaphragm is connected to the crankcase through a vacuum tube. A nozzle channel connecting the carburetor throat with the fuel chamber also allows the fuel chamber to be at less than atmospheric pressure.

The chamber on the other side of the diaphragm is vented to atmosphere, and therefore, is always at atmospheric pressure.

With the two pressure differentials, the diaphragm will flex toward the lowest pressure -- towards the fuel chamber. As the diaphragm flexes, it raises the float arm which, because of a return spring, is in constant contact with the diaphragm. The float arm is hinged. As one side goes up, the other side comes down and allows the inlet valve to open. At the same time, the needle valve falls away from the valve seat. As soon as the inlet valve opens, fuel flows under pressure from the fuel pump into the fuel chamber.

When the piston is on its downward stroke, the crankcase, the carburetor throat, and the fuel chamber are all at a higher pressure than atmosphere. The fuel chamber filled with fuel at a higher pressure now flexes toward the side with the lower pressure -- the side vented to atmosphere.

The return spring pushes the float arm down against the diaphragm. The other side of the float arm raises up and pushes the needle valve against its seat closing the inlet valve.

On the next piston downward stroke, the diaphragm flexes back again forcing the fuel in the fuel chamber to be ejected through a jet into the carburetor throat. On the same stroke the fuel chamber is replenished with fresh fuel through the open needle valve. This cycle repeats itself, sending a squirt of fuel into the carburetor throat each downward stroke of the piston.

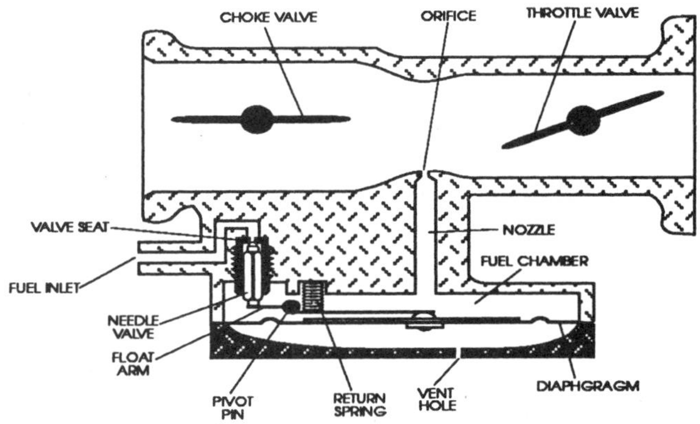

Cross-section drawing of a diaphragm carburetor -- the type used on engines covered in this manual.

In order to obtain the proper air/fuel mixture for all engine speeds, some models have high and low speed jets. These jets have adjustable needle valves which are used to compensate for changing atmospheric conditions. In almost all cases, the high-speed circuit has fixed high-speed jets and are not adjustable.

A throttle valve controls the flow of air/fuel mixture drawn into the combustion chambers. A cold engine requires a richer fuel mixture to start and during the brief period it is warming to normal operating temperature. A choke valve is placed ahead of the metering jets and venturi. As this valve begins to close, the volume of air intake is reduced, thus enriching the mixture entering the cylinders.

When this choke valve is fully closed, a very rich fuel mixture is drawn into the cylinders.

FUEL/OIL MIXTURE

(Engines Without Oil Injection)

Most of the engines covered in this manual are equipped with an oil injection system --

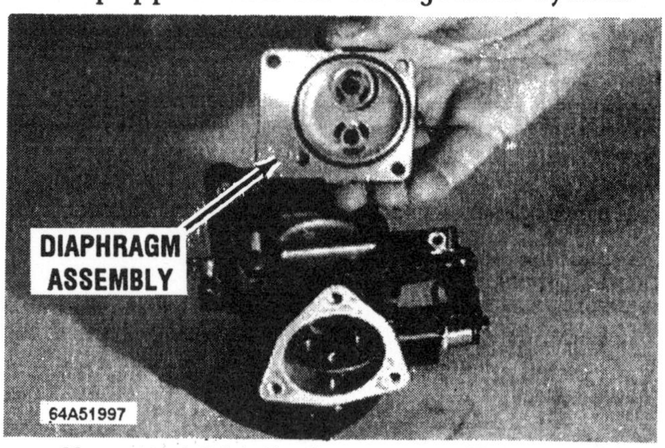

Close view of the diaphragm assembly removed from the carburetor.

replacing the method of mixing oil with the fuel. However, one example of a model using the mixing method is the Super Jet.

A new or rebuilt engine must be properly "broken-in" if it is to develop maximum performance. An engine incorrectly "broken-in" will never be able to achieve the maximum rated horsepower. During the initial "breaking-in" period, the fuel/oil ratio should be very rich, about 20:1 for the first two to four tank fulls -- twenty parts of fuel to one part oil.

Two-stroke oil must be added to the fuel tank at the ratio of 25:1 for the first ten hours of operation after the unit is brought out of storage. This ratio will **ENSURE** adequate lubrication of moving parts which have been drained of oil during the storage period. Operation of an engine without the proper amount of oil will quickly lead to a significant loss of horsepower.

After the first ten hours of operation, a lower ratio of fuel/oil mixture may be used. In the past, manufacturers of two-stroke engines gave an absolute minimum of 100:1. However, this is a very lean mixture. Yamaha recommends a minimum mixture of 50:1.

However, experienced two-stroke mechanics run their own units between 16:1 and 32:1 on the premise that it is cheaper to replace a fouled spark plug than to have a complete engine overhaul with rebored cylinders, oversize pistons and rings. These same mechanics who own oil injected units add an extra ounce of oil per each gallon of fuel. The addition of this extra oil may prevent engine seizure in the event of an oil pump failure or clog in an oil delivery line.

Use only two-stroke outboard marine oil in the mixture -- never automotive oils. Four-stroke automotive engine oil is not formulated to burn completely -- only to lubricate. Therefore, automotive oil, if used in a two-stroke engine, will leave an undesirable residue in the combustion chamber.

Air/Fuel Mixture

A suction effect is created in the intake manifold each time the piston moves upward in the cylinder. This suction draws air through the throat of the carburetor. A restriction in the throat, called a venturi, controls air velocity and has the effect of reducing air pressure at this point.

The difference in air pressures at the throat and in the fuel chamber, causes the fuel to be pushed out of a metering jet extending down into the fuel chamber. When the fuel leaves the jet, it mixes with the air passing through the venturi. This air/fuel mixture should then be in the proper proportion for burning in the cylinders for maximum engine performance.

Water Separator Filter
Yamaha SuperJet

A water separating fuel filter is installed on the Yamaha SuperJet between the filler nozzle and the fuel check valve. This filter removes water and fuel system contaminants, such as dirt, rust and other solids, thus reducing potential problems. The bottom screw should be removed every three or four tankfulls of gas to allow the water to drain from the filter. This filter should be replaced each season. Keeping this separator filter fairly clean is one of the easiest -- what could be more simple than removing a screw -- methods of helping to ensure an adequate supply of clean fuel to the carburetor under all conditions.

6-3 FUEL PUMP

As mentioned several times earlier in this chapter the fuel pump on all engines covered in this manual is an integral part of the carburetor. However, on engines with a triple carburetor installation -- one carburetor serving each cylinder -- only the No. 1 and No. 2 carburetors have the fuel pump -- the No. 3 carburetor receives fuel from the fuel pump which is a part of the No. 2 carburetor.

Fuel pump service is included in the overhaul procedures in the Disassembling and Assembling portions of this chapter.

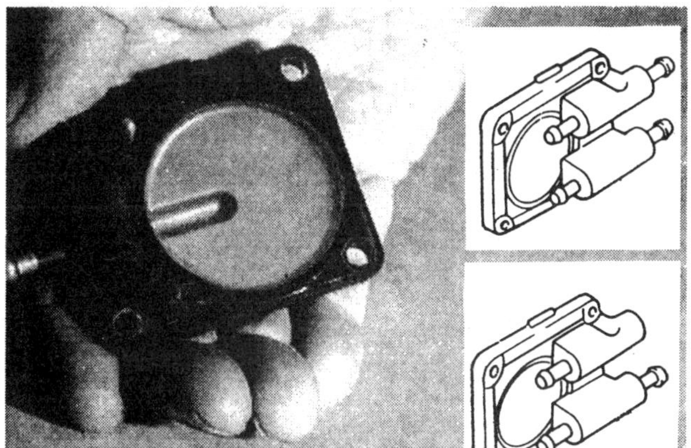

Close view of the inside of the fuel pump cover. The fitting arrangement may differ, depending on the particular installation, as indicated in the "inserts".

Integral Fuel Pump
Description and Operation

The fuel pump consists of a series of diaphragms and check valves operated by crankcase pressure. The pump feeds fuel directly into the fuel chamber through the inlet valve.

As the piston moves upward, a suction, or negative pressure, is created in the crankcase. This low pressure acts upon the inner diaphragm through the carburetor. The inner diaphragm is, therefore, pulled inward. When the diaphragm moves inward, the check valve opens and fuel is drawn from the bottom of the fuel pump exterior chamber into the fuel pump interior chamber.

As the piston moves downward, a positive pressure is created in the crankcase causing the inner diaphragm to be pushed outward. The delivery check valve opens under pressure and allows fuel to flow into the upper part of the exterior chamber and on to the inlet valve of the carburetor.

The function of the outer diaphragm is to absorb the pulsations of the fuel and allow a smooth uninterrupted fuel flow.

If the fuel pump diaphragm tears or is punctured, fuel will enter the crankcase through the pulse line causing an overrich mixture. This mixture will foul the plugs and in extreme cases flood the crankcase.

6-4 FUEL IN THE SYSTEM

The fuel system includes the fuel tank, fuel pump, fuel filters, carburetor, connecting fuel lines, and the associated parts to connect it all together. Regular maintenance of the fuel system to obtain maximum performance, is limited to changing the fuel filters at regular intervals and using fresh fuel.

Even with the high price of fuel, removing gasoline that has been standing unused over a long period of time, is still the easiest and least expensive preventive maintenance possible. In most cases this old gas, even with some oil mixed with it, can be used without harmful effects in an automobile using regular gasoline.

If a sudden increase in gas consumption is noticed, or if the engine does not perform properly, a carburetor overhaul, including boil-out, or replacement of the fuel pump may be required.

Leaded Gasoline

The manufacturers of the units covered in this manual recommends the engines be operated using either regular unleaded or regular leaded gasoline with a minimum octane rating of 84 or higher.

In the United States, the Environmental Protection Agency (EPA) required leaded fuel -- "Regular" gasoline to be phased out back in 1993. This requirement was accomplished.

Lead in gasoline boosts the octane rating (energy). Therefore, if the lead is removed, it must be replaced with another agent. Unknown to the general public, many refineries have added alcohol in an effort to hold the octane rating.

Alcohol in gasoline can have a deteriorating effect on certain fuel system parts. Seals can swell, pump check valves can swell, diaphragms distort, and other rubber or neoprene composition parts in the fuel system can be affected.

Since about 1981, every effort has been made to use materials that will resist the alcohol being added to fuels.

Fuels containing alcohol will slowly absorb moisture from the air. Once the moisture content in the fuel exceeds about 1%, it will separate from the fuel taking the alcohol with it. This water/alcohol mixture will settle to the bottom of the fuel tank. The engine will fail to operate. Therefore, storing this type of gasoline for use in marine engines is not recommended for more than just a few days.

Removing Fuel from the System

For many years there has been the widespread belief that simply shutting off the fuel at the tank and then running the engine until it stops is the proper procedure before storing the engine for any length of time. Right? **WRONG.**

It is **NOT** possible to remove all of the fuel in the carburetor by operating the engine until it stops. Some fuel is trapped in passages. The **ONLY** guaranteed method of removing **ALL** of the fuel is to take the time to remove the carburetor, and drain the fuel.

If the engine is operated with the fuel supply shut off until it stops the fuel and oil mixture inside the engine is removed, leaving bearings, pistons, rings, and other parts with little protective lubricant, during long periods of storage.

Proper procedure involves: Shutting off the fuel supply at the tank; disconnecting the fuel line at the tank; operating the engine until it begins to run **ROUGH;** then stopping the engine, which will leave some fuel/oil mixture inside; and finally removing and draining the carburetor. By disconnecting the fuel supply, all **SMALL** passages are cleared of fuel even though some fuel is left in the carburetor. A light oil should be put in the combustion chamber as instructed in the Owner's Manual.

For short periods of storage, simply running the carburetor dry may help prevent severe gum and varnish from forming in the carburetor. This is especially true during hot weather.

6-5 TROUBLESHOOTING

The following paragraphs provide an orderly sequence of tests to pinpoint problems in the fuel system. It is very rare for the carburetor by itself to cause failure of the engine to start.

FUEL PROBLEMS

Many times fuel system troubles are caused by a plugged fuel filter, a defective fuel pump, or by a leak in the line from the fuel tank to the fuel pump. A defective choke may also cause problems. **WOULD YOU BELIEVE,** a majority of starting troubles which are traced to the fuel system are the result of an empty fuel tank or aged "sour" fuel.

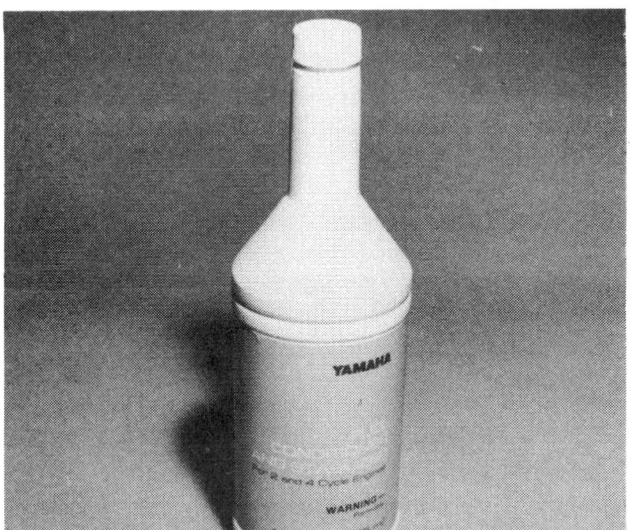

Yamaha Gasoline Stabilizer and Conditioner -- a very effective additive — may be used to prevent fuel from "souring" for up to twelve full months.

"Sour" Fuel

A very common cause of hard starting after an engine has been idle for some time is the fuel becoming "sour".

Under average conditions (temperate climates), fuel will begin to breakdown in about four months. A gummy substance forms in the bottom of the fuel tank and in other areas. The filter screen between the tank and the carburetor and small passages in the carburetor will become clogged. The gasoline will begin to give off an odor similar to rotten eggs. Such a condition can cause the owner much frustration, time in cleaning components, and the expense of replacement or overhaul parts for the carburetor.

Even with the high price of fuel, removing gasoline that has been standing unused over a long period of time is still the easiest and least expensive preventative maintenance possible. In most cases, this old gas can be used without harmful effects in an automobile using regular gasoline.

The gasoline preservative additive Yamaha Fuel Conditioner and Stabilizer for 2 and 4-Cycle Engines, will keep the fuel "fresh" for up to twelve months. If this particular product is not available in your area, other similar additives are produced under various trade names.

Choke Problems

When the engine is hot, the fuel system can cause starting problems. After a hot engine is shut down, the temperature inside

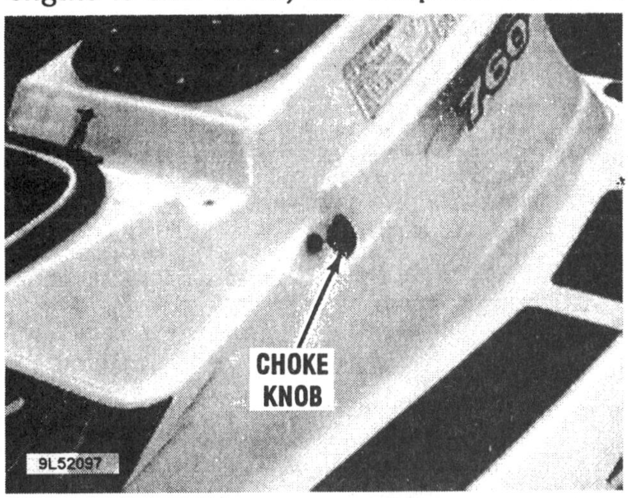

The choke knob, cable, and choke valve must always be properly adjusted for efficient operation and ease of engine starting.

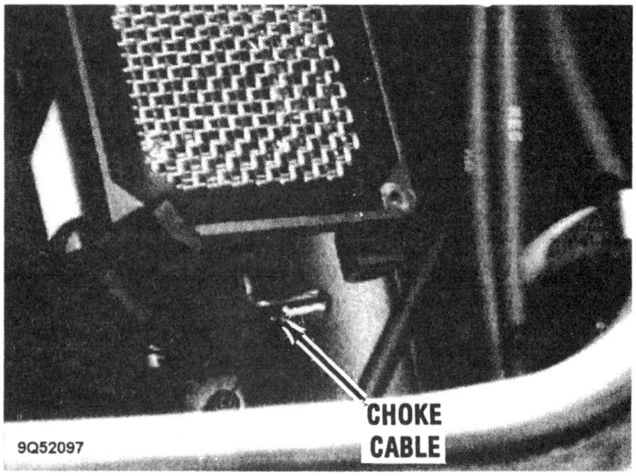

Free movement of the choke cable is essential for proper engine operation, especially during cold startup.

the fuel bowl may rise to 200°F and cause the fuel to actually boil. All carburetors are vented to allow this pressure to escape to the atmosphere. However, some of the fuel may percolate over the high-speed nozzle.

If the choke should stick in the open position, the engine will be hard to start. If the choke should stick in the closed position, the engine will flood making it very difficult to start.

In order for this raw fuel to vaporize enough to burn, considerable air must be added to lean out the mixture. Therefore, the only remedy is to remove the spark

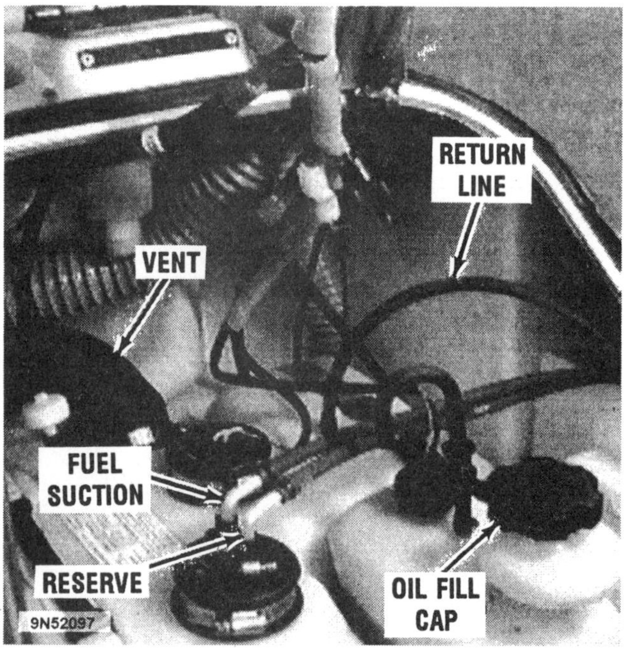

The fuel supply and return lines should be checked regularly for kinks and damage along with the fittings for any possible leaks.

Mikuni carburetor removed, on a "suitable" work surface ready to be disassembled and serviced.

plugs; ground the leads; crank the engine through about ten revolutions; clean the plugs; install the plugs again; and start the engine.

Rough Engine Idle

If an engine does not idle smoothly, the most reasonable approach to the problem is to perform a tune-up to eliminate such areas as: fouled or faulty spark plugs.

Other problems that can prevent an engine from running smoothly include: An air leak in the intake manifold; uneven compression between the cylinders; and sticky or broken reeds.

Of course any problem in the carburetor affecting the air/fuel mixture will also prevent the engine from operating smoothly at idle speed. These problems usually include: a weak float arm return spring; leaking needle valve and seat; defective choke; and improper adjustments for idle mixture or idle speed.

Excessive Fuel Consumption

Excessive fuel consumption can be the result of any one of two conditions, or both may apply.

1- Inefficient engine operation.

2- Poor boating habits of the operator.

If the fuel consumption suddenly increases over what could be considered normal, then the cause can probably be attributed to the engine or watercraft and not the operator.

Check the fuel system for possible leaks. A leak between the tank and the pump many times will not appear when the engine is operating, because the suction created by the pump drawing fuel will not allow the fuel to leak. Once the engine is turned off and the suction no longer exists, fuel may begin to leak.

If a minor tune-up has been performed and the condition still exists, then the problem most likely is in the carburetor and an overhaul is in order.

Engine Surge

If the engine operates as if the load on the craft is being constantly increased and decreased, even though an attempt is being made to hold a constant engine speed, the problem can most likely be attributed to the fuel pump, or a restriction in the fuel line between the tank and the carburetor.

6-6 CARBURETOR MODELS MIKUNI BN38 AND BN44

As mentioned earlier in this chapter on Page 6-1, both of these carburetors used on the engines powering the PWCs covered in this manual are diaphragm type units. Both have an integral fuel pump and operate on the same principle. Actually these two carburetors could be considered identical as far as service procedures are concerned. The difference between the two is in the size of the bore, the venturi, the jets, and other engineering type changes.

Some engines use a single carburetor unit, others use a dual installation and three cylinder engine models use a triple set-up -- three carburetors -- one serving each cylinder. On a triple carburetor installation, only the No. 1 and No. 2 carburetors have the fuel pump -- the third does not.

Because these two carburetors are so similar, complete service procedures to remove, disassemble, clean and inspect, assemble, and make bench adjustments are presented in a single section.

The following table lists the model PWC, years of production, and the Mikuni carburetor used, at press time. Just a quick glance at the table reveals, single, dual, and triple carburetor installations.

Identification

The following table lists the model PWC, approximate years of production, and the Mikuni carburetor used, at press time. As mentioned earlier in Chapter 1, the manufacturer reserves the right to discontinue a model within a production year. By the same token, the manufacturer may introduce a new model within the year. For this reason the phrase "approximate years of production" is used.

CARBURETOR INSTALLATIONS

MODEL	Years Of Production	Mikuni Carburetor
Super Jet 650	1992-1993	Single BN 44
Super Jet 700	1994-1997	Dual BN 38
WaveRunner	1991-1992	Single BN 44
WaveRunner III 700	1992-1997	Single BN 44
VXR 650 & PROVXR 700	1993	Single BN 44
WaveRunner 700	1993-1995	Single BN 44
WaveRaider 700	1996	Dual BN 44
WaveRaider Deluxe	1994-1995	Dual BN 38
WaveRaider 1100	1995-1996	Triple BN 38
WaveBlaster 700	1994-1995	Single BN 44
WaveBlaster 700	1996-1997	Dual BN 38
WaveBlaster II	1996-1997	Dual BN 44
WaveVenture 760	1995-1997	Dual BN 38
WaveVenture 1100	1995-1997	Triple BN 38
GP 760	1997	Dual BN 44
GP 1200	1997	Triple BN 44

6-7 SERVICE CARBURETOR Mikuni BN 38 and BN 44

This section provides complete detailed illustrated procedures for removal, disassembly, cleaning and inspecting, assembling including bench adjustments, installation and operating adjustments for the Mikuni BN 38 and Mikuni BN 44.

At press time, these units were installed on the PWCs listed in the above table.

As the table indicates, this carburetor may be installed as a single unit, a dual installation, or as a triple set-up with each carburetor serving a single cylinder. When the triple carburetor installation is used, the No. 3 carburetor does not have the integral fuel pump.

REMOVAL AND DISASSEMBLY

Good shop practice dictates a carburetor repair kit be purchased and new parts be installed any time the carburetor is disassembled.

Make an attempt to keep the work area organized and to cover parts after they have been cleaned. This practice will prevent foreign matter from entering passageways or adhering to critical parts.

Dual carburetor and triple carburetor installations are removed as a set and may be serviced on the bench **WITHOUT** separating them.

1- Remove the Philip head screws securing the flame arrestor cover to the carburetor/s and then lift the cover and arrestor screen/s away from the lower cover.

WORDS OF WISDOM

DO NOT attempt to remove the phillips head screws securing the lower flame arrestor cover to the carburetor/s at this time -- while the carburetor bodies are still attached to the intake manifold. If a screw or washer is accidentally dropped into the lower funnel shaped cover, the screw/washer will almost certainly find its way down through the carburetor, the intake

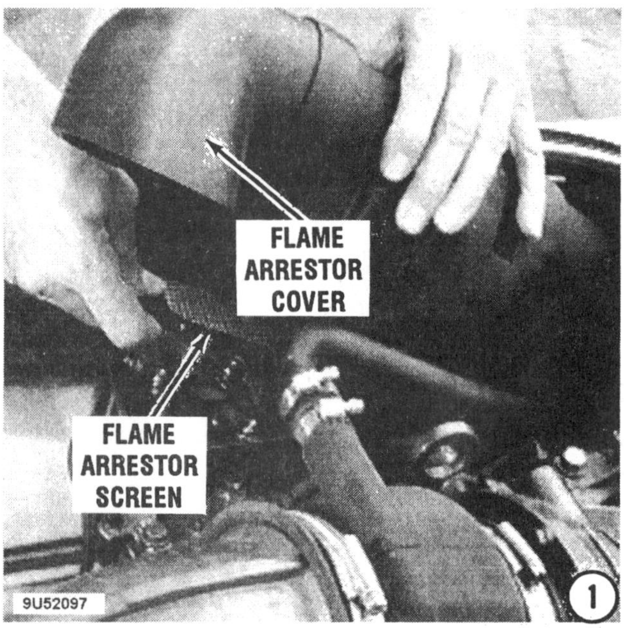

manifold and into the crankcase. If allowed to remain there, the screw/washer will reek havoc on pistons, rings and cylinder walls!

If a screw or washer is lost in this manner, the engine **MUST** be completely disassembled to locate the part to avoid expensive and extensive damage. The moral of this story is -- leave the lower cover in place until the carburetor/s are on the workbench.

Fuel and Vacuum Hose Disconnect

2- Identify the three hoses at each carburetor. (The accompanying illustration shows the carburetor on the bench to clearly indicate the hose fittings.) The hose attached to the plastic fitting at the outer end of the fuel pump is the fuel supply hose. The other end of this hose is attached to an in-line fuel filter mounted on the engine compartment wall. The second hose attached mid-way at the fuel pump is a vacuum hose. The other end of this hose is attached to the crankcase. The third hose attached to the carburetor body is an excess fuel return hose and leads back to the fuel tank.

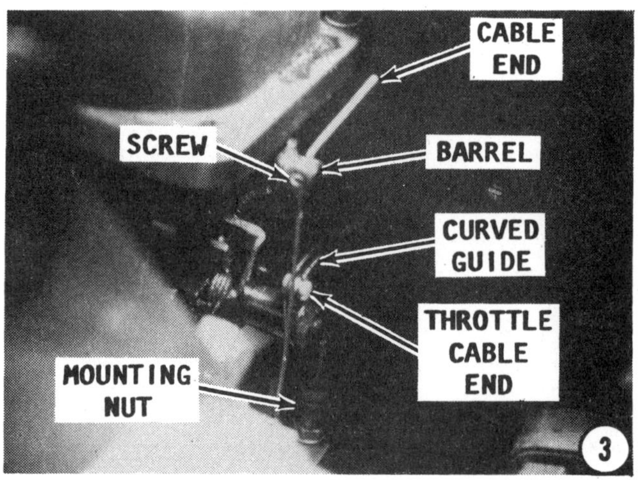

Mark the three hoses and their respective fittings on each carburetor and fuel pump **BEFORE** disconnecting them. The No. 3 carburetor on a triple installation does not have a fuel pump.

Take time to plug the disconnected ends of all hoses with a golf tee, pencil end, or similar item to prevent contaminants from entering the fuel system. Disconnect and tag the fuel hoses. Disconnect the linkage as described in the following paragraphs.

3- Observe the method used in securing the throttle or choke cable end to the shaft. If the cable is threaded through a hole in a barrel, and then the end anchored in place with a small screw through the barrel, the cable must be marked at the point it enters the barrel, to **ENSURE** installation back in exactly the same position from which it was removed.

Obtain some "whiteout", or some masking tape, or equivalent. Mark the point on the cable at which it is inserted into the barrel, so the mark will not be disturbed when the cable is removed from the barrel. Marking the cable at this point will **ENSURE** the cable can be installed with the same cable tension and throttle or choke valve settings.

Loosen the small screw securing the choke cable to the barrel and slide the cable end free of the barrel. Loosen the two nuts securing the cable to the mounting bracket and pull the cable free of the slot. If the throttle cable is secured to the throttle shaft in the same manner, loosen the small screw on the barrel and slide the throttle cable end free. If the throttle cable lies over a curved guide, loosen the two nuts -- one on either side of the bracket -- and slide the cable away from the bracket. Unhook the cable end from the guide.

4- Back off the two mounting nuts for each carburetor. It will probably be necessary to lift

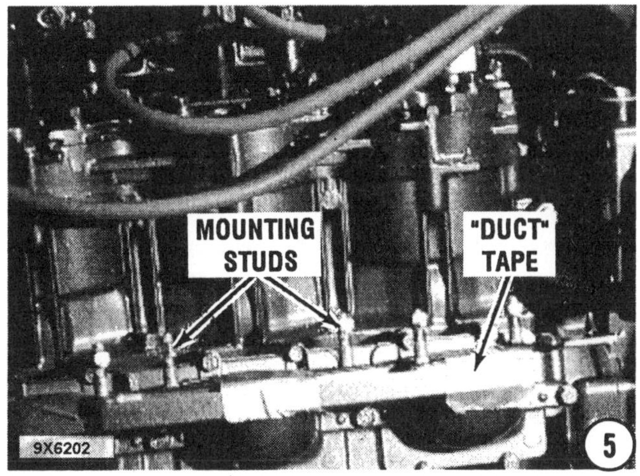

the carburetor up on the studs while the nuts are loosened, because there is very little clearance between the mounting flange and the carburetor. Therefore, the carburetor must be raised to enable the nuts to clear the last threads on the studs. Remove the nuts and lockwashers from all studs.

5- Lift the carburetor/s up and free of the mounting studs. Remove the cable mounting bracket and two gaskets -- one on each side of the bracket.

Move the carburetor/s as an individual -- or as a set -- with the carburetors attached together -- to a suitable work surface. Cover the mani-

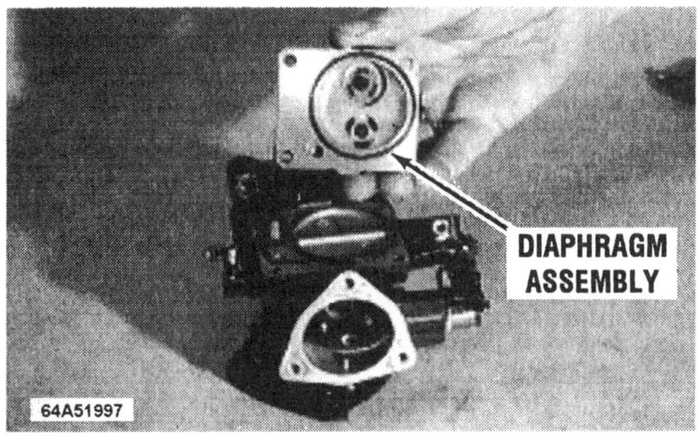

Diaphragm assembly removed from the carburetor.

Inside view of fuel pump cover. Only the No.1 and No. 2 carburetors on a triple installation have the pump.

fold openings with "duct" tape to prevent contaminants from entering the block.

GOOD WORDS

The following procedures pickup the work after the carburetor has been removed from the engine and moved to a suitable work surface. As mentioned earlier, dual or triple carburetors need not be separated for normal carburetor service work. Make an attempt to keep the area clean and to cover parts with a shop cloth to prevent them from being contaminated with dust or dirt. Also it would be helpful to keep parts in order as an aid during assembling.

The carburetor in this section was separated for photographic purposes.

Carburetor Disassembling

6- Remove the bolts and lockwashers securing the lower flame arrestor cover to the carburetor, and then remove the cover and gasket.

SPECIAL FUEL PUMP WORDS

This design fuel pump consists of many layers of components. Some of these components may be stuck together and appear to be one gasket instead of a stock of different items. If the fuel pump is to be returned to service without replacing any of the fragile gaskets and check valves made of plastic film, then **DO NOT ATTEMPT** to separate any stack of components that is stuck together. Such action will surely rip or stretch the delicate components.

Lay the parts out in order of removal, as an aid to later assembly.

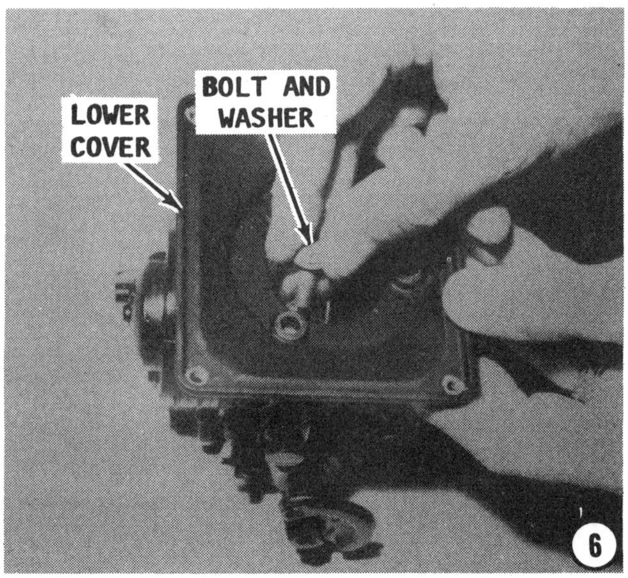

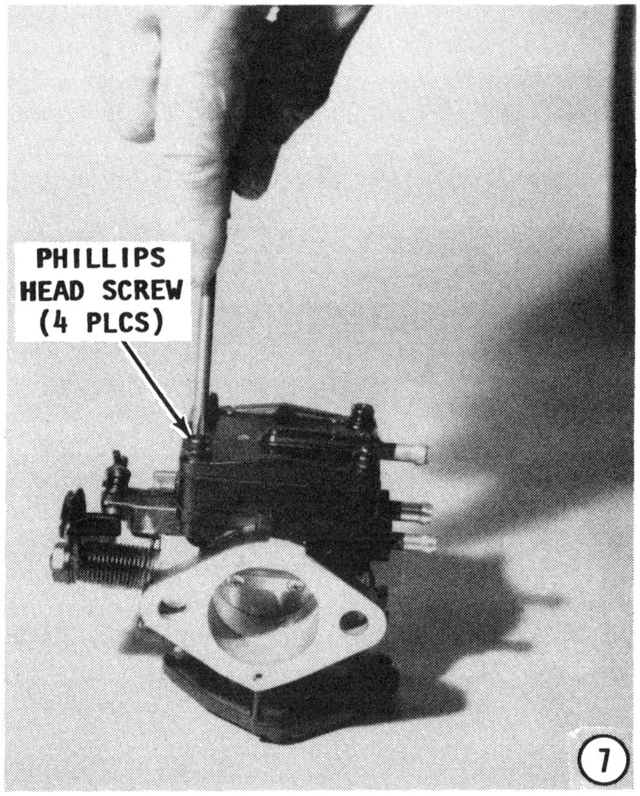

7- Scribe a mark along the entire thickness of the fuel pump to ensure all components will be positioned correctly during installation. Remove the four Phillips head screws and lockwashers securing the fuel pump cover to the carburetor.

8- Remove the fuel pump cover and gasket.

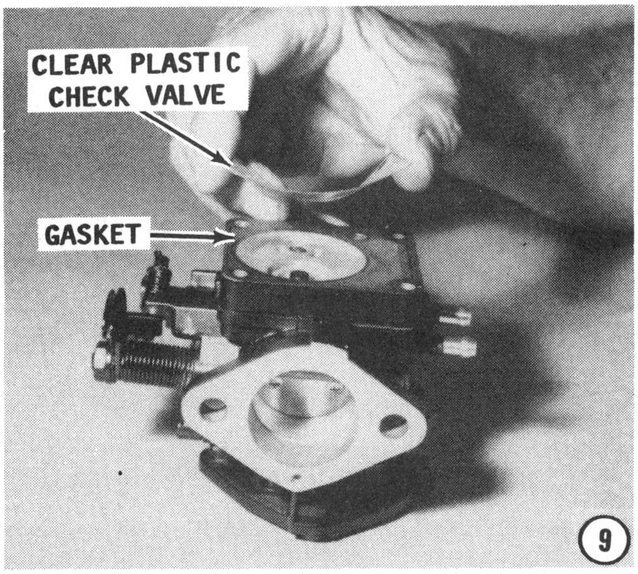

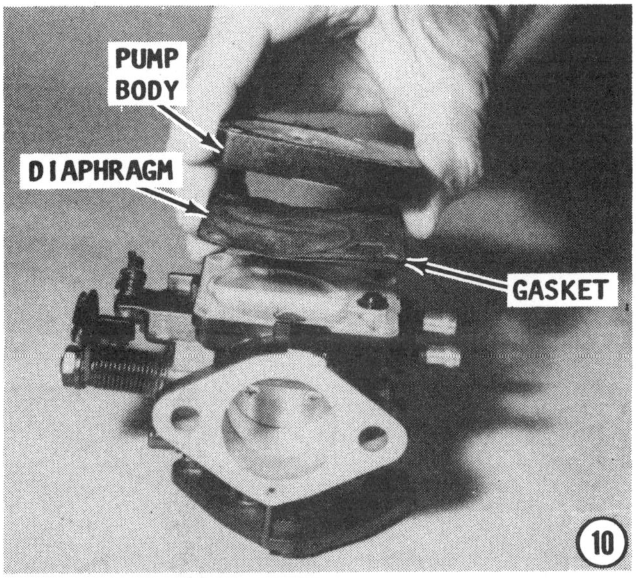

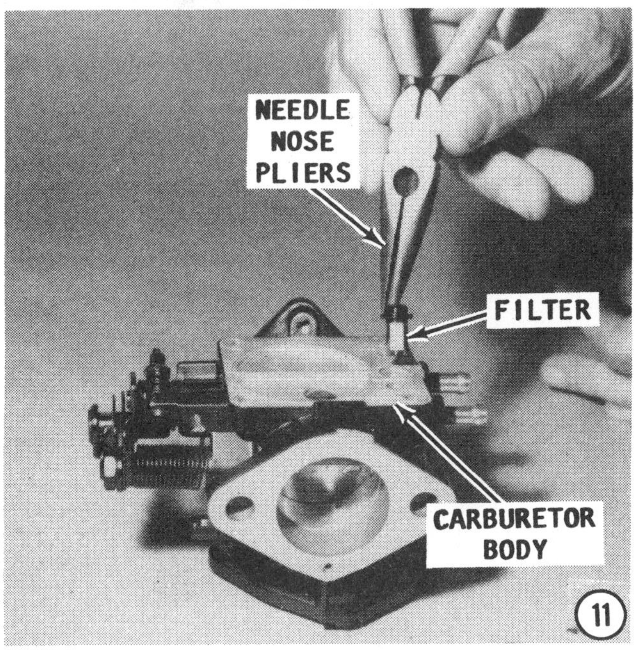

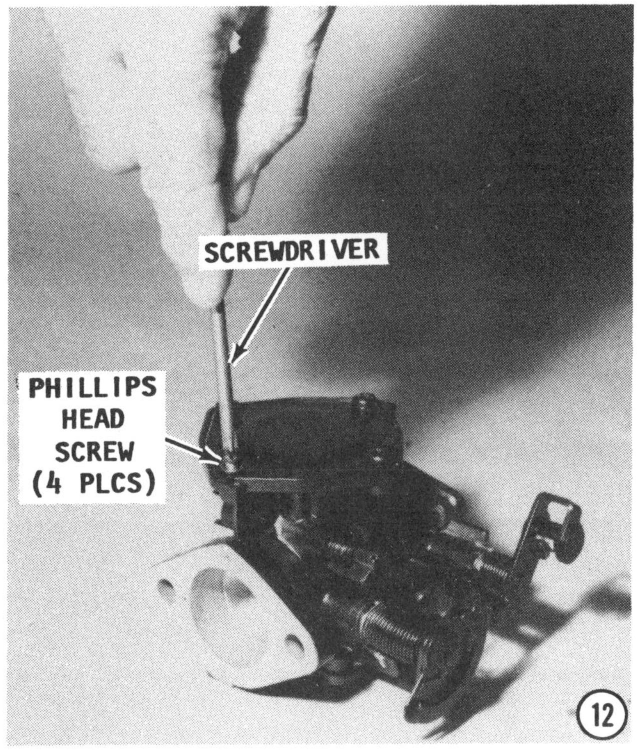

9- Remove the clear plastic check valve and gasket.

10- Lift off the pump body, diaphragm, and gasket.

11- Using a pair of needlenose pliers, withdraw the small fuel filter in the carburetor body.

12- Remove the four Phillips head screws securing the diaphragm cover to the carburetor.

13- Lift off the diaphragm cover.

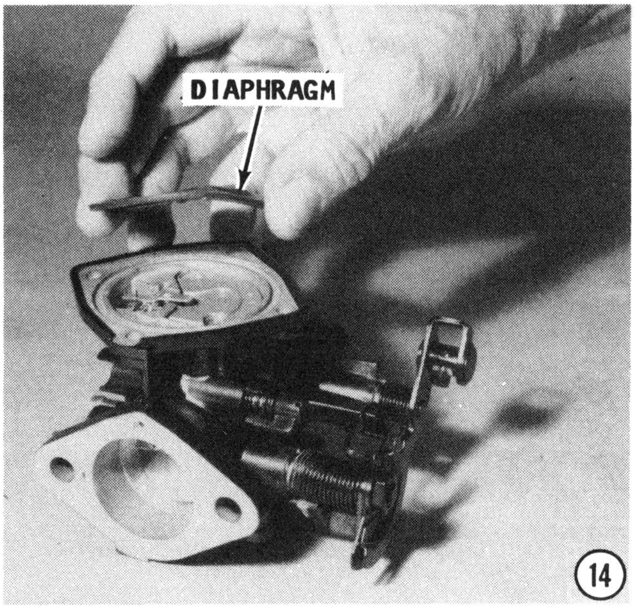

14

14- Remove the diaphragm from the fuel chamber.

15- Obtain a stubby Phillips head screwdriver and a hammer. Now, tap lightly on the end of the screwdriver while attempting to remove the hinge screw. Do not attempt to remove this screw "cold" -- without tapping the screwdriver -- because the head will almost certainly be stripped!

16- Lift out the float arm and float pin. The needle valve will remain hanging on the

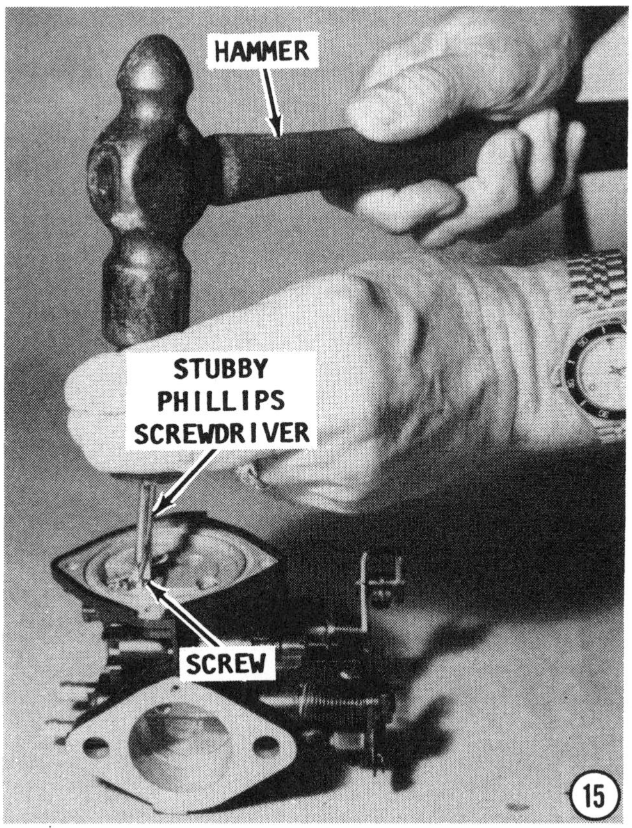

15

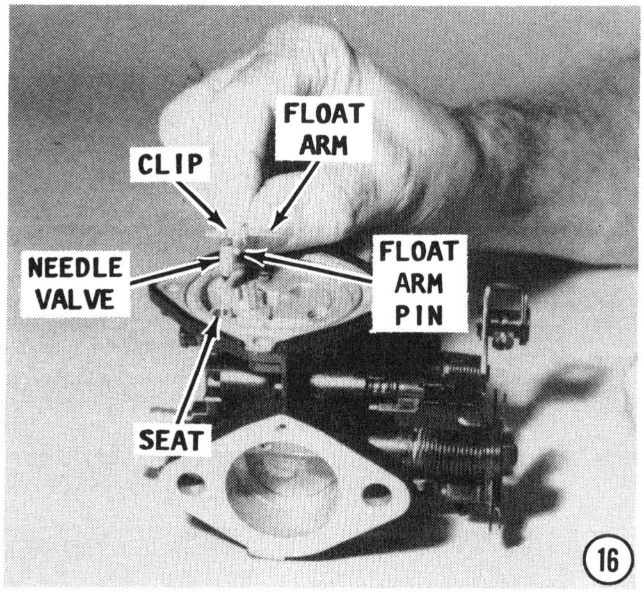

16

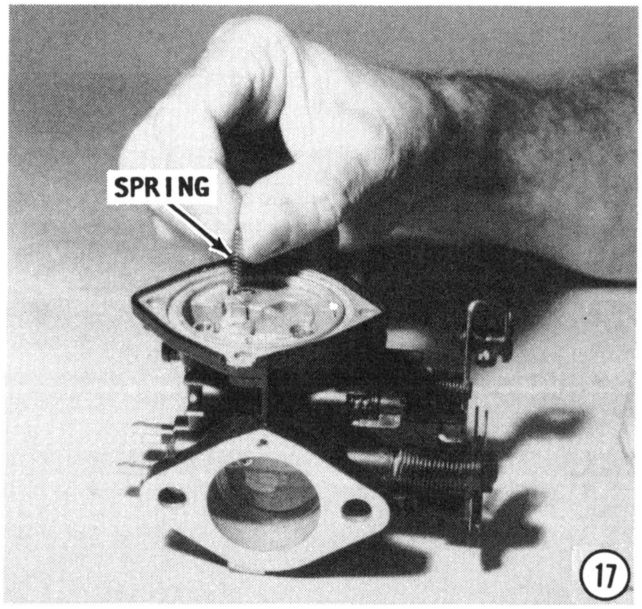

17

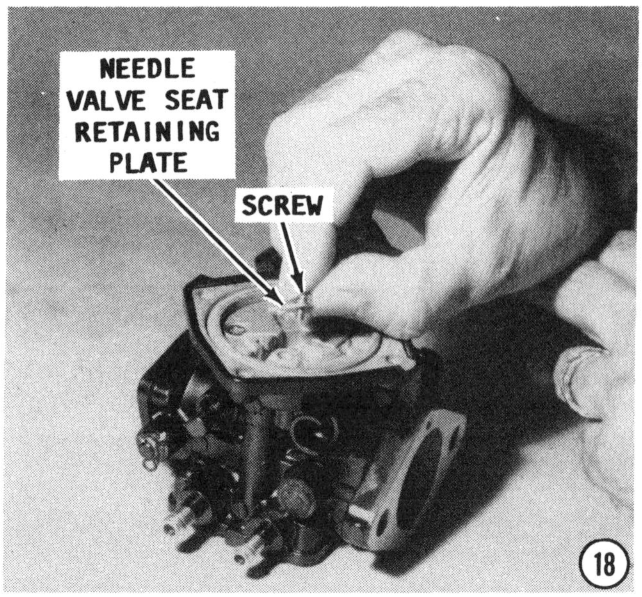

18

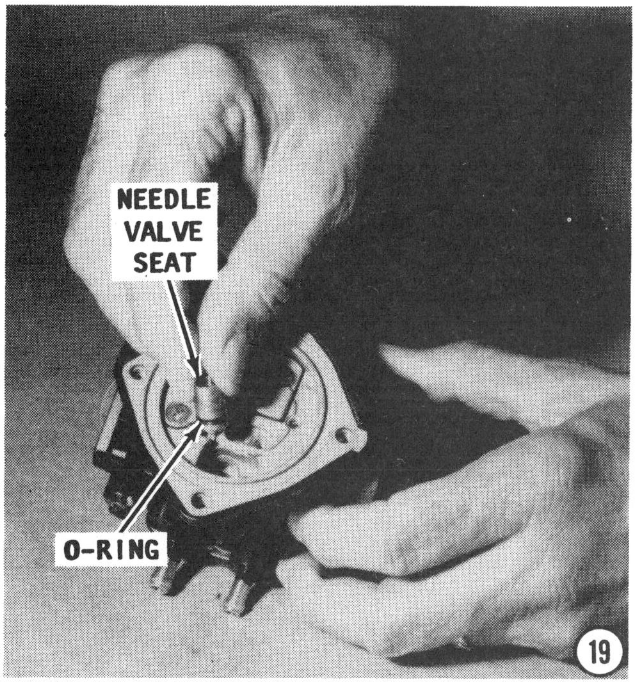

pin by the clip. Lift the valve from the seat.

17- Remove the spring from its recess in the fuel chamber.

18- Use the stubby Phillips head screwdriver and a hammer from Step 15 and lightly tap the end of the screwdriver while attempting to remove the screw securing the retaining plate to the fuel chamber. Remove the screw and plate.

19- Lift out the needle valve seat from the fuel chamber. Remove and discard the O-ring around the seat.

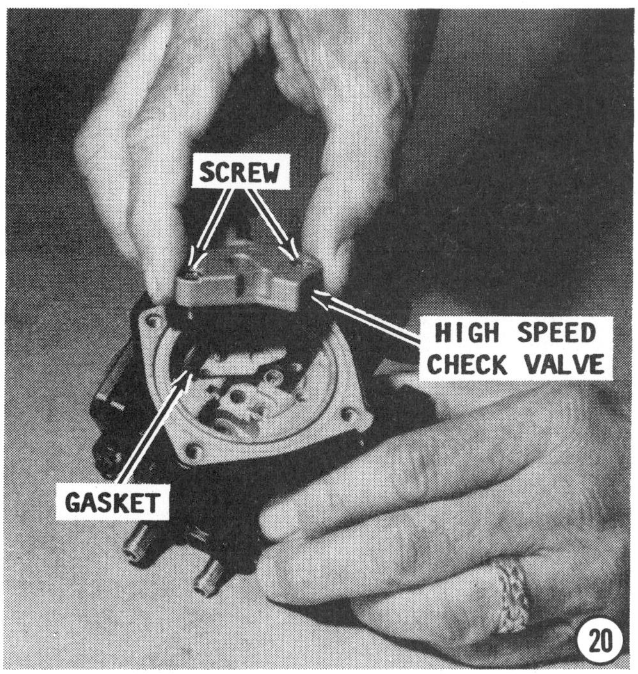

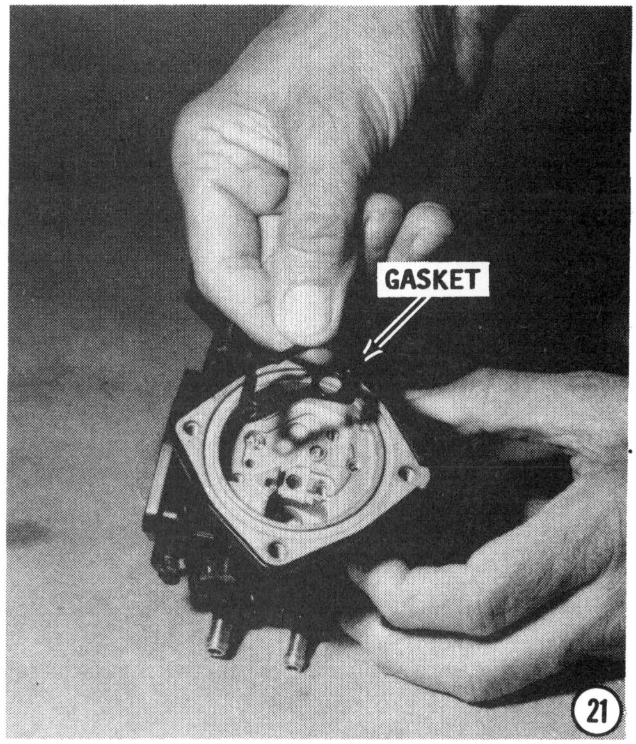

20- If necessary, use the "tapping method" to remove the two small screws securing the high speed check valve housing to the carburetor. Remove the check valve housing.

21- Remove and discard the gasket.

22- Use the correct size screwdriver to remove the main jet (the larger of the two jets), from the fuel chamber.

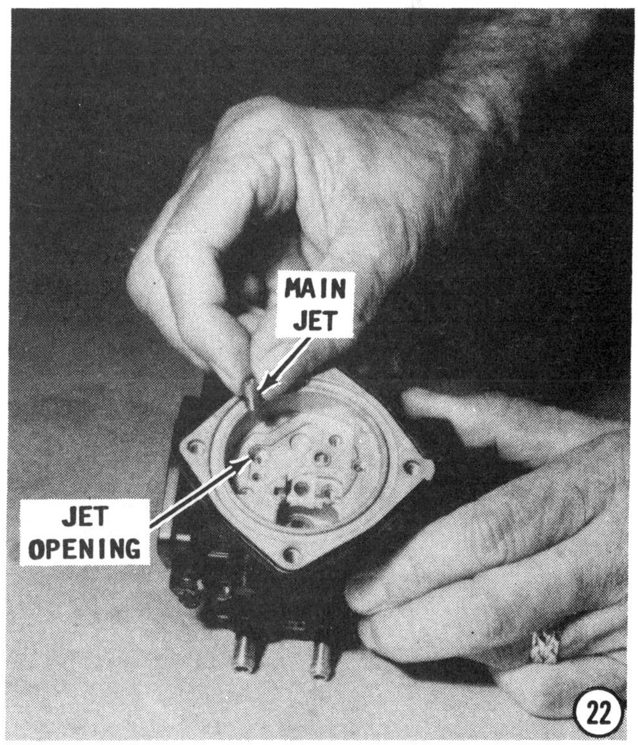

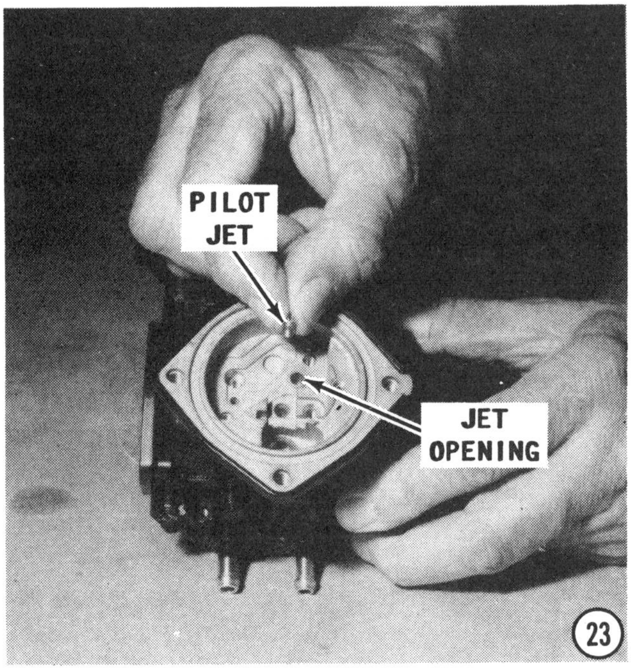

23- Use the correct size screwdriver and remove the pilot jet from the fuel chamber.

24- Remove the small Phillips head screw from the underside of the high speed check valve. Lift off the retainer. Note how a small post on the underside of the retainer indexes into a hole in the housing.

25- CAREFULLY lift off the clear plastic flap. **TAKE CARE** not to lose this item. This flap controls the flow of fuel in one direction and prevents the engine from "faltering" when the throttle is suddenly changed from wide open, to idle, and then back to wide open again.

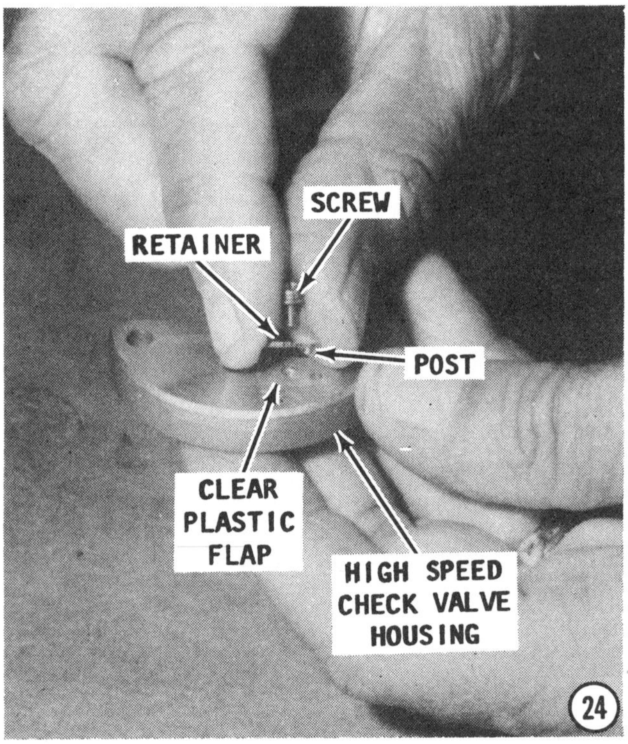

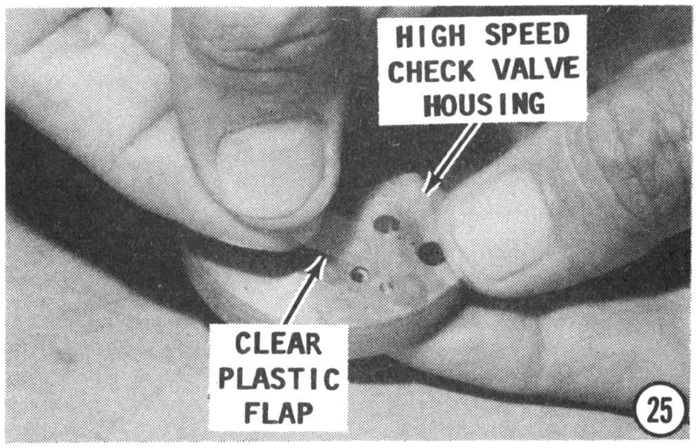

SPECIAL WORDS

Observe the letters **"L"** and **"H"** embossed next to the two mixture adjusting screws. The **"L"** denotes the low speed mixture adjusting screw, and the **"H"** denotes the high speed mixture adjusting screw. Each screw may have a plastic limiter cap installed on the screw head. A tab on the cap indexes into a slot in the collar cast in the carburetor body around the screw. The rotation of the screw is limited by the tab in the slot - hence the name "limiter cap".

26- Pull off the limiter cap on the low speed mixture adjusting screw -- the screw next to the embossed **"L"**.

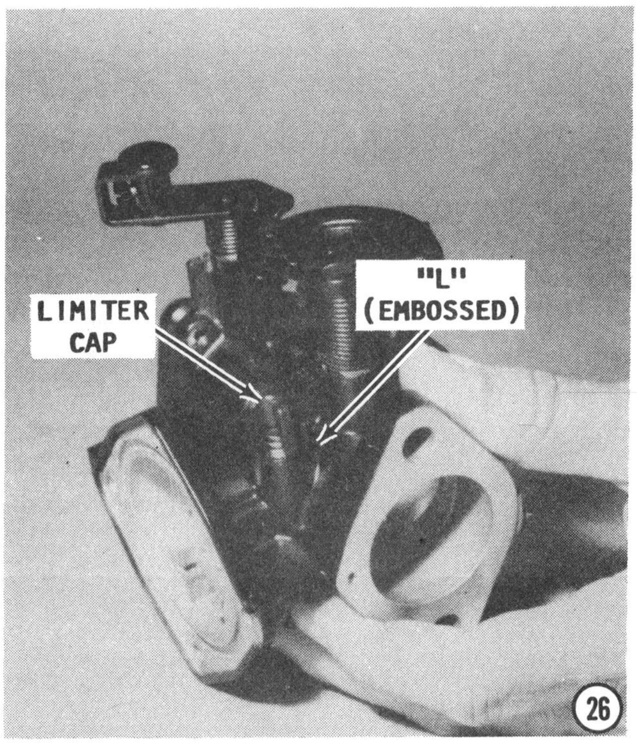

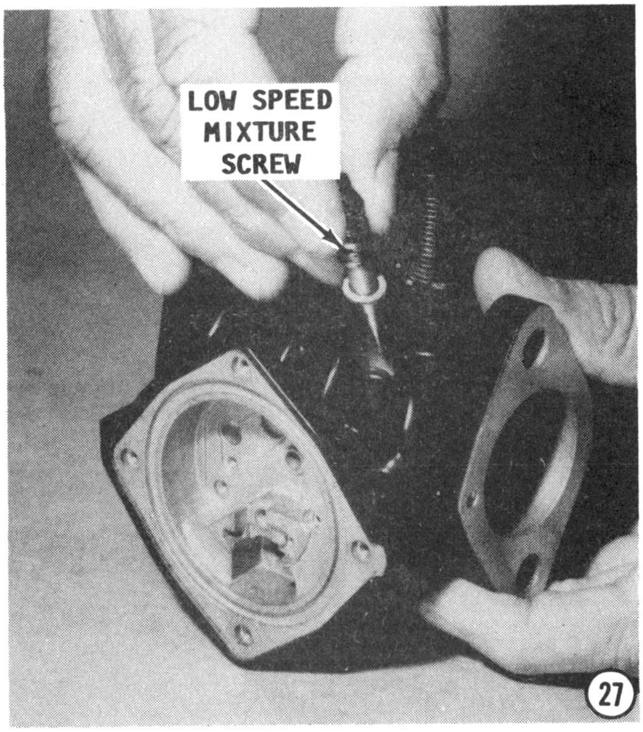

27- Back out the low speed mixture screw.

28- Pull off the limiter cap on the high speed mixture adjusting screw -- the screw next to the embossed **"H"**.

29- Back out the high speed mixture adjusting screw.

CLEANING AND INSPECTING

NEVER dip rubber parts, plastic parts, or diaphragms in carburetor cleaner. These

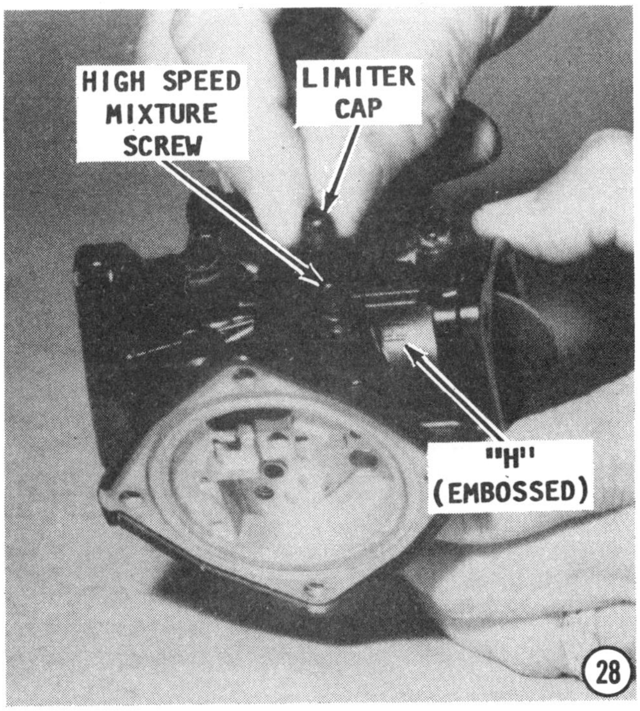

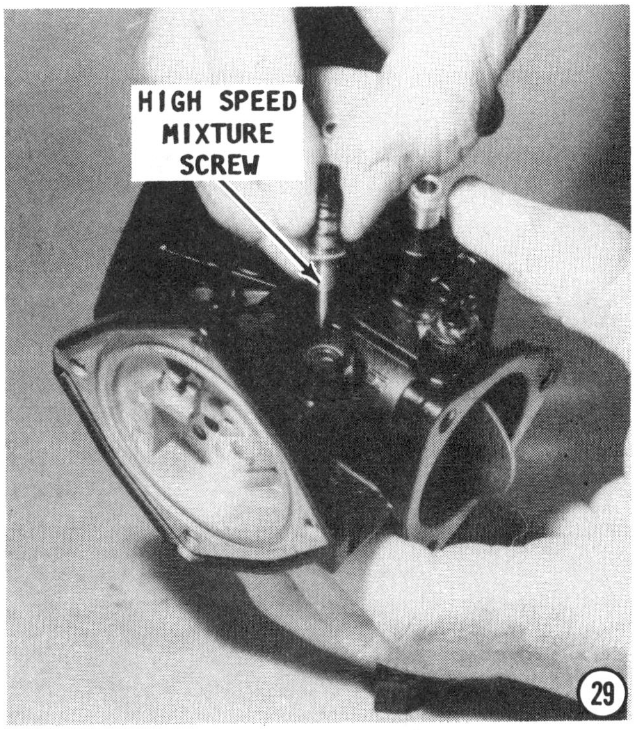

parts should be cleaned **ONLY** in solvent, and then blown dry with compressed air.

Place all metal parts in a screen-type tray and dip them in carburetor cleaner until they appear completely clean, then blow them dry with compressed air.

Blow out all passages in the castings with compressed air. Check all parts and passages to be sure they are not clogged or contain any deposits. **NEVER** use a piece of wire or any type of pointed instrument to clean drilled passages or calibrated holes in a carburetor.

Move the throttle shaft back and forth to check for wear. If the shaft appears to be too loose, replace the complete throttle body because individual replacement parts are **NOT** available.

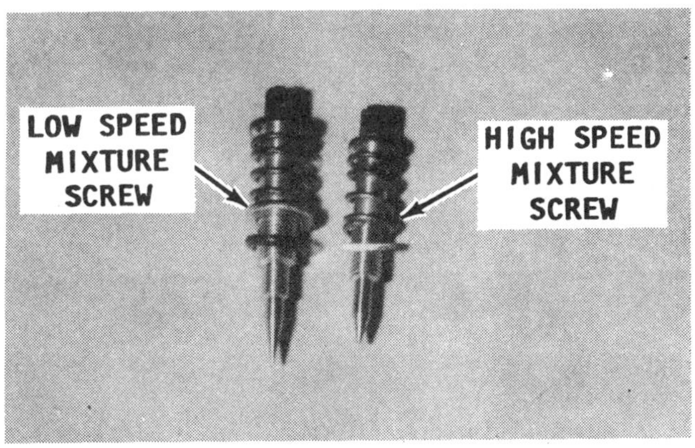

Comparison of the low speed and high speed mixture screws. Notice how the high speed screw is slightly shorter than the low speed screw.

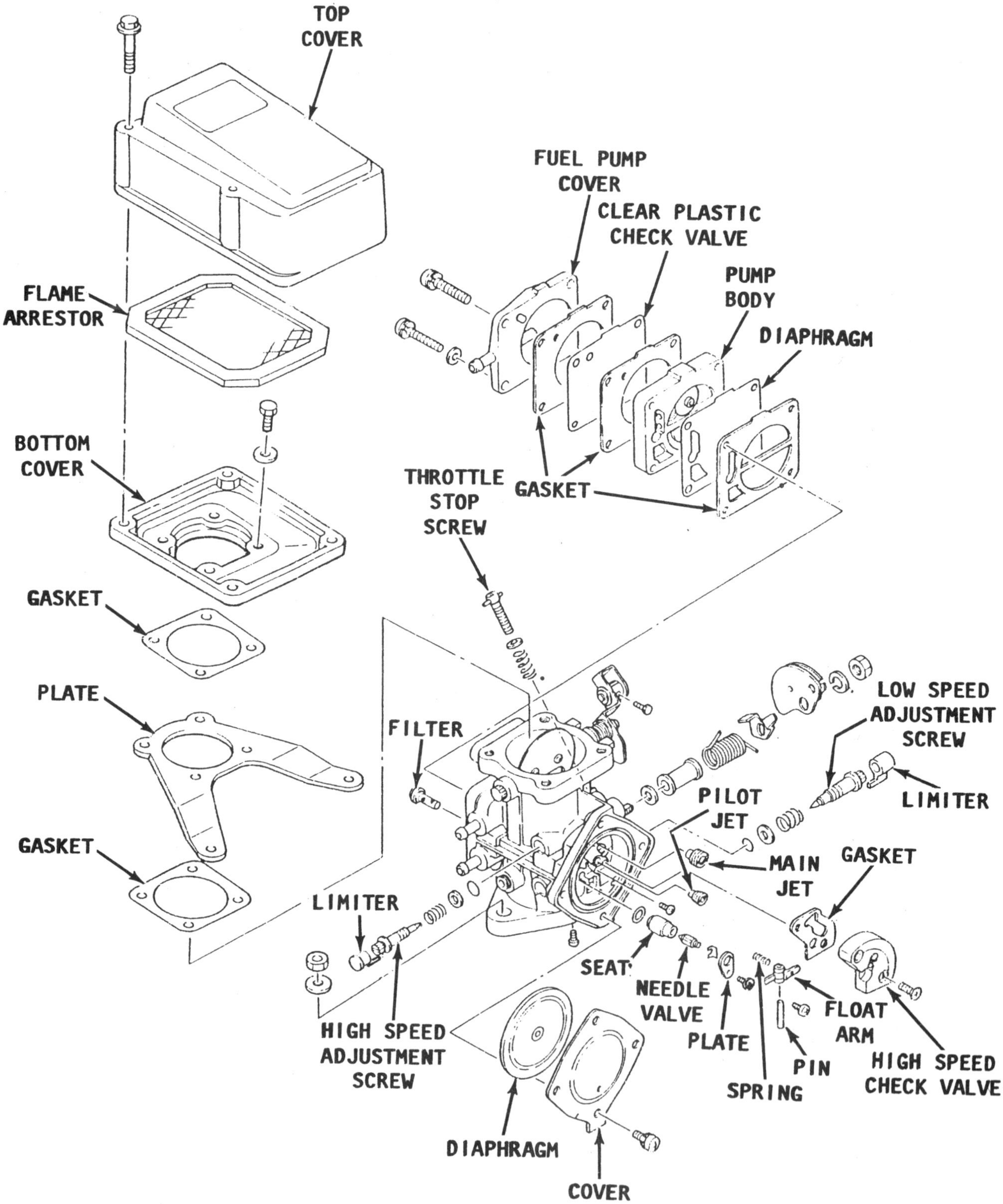

Exploded drawing of a typical Mikuni carburetor installed on a Model 650 Series engine. Major parts have been identified. This carburetor is very similar to the unit installed on a Model 700 or Model 1100 series engine, as shown on the next page.

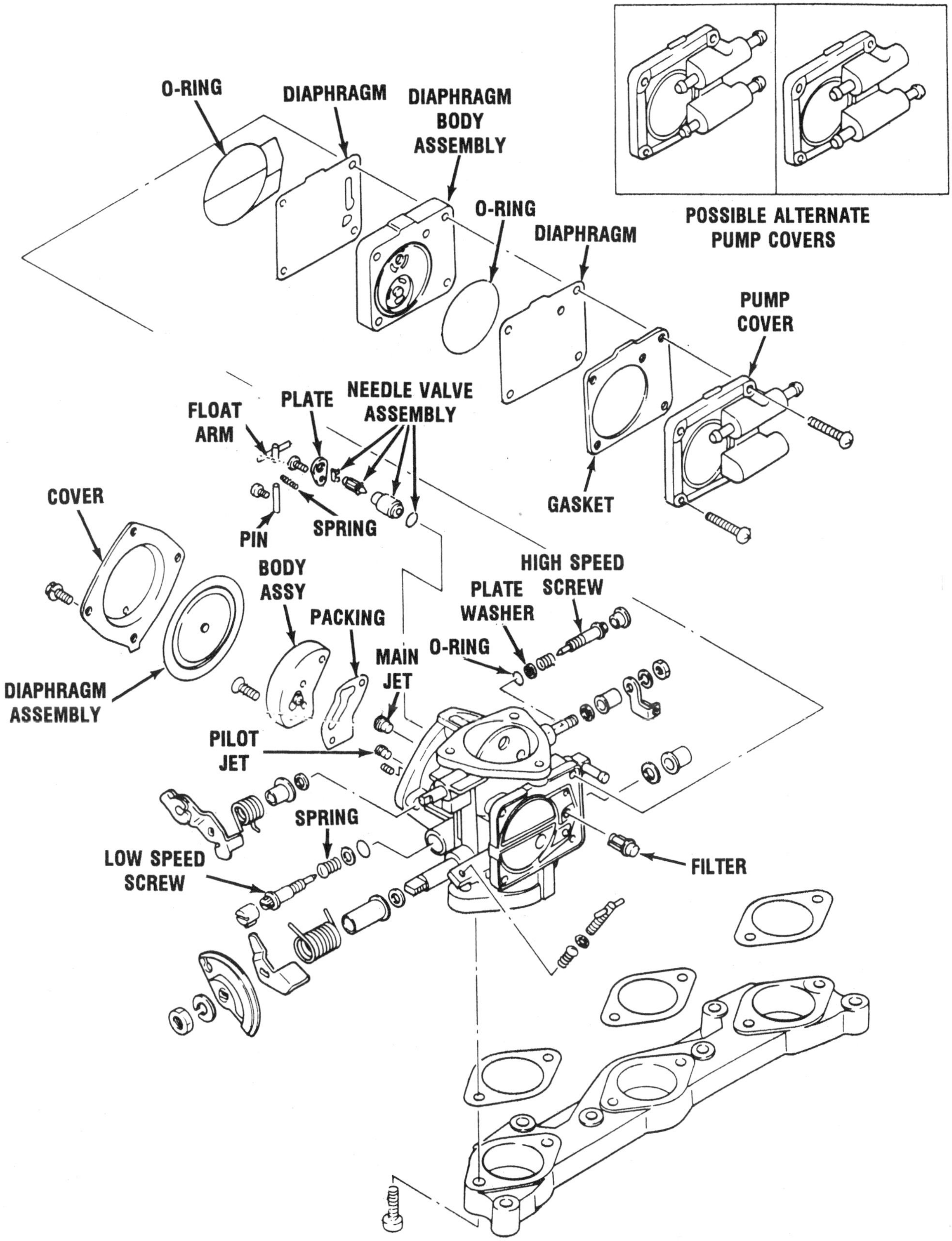

Exploded drawing of a typical Mikuni carburetor installed on a Model 700 or Model 1100 Series engine. Major parts have been identified. You will note how similar this unit is to the unit installed on the Model 650 Series on the previous page.

CRITICAL AREA

Inspect the condition of both the choke and thottle shafts. Most shaft designs incorporate a cutout portion to enable the butterfly valve to lay flat against the shaft. Two small holes are drilled in this cutout portion to accomodate the small screws securing the valve to the shaft. The weakest point of the shaft is at the screw holes. Small cracks form at the holes due to metal fatigue. These cracks elongate the threaded holes and the small screws shake loose. Once loose, they are sucked into the carburetor, then the intake manifold, and into the crankcase -- eventually finding their way into the combustion chamber. One of these small screws can then cause very expensive damage to pistons, rings and cylinder walls. Therefore, check the cutout in the shaft **CLOSELY** for any evidence of a small crack.

Inspect the main body, airhorn, and venturi cluster gasket surfaces for cracks and burrs which might cause a leak. Check to be sure the float arm return spring has not been stretched. Check the float arm needle contacting surface and replace the diaphragm if this surface has a groove worn in it.

Inspect the tapered section of the low and high speed adjusting needles and replace any that have developed a groove.

As previously mentioned, most of the parts which should be replaced during a carburetor overhaul are included in overhaul kits available from your local marine dealer. One of these kits will contain a matched fuel inlet needle and seat. This combination should be replaced each time the carburetor is disassembled as a precaution against leakage.

Make a thorough inspection of the fuel chamber and fuel pump diaphragms for the tiniest pin hole. If one is discovered, the hole will only get bigger. Therefore, the diaphragms must be replaced in order to obtain full performance from the engine.

Inspect the two vent holes in the first pump body. These holes **MUST** be clean. If these two holes are not perfectly clear, the diaphragm in the fuel pump will not function properly — full fuel volume will not be pumped.

ASSEMBLING

Special Words on Mixture Screws

Observe the low and high speed mixture screws. They appear to be very similar, but they are **NOT** interchangeable. To identify the correct screw, place them side by side as shown in the lower right illustration on Page 6-15. The low speed screw is longer then the high speed screw. The low speed screw is installed on the linkage side of the carburetor -- next to the embossed "L". The high speed screw is installed on the opposite side -- close to the fuel supply and return fittings -- next to the embossed "H".

Both screws are adjusted later at the completion of the assembling procedures.

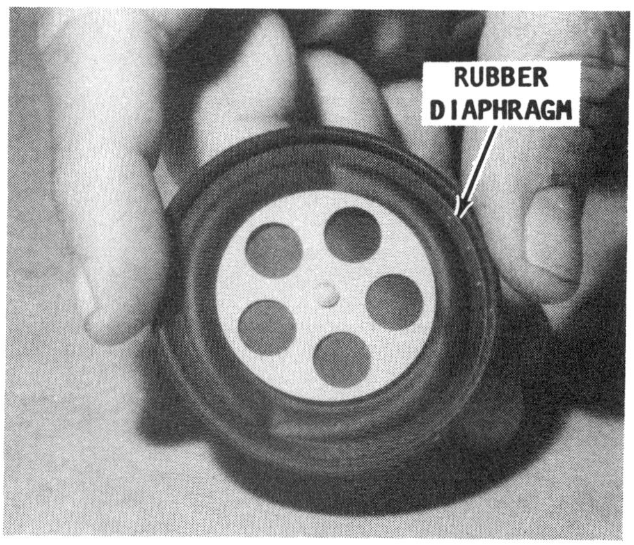

The pump diaphragm must be carefully inspected and replaced if any damage is discovered or even suspected. The tiniest "pin" hole is sufficient cause for replacement.

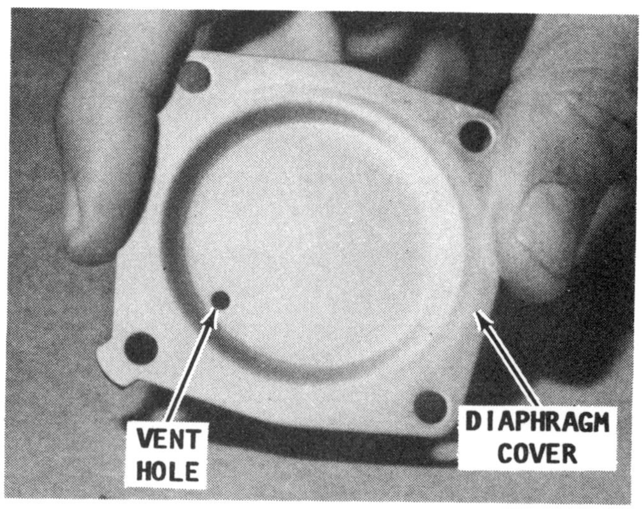

Carefully clean the vent hole in the diaphragm cover. One side of the rubber diaphragm is vented to the atmosphere thru this hole. Diaphragm action is seriously impaired if the hole becomes blocked -- even by the smallest obstruction.

Therefore, thread each screw in just a few turns at this time.

1- Install the low speed mixture screw just a few turns on the linkage side of the carburetor -- next to the embossed "L".

2- Index the tab on the limiter cap into the slot in the collar and snap the cap squarely down over the screw head.

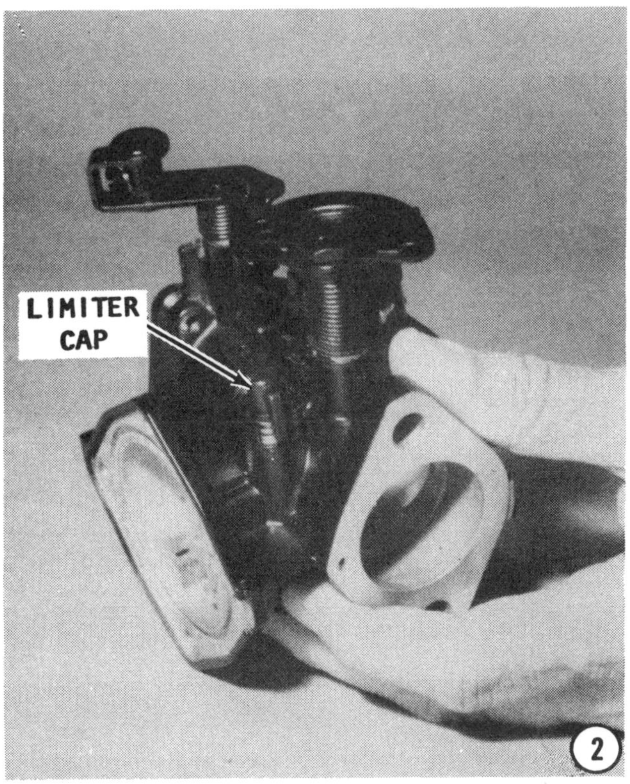

3- Install the high speed mixture screw just a few turns on the same side as the fuel supply and return fittings -- next to the embossed "H".

4- Index the tab on the limiter cap into the slot in the collar and snap the cap squarely down over the screw head.

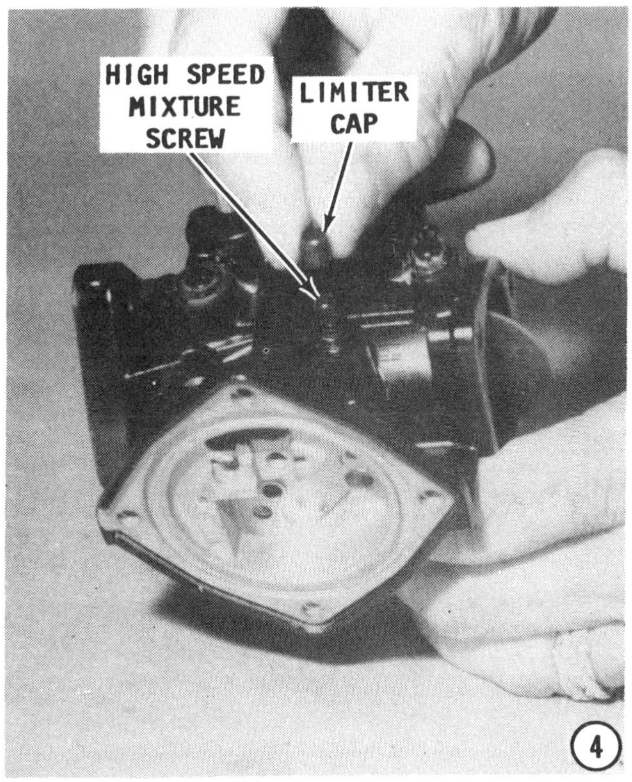

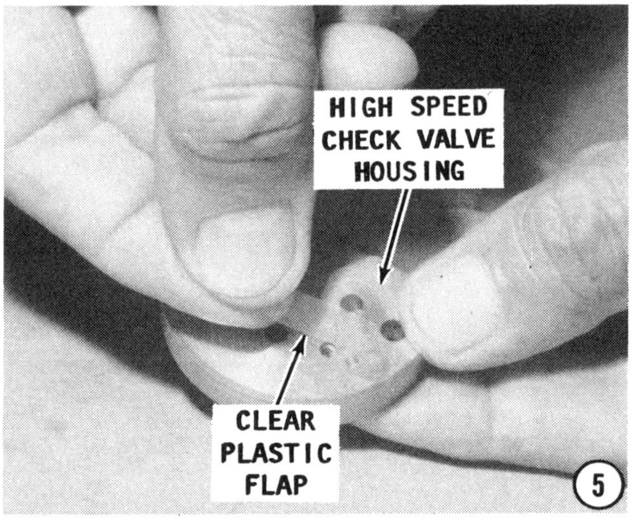

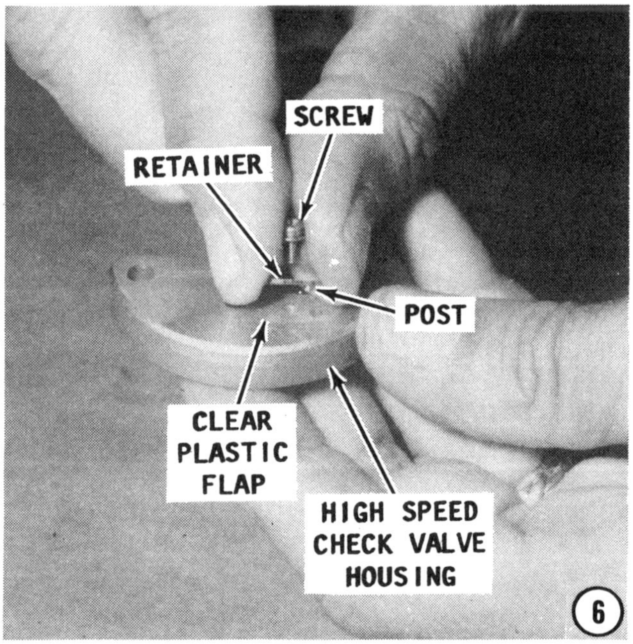

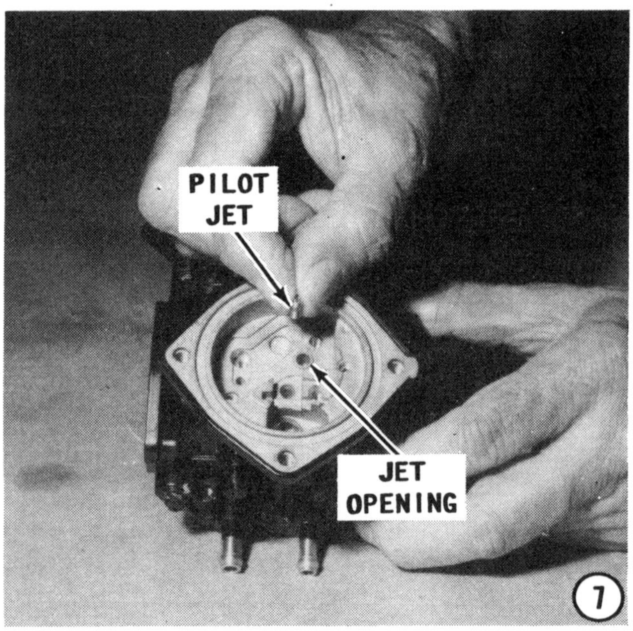

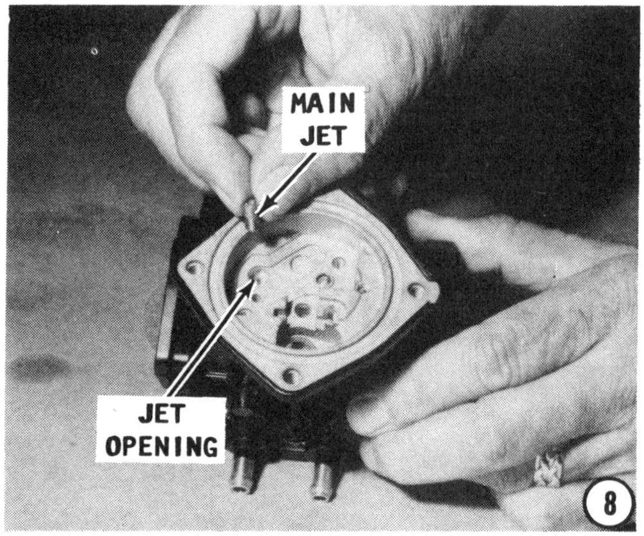

5- Align the two holes in the clear plastic flap with the two holes on the underside of the high speed check valve housing. If the four holes align, the flap is installed properly. If the holes will not align, the flap is upside-down.

6- Position the retainer over the plastic flap, with the post on the underside of the retainer indexed into both the hole in the plastic flap and the hole in the housing. Install and tighten the screw securing both parts to the housing.

7- Install the pilot jet (the smaller of the two), into the jet opening in the fuel chamber. Tighten the jet securely using the proper size screwdriver.

8- Install the main jet into the jet opening in the fuel chamber. Again, using the proper size screwdriver tighten the jet securely.

9- Position the high speed check valve housing gasket into the recess in the fuel chamber.

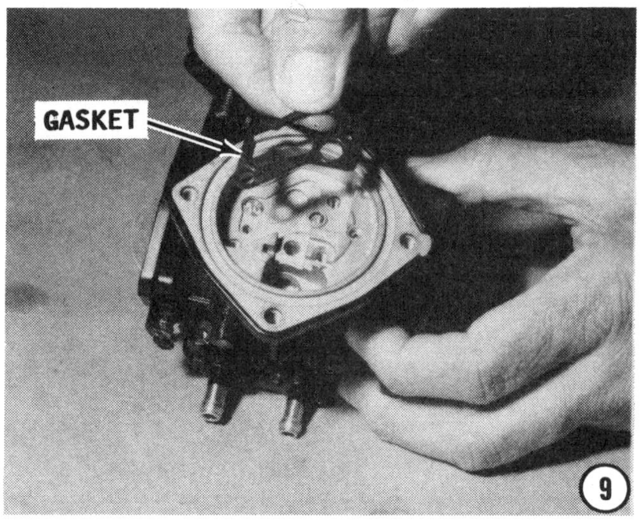

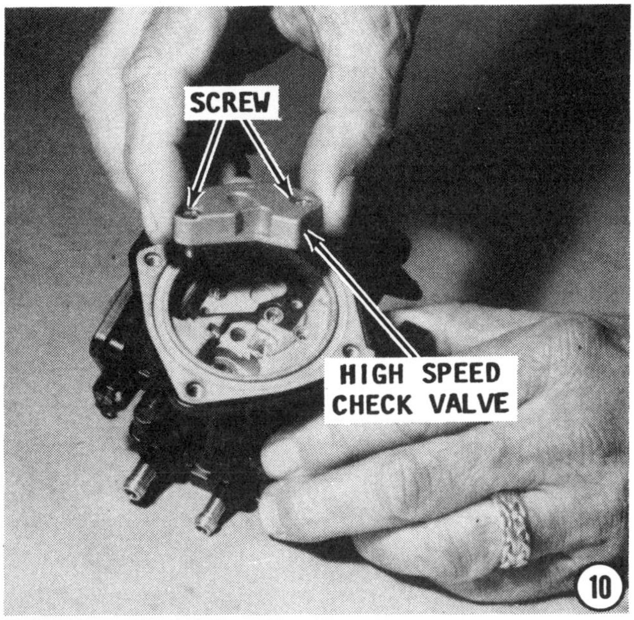

10- Place the high speed check valve over the gasket. Secure it in place with two Phillips head screws. Tighten the screws to a torque value of 1.5 ft lb (2Nm).

11- Install a new O-ring around the needle valve seat. Lower the seat into the recess in the fuel chamber.

12- Install the seat retainer over the seat. Secure the seat in place with the Phillips head screw. Tighten the screw to a torque value of 0.7 ft lb (1Nm).

13- Lower the spring into the recess in the fuel chamber.

14- Slide the needle valve clip over the square tab on the float arm. Slide the float arm over the pin, as shown. Lower the assembly down into place and at the same time: guide the needle valve into the needle

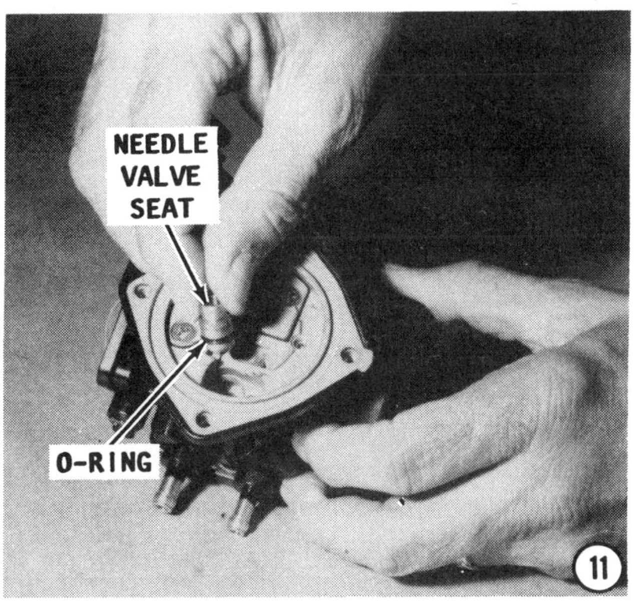

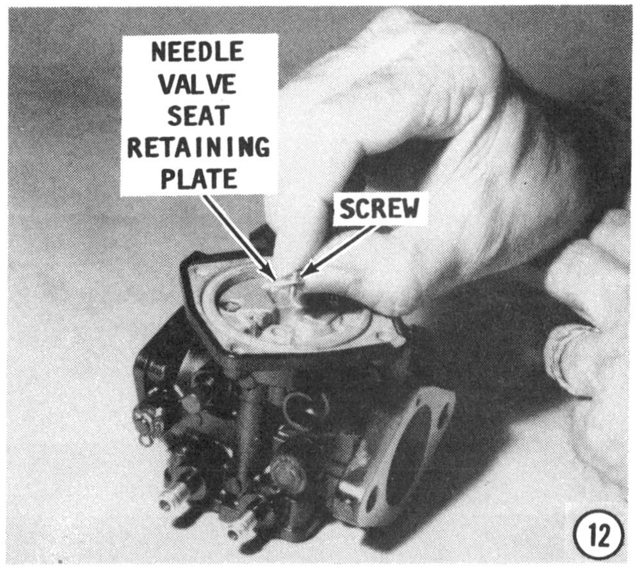

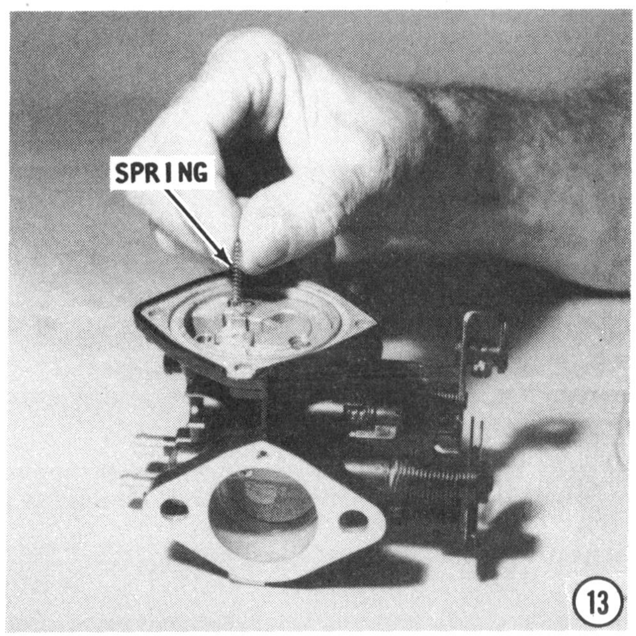

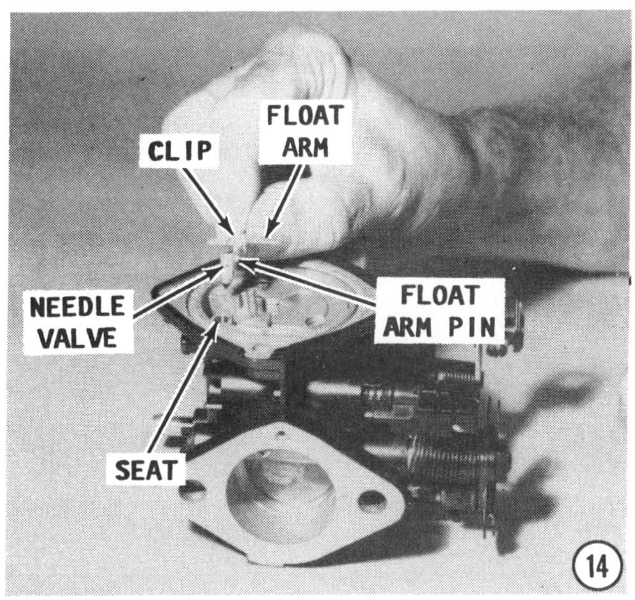

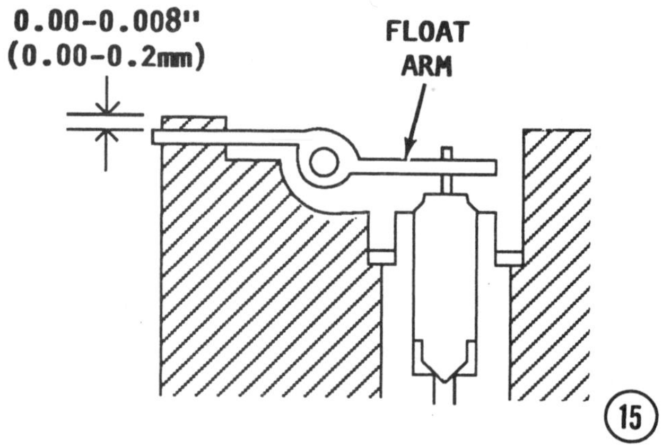

seat; place the float pin into the elongated slot in the fuel chamber; and position the dimple in the float arm over the spring. Secure the pin to the carburetor with the small Phillips head screw. Tighten the screw to a torque value of 0.7 ft lb (1Nm).

Float Arm Adjustment

15- The float arm adjustment is correct when three conditions are satisfied:

a) The top of the float arm is parallel to the fuel chamber surface.

b) The distance between the top surface of the float arm and the diaphragm contact surface of the carburetor is between 0.00-0.008" (0.0-0.2mm).

c) The float arm makes contact with the needle valve, but does not apply any pressure to the valve.

If any of these conditions are not satisfied, then replace the float arm and/or return spring. Do not attempt to bend the

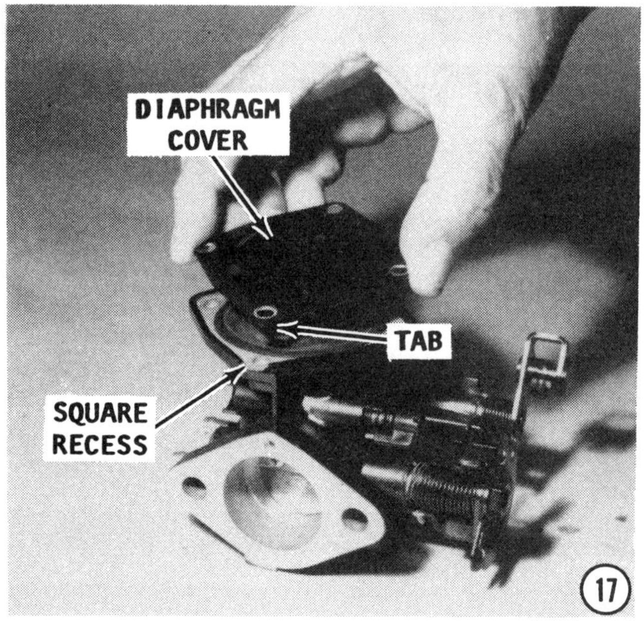

float arm or to change the characteristics of the old return spring.

Depress the rounded end of the float arm. The needle valve should lift smoothly and return inside the seat when the arm is released.

16- Place the diaphragm over the fuel chamber with the float post on the underside facing **DOWN** to rest against the float arm.

17- Position the diaphragm cover over the diaphragm with the tab in the cover corner indexed into the square recess in the carburetor body.

18- Secure the cover to the carburetor with the four Phillips head screws. Tighten

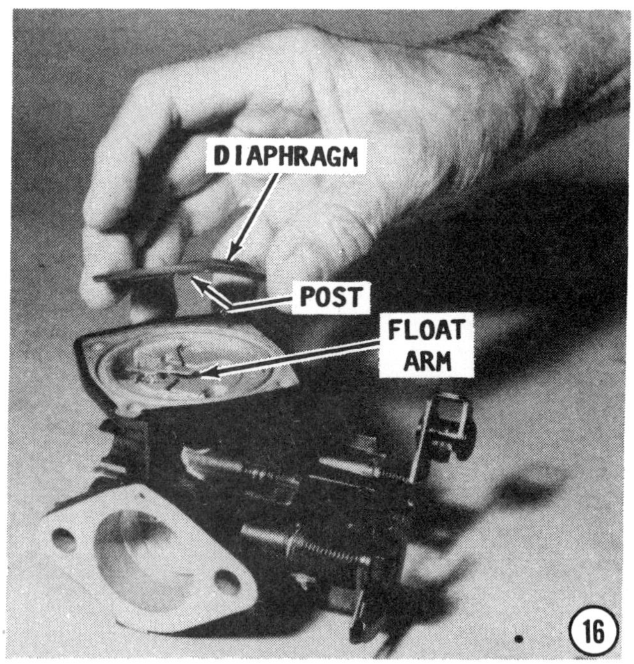

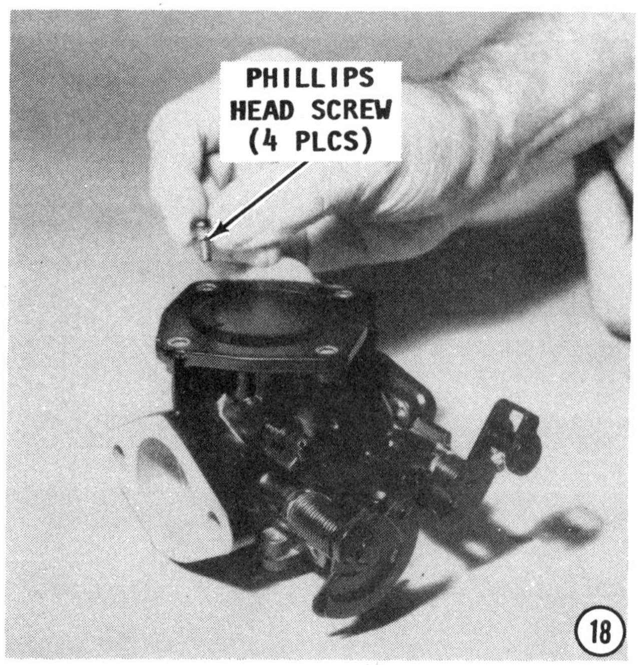

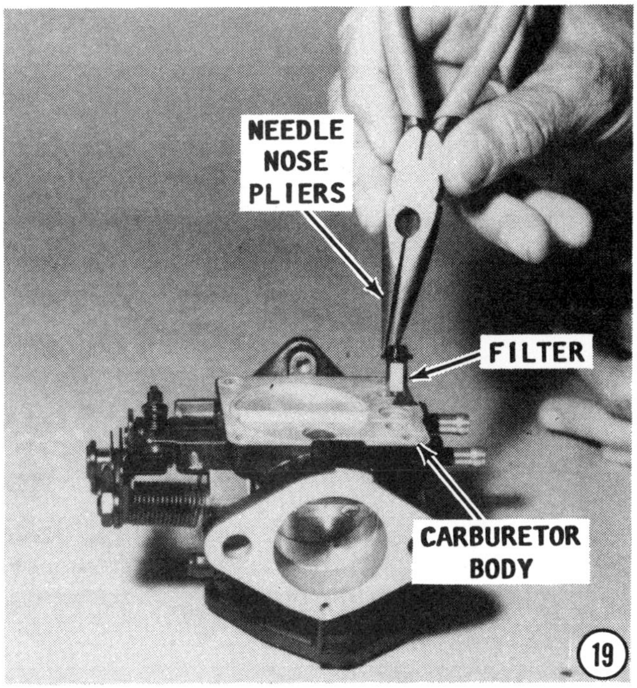

the screws alternately and evenly to a torque value of 3 ft lb (4Nm).

19- Lower the fuel filter into the recess in the carburetor body.

Fuel Pump Assembling

First these words: Take care to install all **seven** layers of diaphragms, gaskets, and check valves (made from plastic film), with their tabs facing **UPWARD** toward the choke valve. The fuel pump components must be carefully stacked and held together until the securing screws may be passed through all layers and threaded into the fuel pump body.

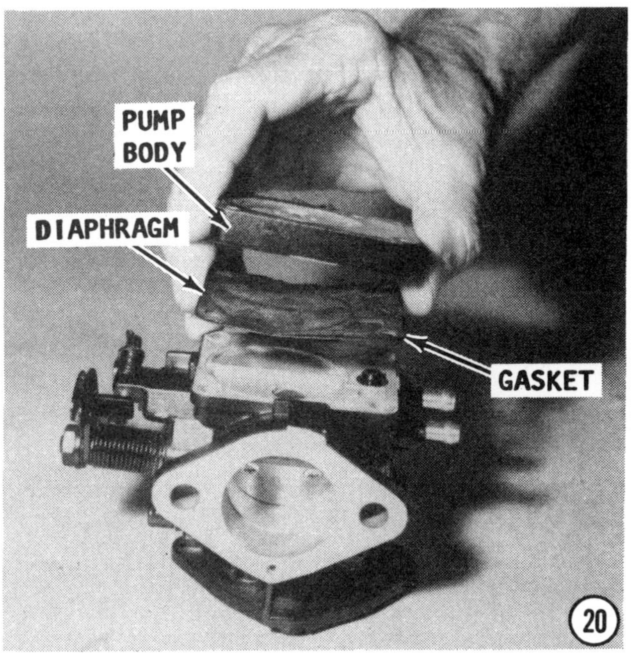

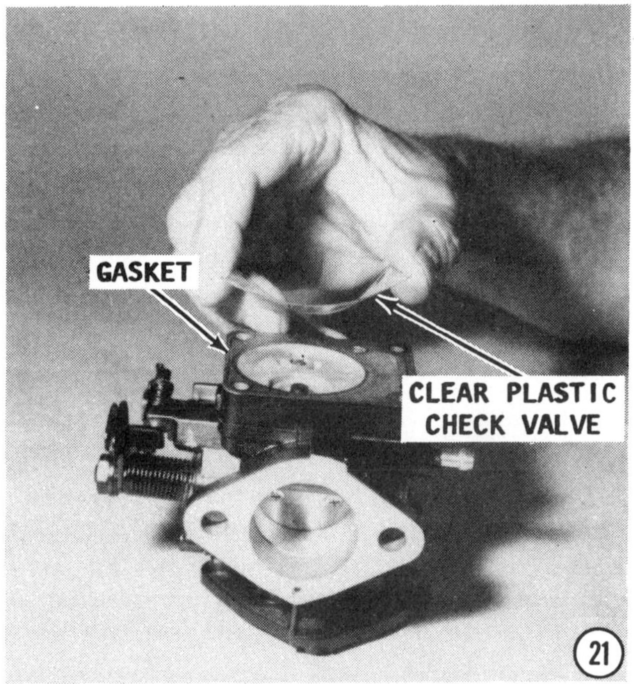

If a gasket, diaphragm or check valve is askew, the slightest pressure from the end of the securing screw will tear the component and affect the performance of the fuel pump.

20- Install the gasket, diaphragm and pump body over the carburetor.

21- Place the gasket, followed by the clear plastic check valve, over the pump body.

22- Position the gasket over the plastic check valve. Finally, place the fuel pump cover over the gasket with the post, on the underside of the cover, indexed into the

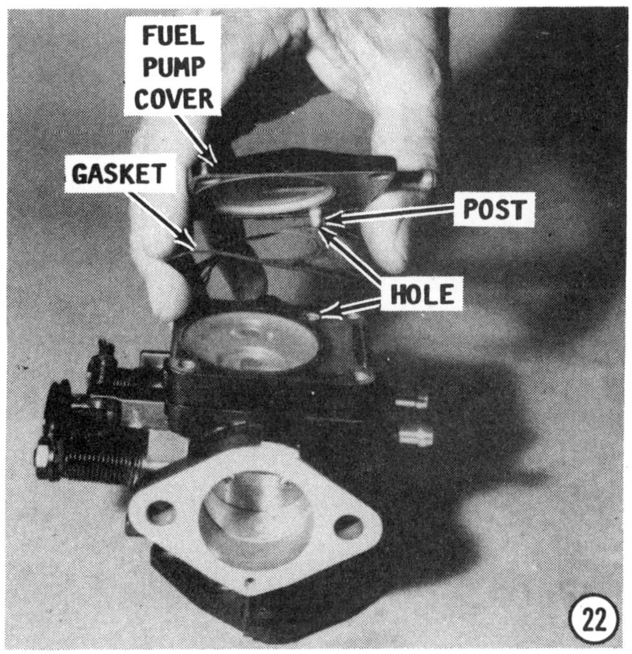

holes in the stack of components between the cover and the pump body. Check to be sure the layers are aligned with all tabs facing **UPWARD.**

23- Visually inspect the screw holes to verify all components are squarely in place and the path for each screw is clear. Continue to hold the stack of components tightly together until all four screws are started into the fuel chamber body.

After the screws are started, tighten them in a diagonal pattern to a torque value of 3 ft lb (4Nm).

BENCH ADJUSTMENTS

Set the low speed and high speed adjustment screws the correct number of turns "out" from a lightly seated position, as listed in the table in the Appendix.

SPECIAL WORDS

If the following adjustments are attempted while the carburetor/s are installed on the

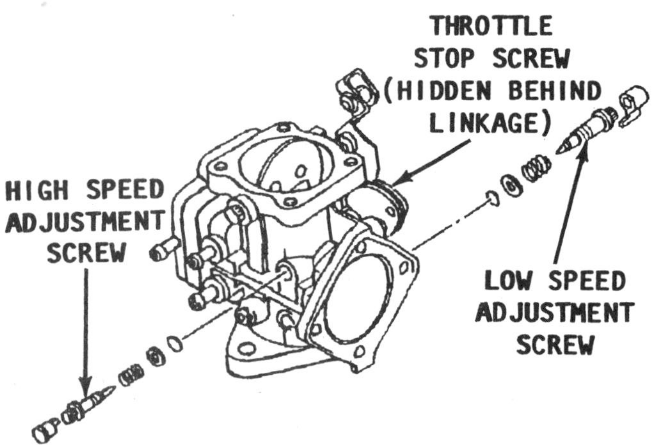

Exploded drawing showing arrangement of parts for the low speed and high speed adjustment screws on a Mikuni BN 38 and BN44 carburetor.

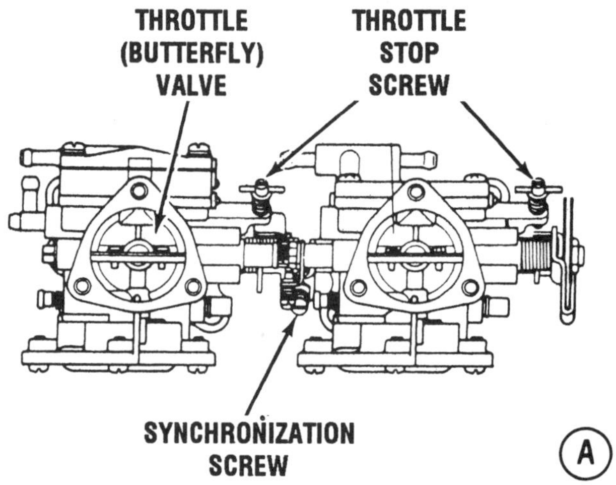

manifold, the flame arrestor cover and the flame arrestor screens must first be removed to enable the choke/throttle (butterfly) valve to be observed.

Low Speed and Idle Mixture Adjustment

Move the craft to a test tank, to a body of water, or connect a flush attachment and hose to the engine. For maximum performance, the idle mixture and the idle rpm should be adjusted under actual operating conditions. Connect a tachometer to the engine.

Lightly seat the low speed adjustment screw. From this position, back the screw out 3/4 to 1 full turn as a preliminary adjustment, at this time.

Start the engine and allow it to warm to operating temperature.

CAUTION

Water must circulate through the jet pump -- to and from the engine, anytime the engine is operating. Circulating water will prevent overheating -- which could cause damage to moving engine parts and possible engine seizure.

NEVER, AGAIN NEVER, operate the engine at high speed with a flush device attached. An engine operating at high speed with such a device attached, might very likely **RUN-AWAY** from lack of a load on the impeller shaft, causing extensive damage.

The throttle stop screw is located on the throttle linkage on the opposite side of the carburetor from the fuel fittings

With the engine operating, slowly rotate the throttle stop screw until the engine idles at 1,200 to 1,300 rpm. Next, rotate the low speed screw inward or outward 1/8th of a turn at a

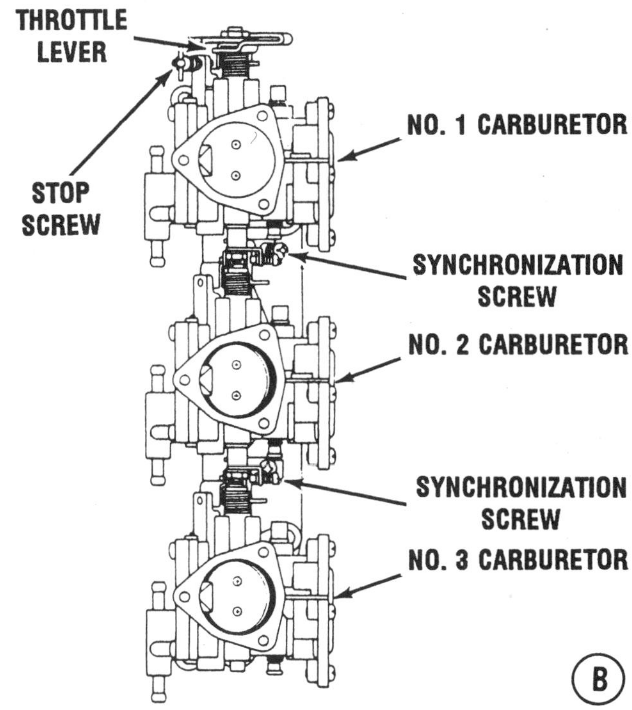

time until the cylinders fire evenly and engine rpm increases. Readjust the throttle stop screw to reduce the rpm to specified idle speed.

Synchronize Throttle Valves
Model 650 and 700 Series
(Illustration "A")

Back off the throttle stop screws on both carburetors until the end of the screws just barely clear the throttle lever.

Make some sort of record as to the position of the throttle stop screws. Consider this as the "set" position. Check to be sure the throttle valve of the No. 2 carburetor is fully closed.

Now, turn the synchronization screw inward or outward until the No. 1 throttle valve is fully closed.

Finally, turn the throttle stop screws on both carburetors to the "set" position, as noted above.

Synchronize Throttle Valves
Model 1100 And 1200 Series
(Illustration "B")

Back off the throttle stop screws on all three carburetors until the end of the screws just barely clear the throttle lever.

Next, back out the throttle stop screws on the No. 1 carburetor until the end of the screw just barely clears the throttle lever. Rotate the throttle stop screw of the No. 1 and No. 2

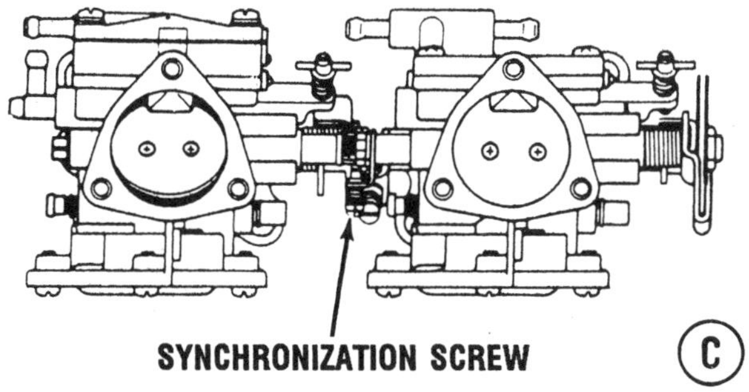

carburetors outward until the ends of both screws just barely clear the throttle lever.

Now, rotate the synchronization screw on the No. 2 carburetor inward until the throttle valves of the No. 2 and No. 3 carburetors are fully closed. **Note:** Turning the synchronization screw inward further than necessary will cause the throttle valve on the No. 3 carburetor to begin to open.

Turn the synchronization screw on the No. 1 carburetor inward until the throttle valve of the No. 1 carburetor is fully closed.

Check to be sure all throttle valves are fully closed. If all valves are not fully closed, repeat this complete adjustment procedure.

Finally, rotate the throttle stop screw to the "set" position noted above.

Synchronize Choke Valves
Model 650 and 700 Series
(Illustration "C")

Rotate the synchronization screw on the No. 1 carburetor inward or outward to bring both choke valves into the fully closed position when the choke lever is turned to the closed position.

Synchronize Choke Valves
Model 1100 And 1200 Series
(Illustration "D")

Begin by backing out the synchronization screw on the No. 1 and No. 2 carburetors until the end of the screw just clears the synchronization lever.

Turn the synchronization screw on the No. 2 carburetor to bring the choke valves of the No. 2 and No. 3 carburetors into a fully closed position when the choke lever is turned to the closed position.

Now, rotate the synchronization screw on the No. 1 carburetor to bring the choke valve on the No. 1 carburetor to the fully closed

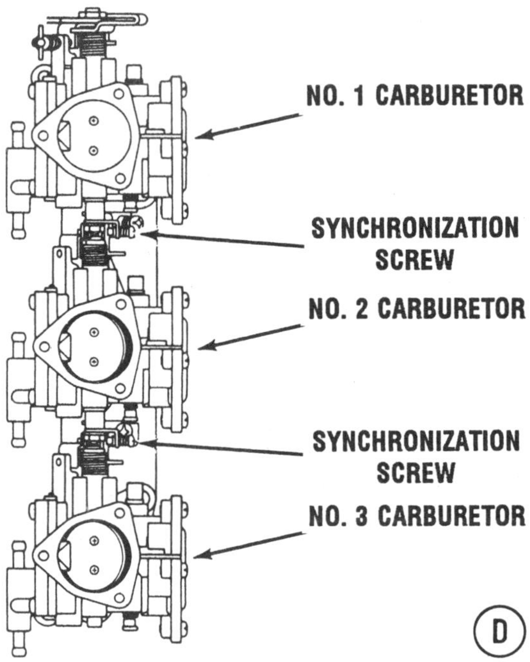

position when the choke lever is turned to the closed position.

Finally, make a check to ensure all three choke valves are fully closed. If they are not fully closed, repeat the complete procedure.

CARBURETOR/S INSTALLATION

1- Remove the "duct" tape covering the manifold openings. Place a new carburetor mounting gasket over the intake manifold studs. Slide the cable mounting bracket over the studs with the cable supports on the outside, followed by another new mounting gasket. Place the carburetor/s over the mounting studs.

2- Place a lockwasher over each carburetor mounting stud. Now, it will probably be necessary to raise the carburetor/s slightly off the studs to provide clearance for start the mounting nuts. Tighten the nuts securely.

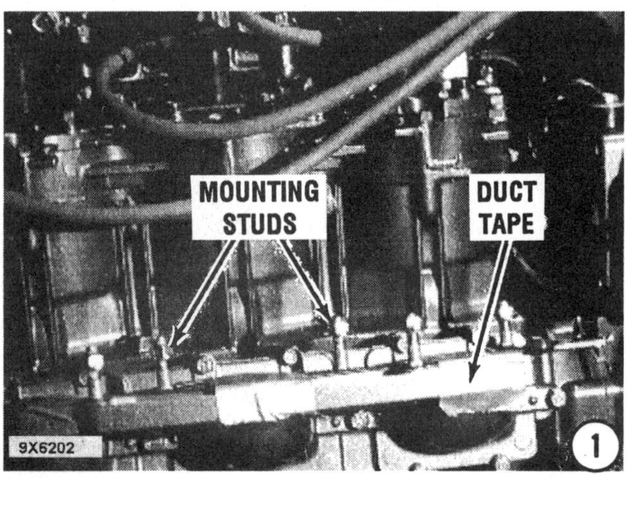

3- Position the flame arrestor screen/s onto the lower flame arrestor cover. Install the top

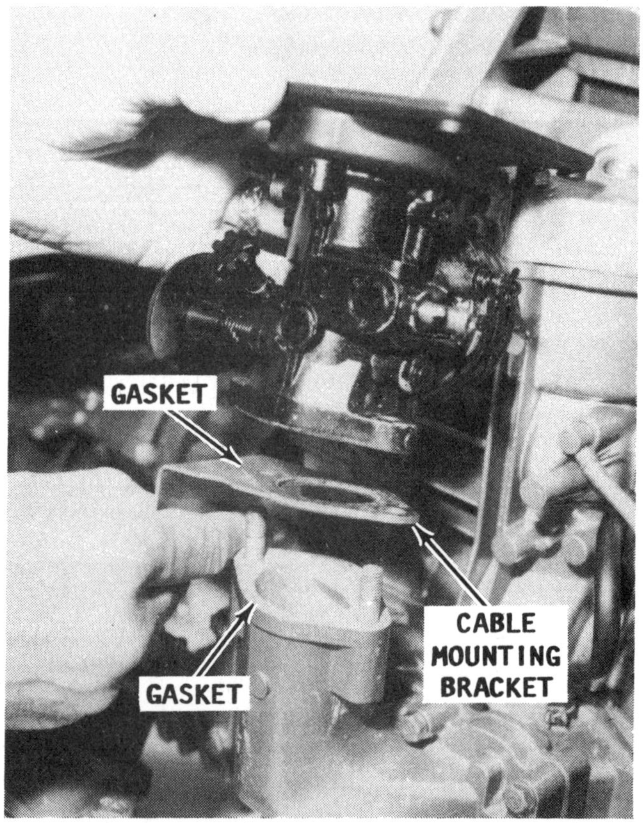

Moving the cable mounting bracket into place between the carburetor and the intake manifold on a single-cylinder engine. A gasket is installed on both sides of the bracket, as shown.

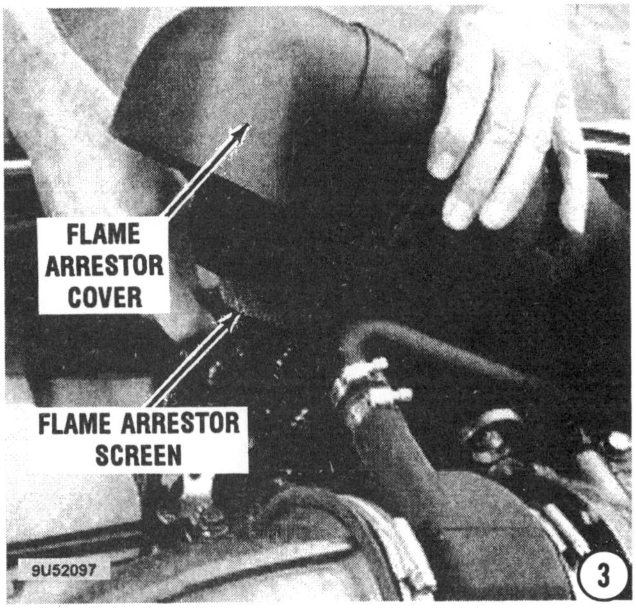

cover and secure the two halves together with the Phillips head screws.

4- Connect the three hoses to the carburetor. If the hoses were not marked as directed in Step 2 of disassembling, proceed as follows: Locate the disconnected vacuum hose leading from the crankcase. Connect this hose to the fitting on the outer fuel pump cover. Locate the disconnected hose leading from the in-line filter usually mounted on the engine compartment wall. Connect this fuel line to the lower fuel fitting on the carburetor body.

Locate the third and last disconnected hose leading from the fuel tank. Connect this hose to the upper fuel fitting on the carburetor body. Install **NEW** sta-straps at all three hose connections.

5- Slide both the throttle and choke cables into their respective slots in the cable mounting bracket. Tighten the two nuts on each cable to secure the cables to the bracket. Hook the

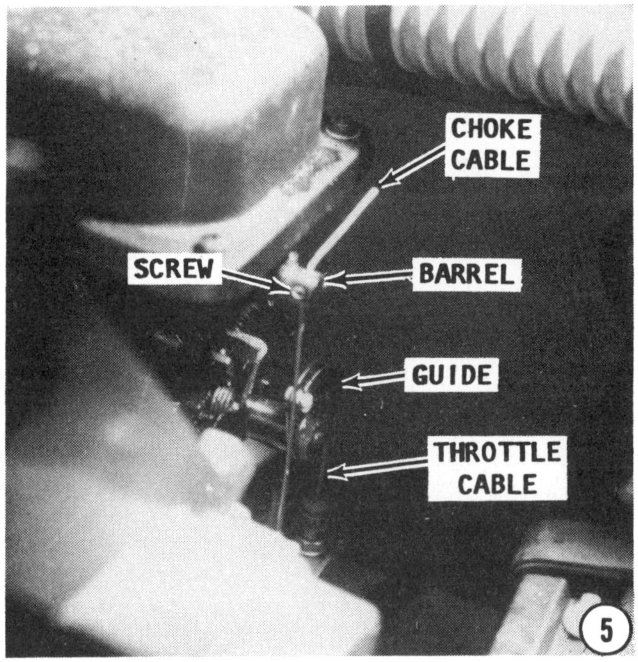

throttle cable end into the guide before sliding the cable into the slot in the mounting bracket.

Measure the distance between the top of the threaded cable guide to the mounting bracket. This distance must be set at 0.67" (17mm). Pass the choke cable end through the barrel until the mark, made in Step 1 of disassembling, is up against the barrel. Tighten the small screw on the barrel to secure the cable in place. If no mark was made, insert the cable into the barrel until no slack remains in the cable, and then temporarily tighten the screw to secure the cable within the barrel. An adjustment follows in the next paragraph.

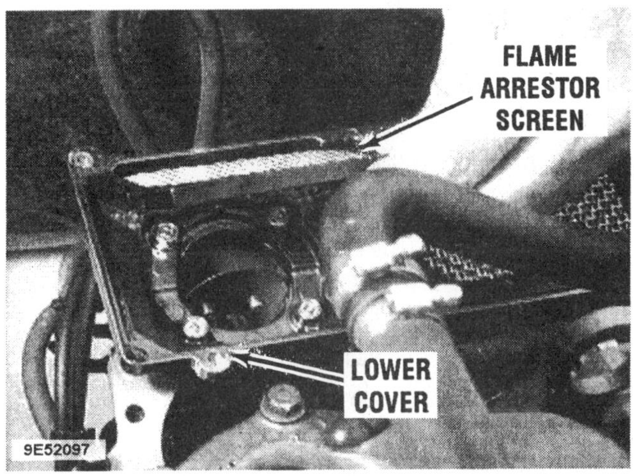

Removing the flame arrestor screen in order to observe the "butterfly" valve during a choke valve adjustment, if the carburetor/s are installed on the intake manifold. Normally, adjustment of the choke valve is considered a "bench adjustment", as described in the text.

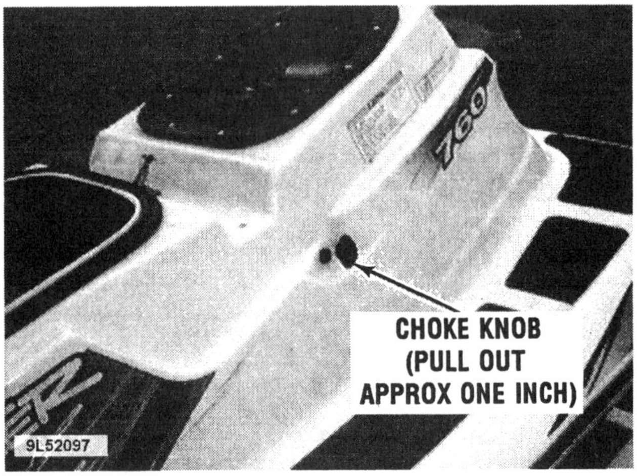

To make the choke cable adjustment, the choke knob is pulled out approximately one inch, as explained in the text.

Choke Cable Adjustment

Remove the flame arrestor cover and the flame arrestor screen, if they are in place. Loosen the small screw securing the choke cable end to the barrel on the choke lever.

Pull the choke knob out until approximately one inch of choke shaft is exposed. With the knob in this position, move the choke valve to the fully closed position and tighten the screw securing the cable to the barrel.

Throttle Cable Adjustment

The idle speed must be adjusted **BEFORE** adjusting the throttle lever free "play". The throttle cable is a fixed length. There is no adjustment of the cable at the carburetor. The handlebar throttle lever should have 0.27-0.39" (7-10mm) free "play" between the throttle lever and the lever stop.

Loosen the locknut and rotate the cable adjuster until the correct clearance is obtained. If the adjuster is turned inward, the free "play"

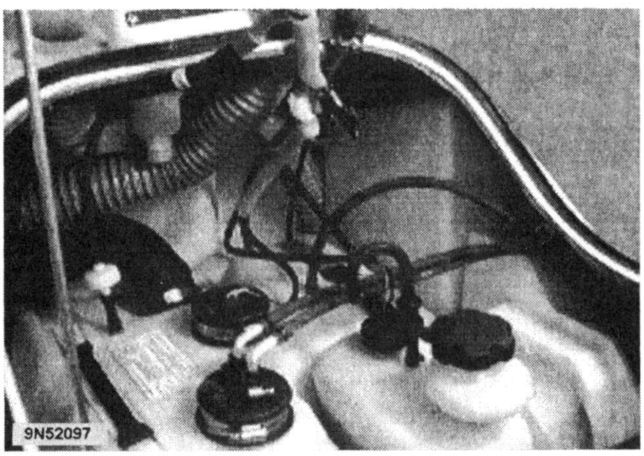

Typical oil tank installation with major items identified.

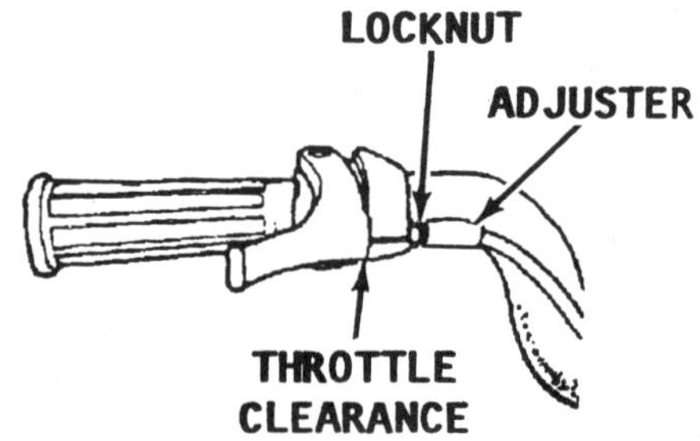

The throttle lever adjustment is explained in the text.

is increased. If the adjuster is turned outward, the free "play" is decreased.

Tighten the locknut to maintain this new adjustment. If the cable has stretched, or has become kinked or frayed, or tends to stick, the entire cable **MUST** be replaced.

At the carburetor, the throttle cable determines the position of the throttle lever and therefore, the position of the throttle "butterfly" valve in the carburetor throat. The throttle stop screw is used to change position of the throttle lever and affects engine idle.

6-8 OIL INJECTION

In recent years a more sophisticated method of mixing oil with the fuel for internal lubrication has become more popular with the manufacturers of personal watercraft. At press time,

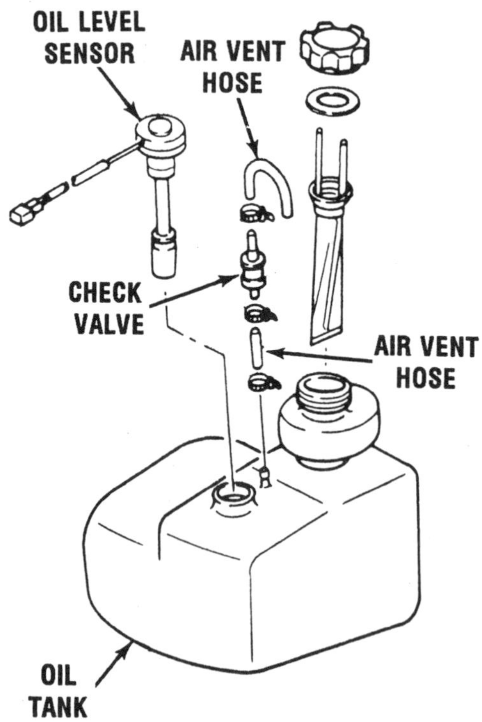

Exploded drawing of a typical oil tank and associated parts, as described in the text. Major parts are identified.

virtually all units covered in this manual were equipped with oil injection, with the exception of the Super Jet and the FX1. The oil injection system replaces the age old method of manually mixing oil with the fuel for lubrication of internal moving parts of a 2-cycle engine.

Yamaha engineers designed and developed their oil injection system as an independent unit, separate from the fuel system until the lubricant enters the cylinder. This system injects oil directly into the intake manifold between the carburetor and the reed valve for each cylinder. Such an arrangement provides immediate oil delivery response to changes in rpm and load demands. Because the oil bypasses the carburetor, gummy deposits in the carburetor passages are avoided.

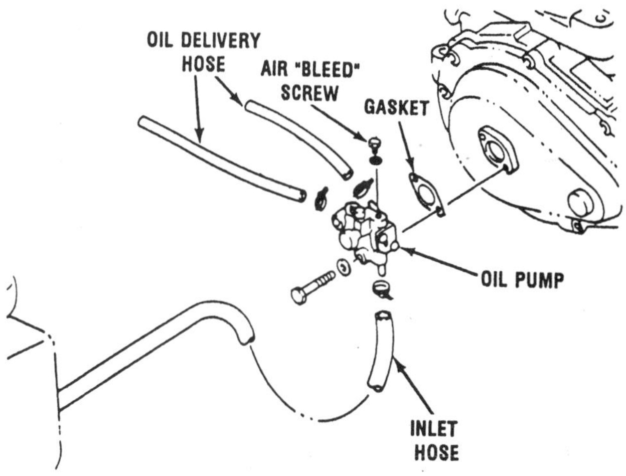

Exploded drawing of associated oil pump parts for a typical two-cylinder engine installation

Oil Mixture

Fill the oil tank to the "Full" mark. Use only Yamalube 2-cycle outboard oil (or an equivalent 2-stroke engine oil with a BIA certified rating TC-W). This oil is suitable for use through a temperature range of 14°F to 140°F (-10°C to 60°C).

The rate of oil injection is controlled by engine rpm. The oil pump is directly coupled to the forward end of the crankshaft. After the initial "break-in" period, oil is injected at the rate giving approximately an 80:1 mixture at low and idle speed. The mixture increases to 40:1 at advanced WOT (wide open throttle).

In order to obtain extra lubrication during the first 10 hours of break-in, the manufacturer recommends a premix of 25:1 mixture be used in the fuel tank. Therefore, any existing unused fuel in the tank should be removed before adding the premixed solution.

Professional mechanics who own oil injected units add an extra ounce of oil per each gallon of fuel. The addition of this extra oil may prevent engine seizure in the event of an oil pump failure or clog in an oil delivery line.

SYSTEM COMPONENTS

Principle components of the oil injection system, as shown in the accompanying exploded drawings and in the functional diagram on the next page are: main oil tank with gauge, sub oil tank, oil filter, a one-way check valve in each feeder hose to each cylinder, a breather valve, an oil injection pump, and a network of hoses to tie it all together. The two exploded drawings on this page illustrate most of the components just listed.

Main Oil Tank

The main oil tank is mounted inside the engine compartment. The oil tank filler is easily accessible when the engine cover is raised. Capacity of the main tank varies from just under a gallon to just over a gallon of oil.

A breather valve for the tank is located next to the filler cap. This breather **MUST** remain open at all times, with the green band on the valve facing the main oil tank.

An oil level sensor mounted on the upper surface of the main tank has a tube extending down into the tank. The sensor reflects the level of oil in the tank.

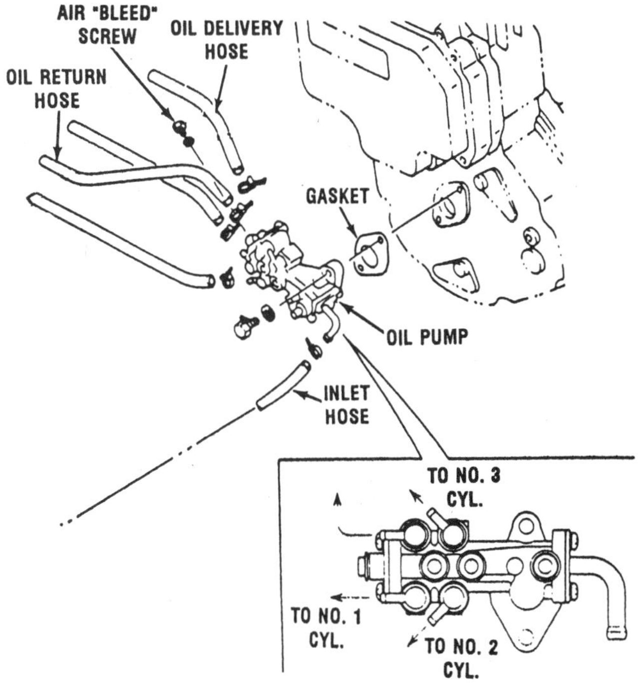

Exploded drawing of associated oil pump parts for a typical three-cylinder engine installation.

A removable "sock" type oil filter is suspended from the tank filler neck and immediately filters new oil added to the tank. Some oil tanks may not have the "sock" type filter. If the filter is not installed, extra care must be exercised to use only clean new oil.

Sub Oil Tank

Some installations may have a small sub oil tank mounted between the main tank and the oil injection pump. This sub oil tank must be inclined at 30° to the vertical with the embossed **"UP"** facing toward the main oil tank.

Oil Injection Pump

The oil injection pump is a positive displacement type unit driven by the crankshaft. A very short shaft -- with a "spade" on the end indexes into a slot on the end of the driveshaft. The short shaft drives a plunger cam. With each revolution of the plunger cam, the plunger moves up and down pumping oil to the cylinders.

The oil leaves the pump and is delivered to each cylinder through separate hoses -- one for each cylinder. A one-way check valve in each delivery hose prevents air from entering the oil pump when the engine is shut down.

SYSTEM INSPECTION

Remove the oil tank filler cap. Inspect the condition of the seal beneath the cap, and replace the seal if it is worn or cracked. Pull out the "sock" type filter -- if one is installed -- or other filter. Rinse the filter in clean solvent and gently blow it dry with compressed air. If the filter is torn, it should be replaced.

The oil tank is equipped with a ventilation hose and a check valve similar to the one installed on the fuel tank.

Before disturbing the ventilation hose, be sure to have a new hose tie wrap or a small hose clamp to replace the one removed. Original equipment tie wraps must be cut to remove them from a hose.

Disconnect the ventilation hose from the fitting on the oil tank. Remove the two tie wraps -- one on each end of the check valve. Clean, and then with a forefinger and thumb wrapped around the White end of the check valve, blow through the White end of the check valve. If the check valve is functioning properly, air should only be able to enter from the White end and escape through the Green end of the valve. If the check valve will not allow air to pass in this direction, the check valve is defective and **MUST** be replaced. A faulty check valve will starve the engine of lubrication and quickly cause extensive and expensive damage.

Test the valve again by attempting to blow through the Green end. The attempt should **FAIL.** Air should not be able to pass in the opposite direction from the White end. If the valve allows air to pass in the wrong direction, it will also allow oil to exit from the tank, through the valve and spill into the hull while the craft is moving through the water. Therefore, replace the valve if it fails to function properly.

Install the check valve with **NEW** tie wraps or hose clamps with the Green end **TOWARD** the tank.

TROUBLESHOOTING OIL INJECTION SYSTEM

Unfortunately, most problems with the oil injection system are only discovered after it is too late. If any hose becomes clogged, kinked, or restricted, the oil delivery to one or more of the cylinders will be reduced.

Insufficient oil delivery to the engine will cause the oil level to drop slower than normal; the engine will overheat due to inadequate lubrication; and moving internal parts will wear more quickly and be severely damaged.

Excessive oil delivery to the cylinders will cause the oil level to drop at a much faster rate than normal. The engine will smoke -- especially at idle speed -- and the spark plugs will become fouled causing the engine to misfire.

First Checks

Oil Delivery

If excessive or reduced oil delivery occurs, as described above, one or more of the following areas may require immediate attention:

Defective oil pump.
Clogged oil tank vent.
Kinked oil hose -- to or from pump.
Blocked oil hose -- to or from pump.
Clogged oil filter.
Air in the system.
Leaking oil hose.
Idle fuel adjustment
Quality of fuel being used.
Quality of two-stroke oil being used.

BAD NEWS

No overhaul kits or spare parts are available for the oil pump used on these units. Therefore, a defective oil pump will have to be replaced.

Systematically check each oil line to and from the pump and the connection at both ends. A free flow of oil through an unrestricted line is **CRITICAL** for adequate engine lubrication.

CAUTION

Any time the oil tank hose is disconnected, the oil injection pump **MUST** be purged ("bled") of any trapped air. Failure to "bleed" the system could lead to engine seizure due to lack of adequate lubrication.

Instruction for "bleeding" the system of air follows.

Purging (Bleeding) Air From Oil Injection System

The following procedures are to be performed any time the oil injection system has been opened -- other than to add oil to the tank -- and air has entered the system.

Prepare about a ten minute supply of 40:1 premix using Yamalube, or equivalent two-stroke oil. "Jury-rig" a setup to provide this mixture to the fuel pump during this purging procedure. Check the level of oil in the oil tank and replenish, as necessary. Start the engine and allow it to warm to operating temperature.

CAUTION

Water must circulate through the jet pump -- to and from the engine -- anytime the engine is operating. Circulating water will prevent overheating -- which could cause damage to moving engine parts and possible engine seizure.

NEVER, AGAIN NEVER, operate the engine at high speed with a flush device attached. An engine operating at high speed with such a device attached, would most likely **RUN-AWAY** from lack of a load on the impeller shaft, causing extensive and expensive damage.

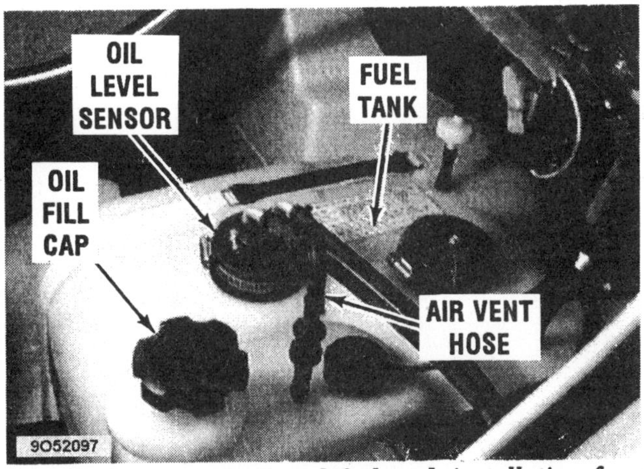

*Another typical oil and fuel tank installation for a Model 700 Series unit -- with different setup than the one shown on Page 6-29. As explained in the text, the air ventilation hose **MUST** be kept clear for the system to function properly.*

SPECIAL WORDS

Because the fuel and oil premix is being fed through the carburetor, in addition to oil from the oil injection system also being fed directly into the cylinders, the engine will be operating on a heavy mixture of oil.

Obtain a small container and have a shop cloth or towel handy to catch any oil drips. Using a pair of needlenose pliers, squeeze the clamp on the No. 1 cylinder oil delivery hose. Gently pull the hose from the fitting on the intake manifold and immediately hold it over the container.

Observe the flow of oil for about four full minutes to verify the pump is functioning properly

MORE SPECIAL WORDS

The oil/fuel mixture prepared earlier will provide adequate lubrication while the system is being purged ("bled").

A steady slow pulsing flow of oil with **NO** air bubbles will indicate the particular line is free of air. Reconnect the line. Repeat the procedure for the other delivery hoses. Once all lines are free of air bubbles, shut down the engine and remove the flushing device.

Replenish the remote oil tank with Yamalube, or other quality two-stroke oil.

FUNPIX1

Using quality fuel with the carburetors properly serviced and adjusted, and the oil injection system functioning correctly gives the engine the chance to operate at peak performance and certainly adds to the enjoyment on the water for the operators.

7
IGNITION

7-1 INTRODUCTION AND CHAPTER COVERAGE

The less a marine engine is operated, the more care it needs. Allowing a marine engine to remain idle will do more harm than if it is used regularly. To maintain the engine in top shape and always ready for efficient operation at any time, the engine should be operated every 3 to 4 weeks throughout the year.

The carburetion and ignition principles of two-cycle engine operation **MUST** be understood in order to perform a proper tune-up on a marine engine.

If you have any doubts concerning your understanding of two-cycle engine operation, it would be best to study the operation

The electrical box is easily opened to gain access to the components housed inside.

The electrical box on the Model 1100 Series engines contains the CDI unit, cranking motor solenoid, and the ignition coil.

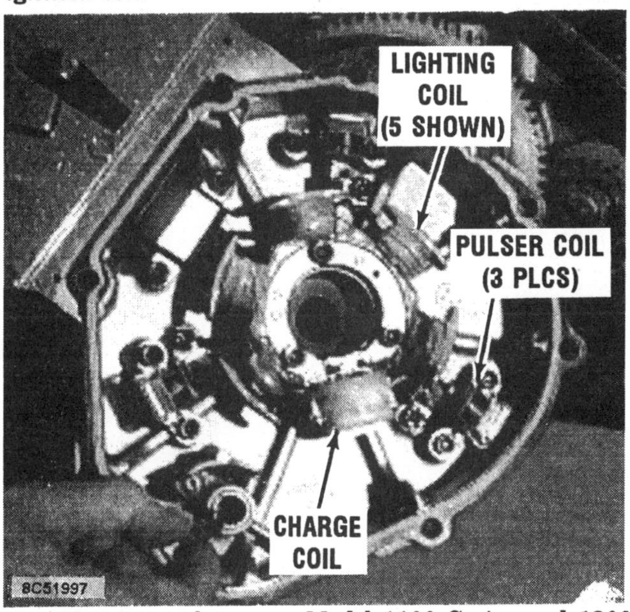

The stator plate on a Model 1100 Series and 1200 Series engine houses the pulser coils, charge coil, and the lighting coils.

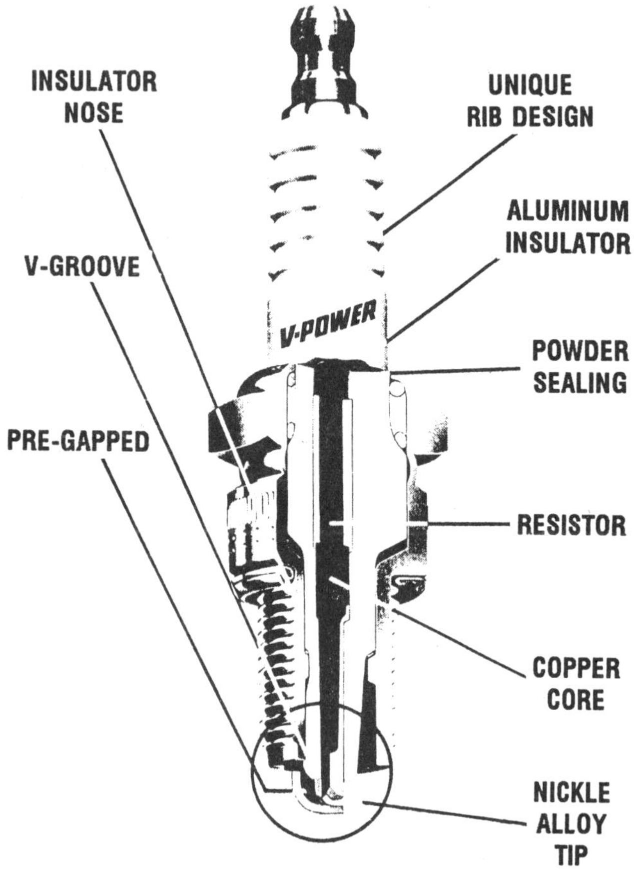

Cross-section drawing of a typical NGK spark plug with some of the features identified.

theory section in the first portion of Chapter 8, before tackling any work on the ignition system.

Ignition System

A Capacitor Discharge Ignition (CDI) is used on all engines covered in this manual. However, some have a digital CDI unit. The CDI units are "black box" type units. They cannot be opened or serviced. Therefore, if troubleshooting indicates the CDI unit is at fault, it **MUST** be replaced.

This spark plug is foul from operating with an overrich condition, possibly an improper carburetor adjustment.

7-2 SPARK PLUG EVALUATION

Removal

Remove the spark plug wires by pulling and twisting on only the molded cap. **NEVER** pull on the wire or the connection inside the cap may become separated or the boot damaged. Remove the spark plugs. **TAKE CARE** not to tilt the socket as you remove the plug or the insulator may be cracked.

Examine

Carefully examine both plugs to determine the firing conditions in the cylinder. If the side electrode is bent down onto the center electrode, the piston is traveling too far upward in the cylinder and striking the spark plug. Such damage indicates the piston pin or the rod bearing is worn excessively.

In most cases, an engine overhaul is required to correct the condition. To verify the cause of the problem, rotate the flywheel by hand. As the piston moves to the full up position, push on the piston crown with a screwdriver inserted through the spark plug hole, and at the same time rock the flywheel back-and-forth. If any play in the piston is detected, the engine must be rebuilt.

Correct Color

A proper firing plug should be dry and powdery. Hard deposits inside the shell indicate too much oil is being mixed with the fuel. The most important evidence is the light gray to tan color of the porcelain which is an indication this plug has bee, running at the correct temperature. This means the plug is one with the correct heat range and also that the air/fuel mixture is correct.

This spark plug has been operating too-cool, because it is rated with a too-low heat range for the engine.

Rich Mixture

A black, sooty condition on both spark plug shells and the porcelain is caused by an excessively rich air/fuel mixture, both at low and high speeds. The rich mixture lowers the combustion temperature so the spark plug does not run hot enough to burn off the deposits.

Deposits formed only on the shell is an indication the low-speed air/fuel mixture is too rich. At high speeds with the correct mixture, the temperature in the combustion chamber is high enough to burn off the deposits on the insulator.

Too Cool

A dark insulator, with very few deposits, indicates the plug is running too cool. This condition can be caused by low compression or by using a spark plug of an incorrect heat range. If this condition shows on only one plug it is most usually caused by low compression in that cylinder. If both plugs have this appearance, then it is probably due to the plugs having a too-low heat range.

Fouled

A fouled spark plug may be caused by the wet oily deposits on the insulator shorting the high-tension current to ground inside the shell. The condition may also be caused by ignition problems which prevent a high-tension pulse from being delivered to the spark plug.

Carbon Deposits

Heavy carbon-like deposits are an indication of excessive oil in the fuel. This condition may be the result of worn piston rings or excessive ring end gap.

*Damaged spark plugs. Notice the broken electrode on the left plug. The missing part **MUST** be found and removed before returning the engine to service, to prevent serious damage to expensive internal parts.*

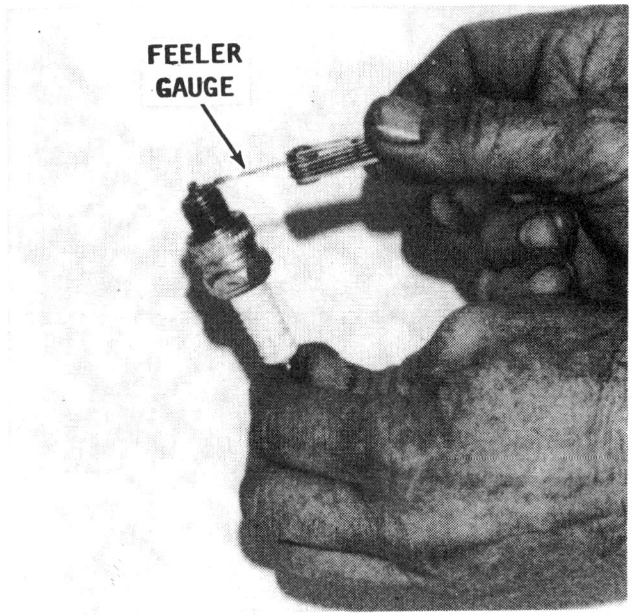

The spark plug gap should always be checked with a wire-type feeler gauge before installing new or used plugs.

Overheating

A dead white or gray insulator, which is generally blistered, is an indication of overheating and pre-ignition. The electrode gap wear rate will be more than normal and in the case of pre-ignition, will actually cause the electrodes to melt. Overheating and pre-ignition are usually caused by overadvanced timing, detonation from using too-low an octane rating fuel, an excessively lean air/fuel mixture, or problems in the cooling system.

Electrode Wear

Electrode wear results in a wide gap and if the electrode becomes carbonized it will form a high-resistance path for the spark to jump across. Such a condition will cause the engine to misfire during acceleration. If both plugs are in this condition, it can cause an increase in fuel consumption and very poor performance at high-speed operation. The solution is to replace the spark plugs with a rating in the proper heat range and gapped to specification.

Red rust-colored deposits on the entire firing end of a spark plug can be caused by water in the cylinder combustion chamber. This can be the first evidence of water entering the cylinders through the exhaust manifold because of an accumulation of scale. This condition **MUST** be corrected at the first opportunity. Refer to Chapter 8, Engine.

7-3 CAPACITOR DISCHARGE IGNITION (CDI) & DIGITAL CDI

A capacitor Discharge Ignition system is used on all engines covered in this manual. As mentioned earlier, some of the engines have a "digital CDI" system. The digital CDI unit is a more sophisticated system than the regular CDI system. The digital readout is incorporated in the instrument package on PWC units identified in the table in the Appendix. The CDI unit uses a micro-computer to select the ignition timing pattern best suited to engine demands. The system is an automatic spark advance with no timing adjustments to be made.

Over-Revolution Limiter

The digital ignition control circuit cuts off ignition to all cylinders if engine rpm reaches 7,175. As soon as engine rpm drops below 7,175, the ignition control circuit returns ignition to all cylinders.

DESCRIPTION AND OPERATION

Three major components are used in the CDI system.

1- Pulser coils are housed under the flywheel. These coils are sometimes called trigger coils, depending on the manufacture of the ignition system. Pulser coils provide a source of AC current and time the electrical pulses.

2- The CDI unit used to convert AC to DC current. The unit stores the DC current, then releases it and automatically controls the timing.

3- Ignition coil, boosts the DC voltage instantly to approximately 20,000 volts to the spark plugs.

Two basic circuits are used with the CDI system, a charge circuit and a pulser circuit.

Charge Circuit

The charge circuit consists of the flywheel magnet, a charge coil, a diode, and a capacitor. As the flywheel magnet passes by the charge coil, a voltage is induced in the coil. As the flywheel continues to rotate and the coil is no longer influenced by the magnet, the magnetic field collapses. Therefore, an alternating current is produced at the charge coil. This AC current is changed to DC by a diode inside the CDI unit.

Special Words

A diode is a solid state unit which permits current to flow in one direction, but prevents flow in the opposite direction. A diode may also be known as a rectifier.

The current then passes to a capacitor, also located inside the CDI unit, where it is stored.

Pulser (Trigger) Circuit

The pulser circuit has its own flywheel magnet, a pulser coil, a diode, and a thyristor. A thyristor is a solid state electronic switching device which permits voltage to flow only after it is triggered by another voltage source.

At the point in time when the ignition timing marks align, an alternating current is induced in the pulser coil, in the same manner as previously described for the charge coil. This current is then passed to a second diode located in the CDI unit where it becomes DC current and flows on to the thyristor. This voltage triggers the thyristor to permit the voltage stored in the capacitor to be discharged. The capacitor voltage passes through the thyristor and on to the primary windings of the ignition coil.

In this manner, a spark at the plug may be accurately timed by the timing marks on the flywheel relative to the magnets in the flywheel and to provide as many as 100 sparks per second for an engine operating at 6000 rpm.

Timing Advance

As mentioned several times in this chapter, all Yamaha engines covered in this manual, are equipped with an automatic advance type CDI system and have no moving or sliding parts. -- therefore, no adjustment. Ignition advance is accomplished electronically -- by the electric waves emitted by the pulser coils. These coils increase their wave output proportionately to engine speed increase, thus advancing the timing.

A detailed table in the Appendix lists the spark plug, spark plug gap, and the degree of timing for idle and WOT (wide open throttle). Once the timing is set it should not be necessary to change unless the ignition system has been serviced and replacement parts have been installed. The system is very reliable and requires very little attention.

Charging System

The charging system consists of the flywheel magnet/s, a lighting coil (alternator), a rectifier, voltage regulator, and the battery.

The lighting coil, so named because it may be used to power the accessories on the craft when used together with a voltage regulator, allows the engine to generate additional electrical current to charge the battery.

As the flywheel magnet/s rotate, voltage is induced in the lighting coil located next to the pulser coils. This alternating current passes through a series of diodes and emerges as DC current. Therefore, it may be stored in the battery. A lighting coil may be identified by its clean laminated copper windings. All other coils are wrapped in tape and their windings are not visible.

The rectifier converts the alternating current into DC, which may then be stored in the battery. The rectifier is a sealed unit and contains four diodes. If one of the diodes is defective, the entire unit **MUST** be replaced.

The voltage regulator stabilizes the power output of the coils and extends the life of the components by preventing power surges.

TROUBLESHOOTING IGNITION CDI SYSTEM AND CHARGING SYSTEM

Always attempt to proceed with the troubleshooting in an orderly manner. The "shot in the dark" approach will only result in wasted time, incorrect diagnosis, replacement of unnecessary parts, and frustration.

1

Begin the ignition system troubleshooting with the spark plug and continue through the system until the source of trouble is located.

Spark Plugs

1- Check the plug wires to be sure they are properly connected. Check the entire length of the wires from the plugs to the magneto under the stator plate. If the wires are to be removed from the spark plug, **ALWAYS** use a pulling and twisting motion as a precaution against damaging the connection.

Attempt to remove the spark plug by hand. This is a rough test to determine if the plug is tightened properly. The attempt to loosen the plug by hand should fail. The plug should be tight and require the proper socket size tool. Remove the spark plug and evaluate its condition as described in Section 7-2.

2- Use a spark tester and check for spark. If a spark tester is not available, hold the plug wire about 1/4" (6.4mm) from the engine. Crank the engine through a few revolutions using the cranking motor and check for spark. A strong spark over a wide gap must be observed when testing in this manner, because under compression a strong spark is necessary in order to ignite the air/fuel mixture in the cylinder. This means it is possible to think a strong spark is present, when in reality the spark will be too weak when the plug is installed. If there is no spark, or if the spark is weak, the trouble is most likely under the flywheel in the stator assembly.

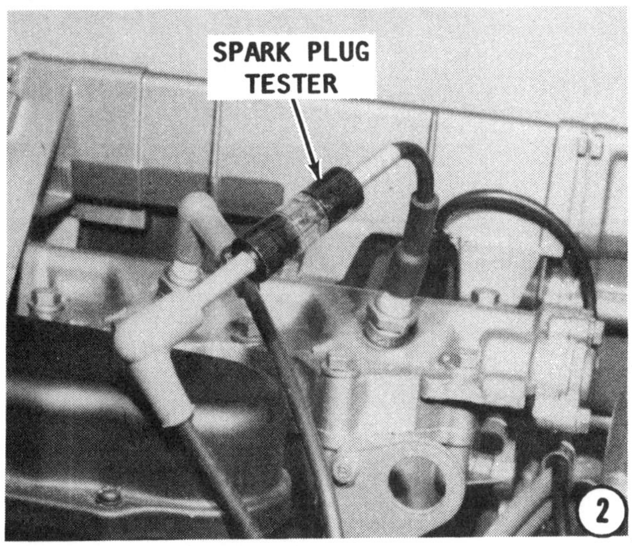

2

Compression

3- Before spending too much time and money attempting to trace a problem to the ignition system, a compression check of all cylinders should be made If a cylinder does not have adequate compression, troubleshooting and attempted service of the ignition or fuel system will fail to give the desired results of satisfactory engine performance.

Remove the spark plug wire by pulling and twisting **ONLY** on the molded cap. **NEVER** pull on the wire because the connection inside the cap may be separated or the boot may be damaged. Remove the spark plug. Insert a compression gauge into the cylinder spark plug hole. Ground the spark plug leads to prevent damage to the ignition coil. If a lead is not grounded, the coil will attempt to match the demand created by the spark trying to jump from the electrode to the nearest ground.

Crank a cold engine through several revolutions with the electric cranking motor. Note the compression reading.

An acceptable pressure reading for an engine covered in this manual is 142 psi (981 kPa) or more. The readings between cylinders should not vary by more than 10%.

7-4 TESTING IGNITION COMPONENTS

General Information

Due to the complex nature of the circuitry and high energy output pulses of micro-second duration, conventional testing devices such as a Volt/Ohm/Ammeter will not measure electrical output with the degree of accuracy required. An Ignition Tester, as used by the local dealer is an electrical device capable of measuring the peak energy output of capacitor discharge ignition units and the pulser coils.

This instrument was designed to troubleshoot the CDI ignition system. Unfortunately this tester may not be easily accessible. Therefore, this chapter includes only those tests which may be performed with instruments normally and easily available. The CDI unit is contained inside the electrical box.

To replace some of the components, the flywheel must be "pulled". Detailed illustrated procedures to accomplish this task are presented in Chapter 8.

WORDS FROM EXPERIENCE

During the tests, if a reading is slightly different from the specifications, but the engine still operates, then there is no real need to replace the affected component, until it actually fails. Bear in mind, in **MOST** cases electrical components are not

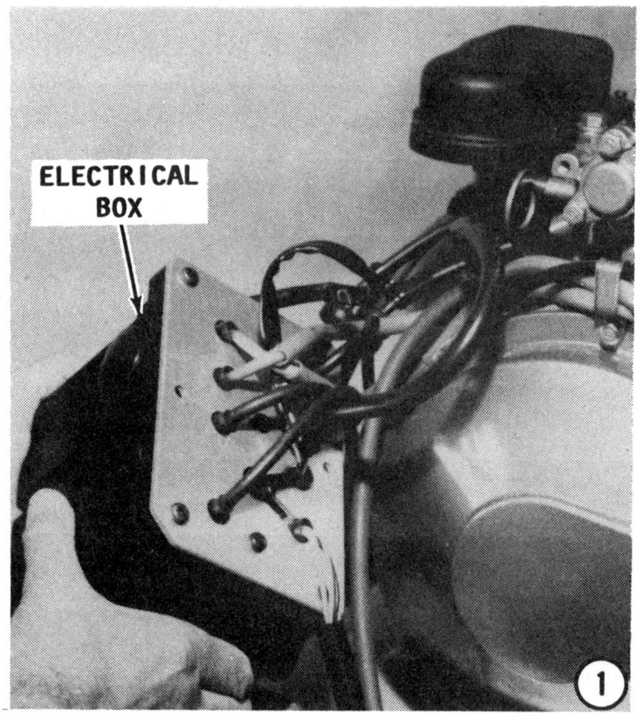

returnable, once the item leaves the store. Therefore, make every attempt to avoid the **BUY** and **TRY** method of troubleshooting. Such a practice will lead only to wasted time, unneeded cash outlay, and frustration.

General Inspections

The ignition components are installed and protected either behind the flywheel or inside the electrical box. On a 3-cylinder Model 1100 Series, some components are housed inside the flywheel cover. For this reason, they will give satisfactory service over a long period of time without any adjustment correction or maintenance. However, the following couple of areas might be worthy of attention.

1- Check the spark plug cap to be sure the cap is tight and free of any cracks or other damage. Replace the cap if it is damaged.

2- Open the electrical box and make a general inspection of the components and wiring inside. These items are well protected inside the box.

Preliminary Tasks
Model 650 & 700 Series

1- Remove the two bolts securing the electrical box to the craft.

2- Remove the Phillips head screws securing the bottom aluminum plate to the electrical box. Note there are two difference size screws used at this location -- the longer screws around the perimeter of the box and the shorter screws in the middle.

3- Separate the electrical box from the aluminum plate.

4- Remove all the Black eyelet leads from the ground screw.

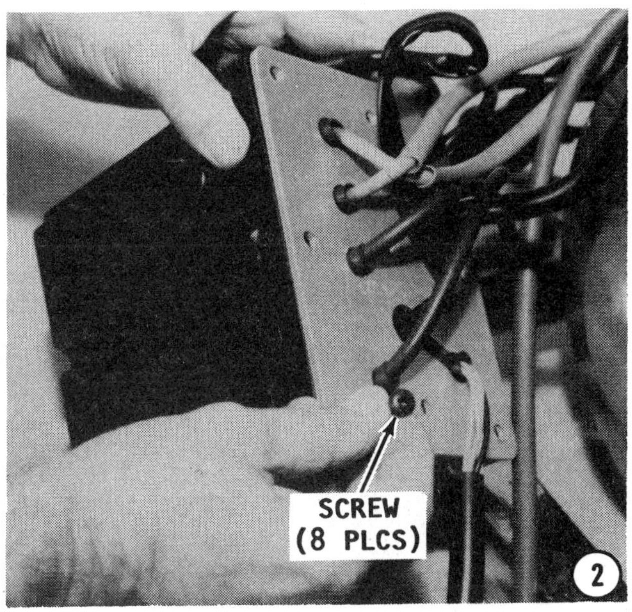

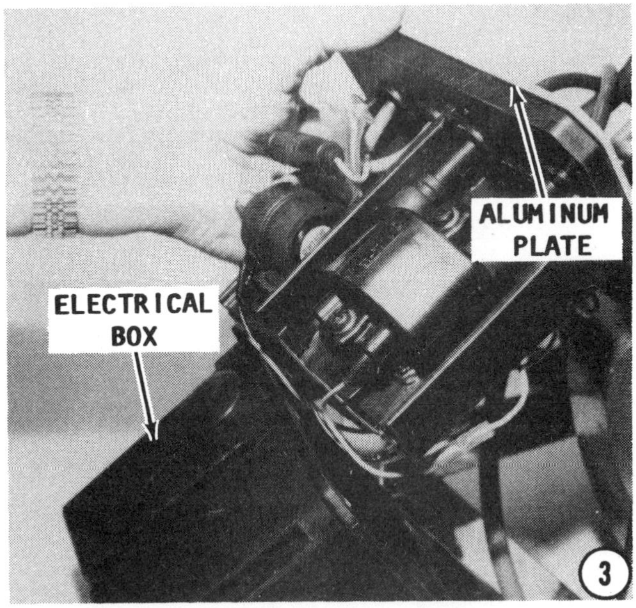

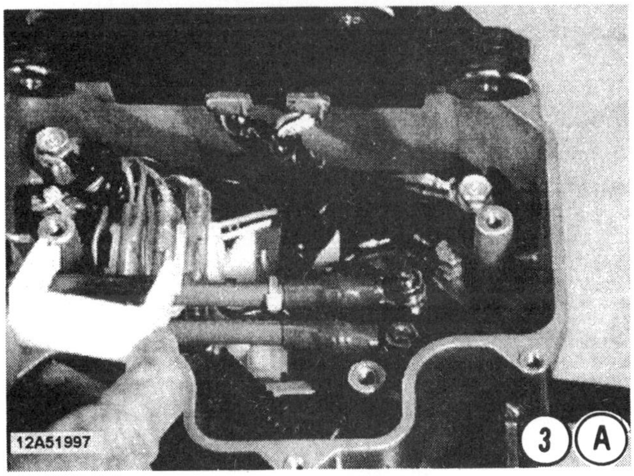

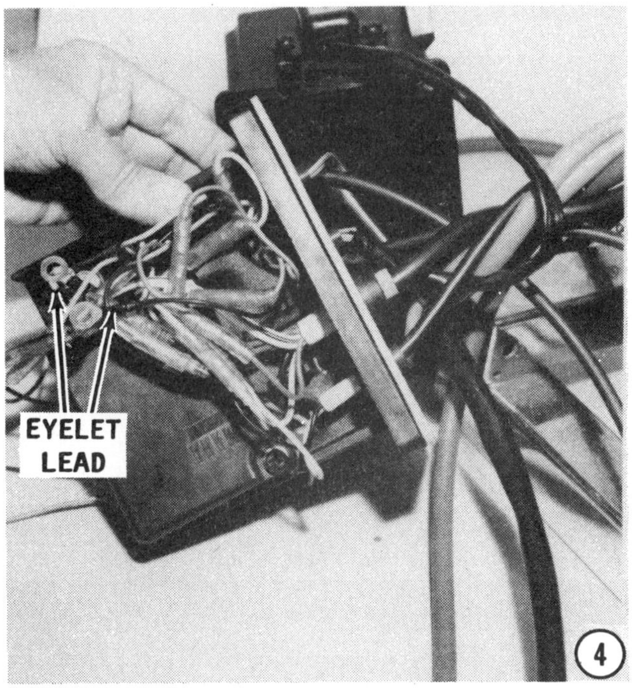

Preliminary Task
Model 1100 and 1200 Series
(Illustration --3A)

Remove the electrical box cover by first removing the five attaching bolts.

Pull the plastic cover over the electrical connections free, exposing the connections.

TESTING WORDS

The following tests can be performed with a shop VOA (volt-ohm-amp) meter. In almost all cases, it is only necessary to make contact with the meter leads to the leads or terminals listed for the test. If the component fails the test it must be replaced for maximum engine performance. When test results differ for certain models, the models will be identified.

PULSER COIL TEST

1- Obtain an ohmmeter and select the appropriate scale for the model being tested, as indicated later in this step. Trace the stator harness from the bottom of the stator plate through the opening in the aluminum plate. Identify the White/Red and the Black pulser coil leads. Disconnect the White/Red at its quick disconnect fitting. Make contact with the meter leads as indicated for the model being serviced.

The meter contacts and the meter reading should be as follows:

All 700 Models plus VXR 650

Meter Lead: Red to White/Red; Black to Black

Results: 12.6 - 15.4 ohms at 68°F (20°C).

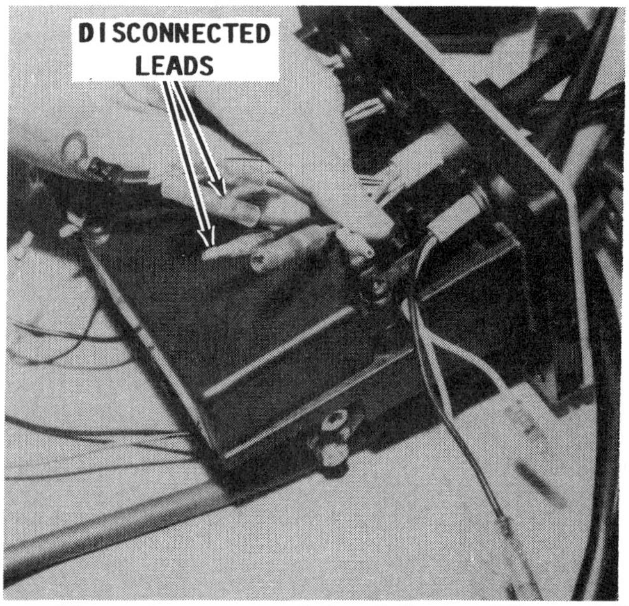

Illustration to support Pulser Coil test and Charge Coil test.

Model 1100 And 1200 Series

These engines have three individual pulser coils, as indicated on the diagram.

Meter Lead:

Coil #1 Red to White/Red; Black to Black

Coil #2 Red to White/Black; Black to Black

Coil #3 Red to White/Green; Black to Black

Results: 248 - 372 ohms at 68°F (20°C).

If the resistance is not within the limits given and the engine does not operate, the pulser coil must be replaced.

To replace the pulser coil, the flywheel cover and flywheel must be removed, see Chapter 8.

If the test is successful, move on to the next text.

CHARGE COIL TEST

Select the appropriate scale on the ohmmeter. Make contact with the meter leads as indicated for the model being serviced.

The meter contacts and the meter reading should be as follows:

700 Models

WaveVenture, WaveRaider,

Meter Lead: Red to Brown/White ; Black to Black

Results: 497.7 - 608.3 Ohms at 68°F (20°C)

Wave\Blaster 760

Meter Lead: Red to Brown; Black to Black

Results: 316.8 - 387.2 Ohms at 68°F (20°C)

WaveRunner, WaveBlaster, SuperJet, VXR650 & PROVXR 700

Meter Lead: Red to Brown/White; Black to Black

Results: 328.5 - 401.5 Ohms

Model 1100 And 1200 Series

WaveVenture, WaveRaider

Meter Lead: Red to Black/Red; Black to Black

Results: 172 - 258 Ohms at 68°F (20°C)

Meter Lead: Red to Blue; Black to Black/Red

Results: 356 - 984 Ohms at 68°F (20°C)

IGNITION COIL TEST

Select the appropriate scale on the ohmmeter. Make contact with the meter leads as indicated for the model being serviced.

The meter contacts and the meter reading should be as follows:

Primary Coil Resistance
All 700 Models plus VXR 650

Meter Lead: Red to Orange; Black to Black

Results: 0.078 - 0.106 Ohms at 68°F (20°C)

1100 And 1200 Models

WaveVenture , WaveRaider

Meter Lead: Red to Black/White; Black to Black

Results: 0.18 - 0.24 Ohms at 69°F (20°C)

Secondary Coil Test
All 700 Models plus VXR 650

High tension leads: 14.3 - 30.5 Ohms at 68°F (20°C)

1100 And 1200 Models

Wave Venture, Wave Raider

Meter lead: Red to Black/White -- high tension lead.

Results: 2.7 - 4.1k Ohms at 68°F (20°C)

CDI RESISTANCE TEST

The following four charts outline testing procedures for the units covered in this manual. The first charts covers the WaveRaider 700 and the WaveVenture 700.

The second chart covers the WaveRaider 1100, WaveVenture 1100, and the 1200 Model.

The third chart covers WaveRunner 650T, 700S; the WaveBlaster 700 & 760; the Super Jet 700; and the VXR 650TX and VXR 700TX.

At first glance, the charts may look complicated -- involved, but actually they are easy to read, understand and use.

The first column at the far left indicates the test lead to be connected to a **POSITIVE** (+) test lead. The row across the top of the chart indicates the test lead to be connect to a **NEGATIVE** (-) test lead. Simply follow the row across to the intersection of the column from the top and satisfactory readings are indicated in the box.

Obtain an ohmmeter and select the 1,000 ohm scale. The unit may remain installed in the electrical panel, provided the leads have been disconnected.

CRITICAL WORDS

Read, believe, and obey: Between each test, make contact with the Black CDI lead to the Orange lead to allow the internal capacitor circuit to discharge. Applying a small current, using the test ohmmeter, charges the internal capacitor, which must then be discharged before proceeding to the next lead test.

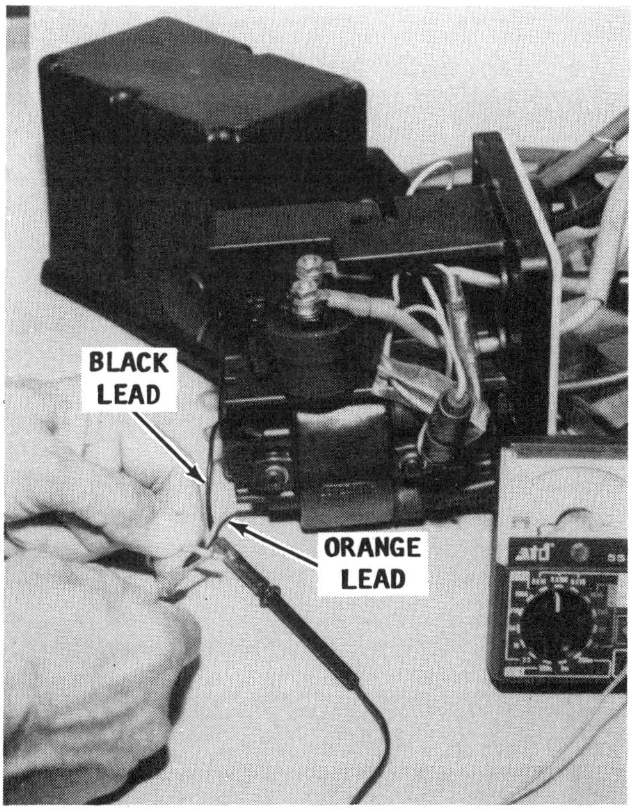

Illustration to support the Primary Coil resistance test.

Illustration to support the Secondary Coil resistance test.

⊕ ⊖	B	Br/W	O	P	W	W/R
B		2~6	•	3~11	10~40	150~600
Br/W	20~80		•	50~200	15~60	500
O	•	•		•	•	•
P	∞	∞	∞		∞	∞
W	∞	∞	∞	∞		∞
W/R	9~36	17~70	•	10~40	50~200	

Chart #1 CDI for the WaveRaider 700 and WaveVenture 760.

⊕ ⊖	B	B/O	B/R	B/W	B/Y	Br	L	P	W	W/B	W/G	W/R
B		280~420	14.4~21.6	280~420	280~420	∞	2.9~4.3	280~420	280~420	60~90	60~90	60~90
B/O	∞		∞	∞	∞	∞	∞	∞	∞	∞	∞	∞
B/R	∞	∞		∞	∞	∞	∞	∞	∞	∞	∞	∞
B/W	∞	∞	∞		∞	∞	∞	∞	∞	∞	∞	∞
B/Y	∞	∞	∞	∞		∞	∞	∞	∞	∞	∞	∞
Br	76~114	120~180	200~300	120~180	120~180		144~216	120~180	120~180	184~276	184~276	184~276
L	19.2~28.8	48~72	240~360	48~72	48~72	∞		56.0~84.0	45.6~68.4	168~252	168~252	168~252
P	∞	∞	∞	∞	∞	∞	∞		∞	∞	∞	∞
W	∞	∞	∞	∞	∞	∞	∞	∞		∞	∞	∞
W/B	200~300	280~420	400~600	280~420	280~420	∞	280~420	280~420	280~420		320~480	320~480
W/G	200~300	280~420	400~600	280~420	280~420	∞	280~420	280~420	280~420	320~480		320~480
W/R	200~300	280~420	400~600	280~420	280~420	∞	280~420	280~420	280~420	320~480	320~480	

Chart #2 CDI for the WaveRaider/WaveVenture 1100, and GP1200.

⊖ Tester	Tester ⊕	①	②	③	④	⑤	⑥	⑦
		B	W	O	B	W/R	P	Br/W
1	B		20^{+20}_{-10}	•	0	300^{+300}_{-150}	7±4	4±2
2	W	∞		∞	∞	∞	∞	∞
3	O	•	•		•	•	•	•
4	B	0	20^{+20}_{-10}	•		300^{+300}_{-150}	7±4	4±2
5	W/R	18^{+18}_{-9}	100^{+100}_{-50}	•	18^{+18}_{-9}		20^{+20}_{-10}	35^{+35}_{-18}
6	P	∞	∞	∞	∞	∞		∞
7	Br/W	40^{+40}_{-20}	30^{+30}_{-15}	•	40^{+40}_{-20}	500^{+500}_{-250}	100^{+100}_{-50}	

Chart #3 CDI for the WaveRunner 650T and 700S &T, also for the WaveBlaster, Super Jet, VXR 650TX and the VXR 700TX.

Color Code
All Charts

B	Black	Br/W	Brown/White
B/O	Black/Orange	O	Orange
B/R	Black/Red	L	Blue
B/W	Black/White	P	Pink
B/Y	Black/Yellow	W	White
Br	Brown	W/B	White/Black
		W/G	White/Green
		W/R	White Red

Unit for all charts is 1,000 ohms.

⊕ ⊖	W	P	W/B	W/R	O	Br	L	B
W		∞	3.8 ~ 16	9.5 ~ 4.0	11 ~ 45	80 ~ 400	3.4 ~ 14	3.8 ~ 16
P	7.5 ~ 35		17 ~ 70	22 ~ 100	40 ~ 300	70 ~ 1,000	16 ~ 70	17 ~ 80
W/B	10 ~ 45	∞		4.4 ~ 18	2 ~ 9	70 ~ 400	6 ~ 26	0 ~ 0.6
W/R	16 ~ 70	∞	4 ~ 17		8 ~ 35	70 ~ 400	13 ~ 60	4 ~ 17
O	∞	∞	∞	∞		∞	∞	∞
Br	26 ~ 150	∞	2.4 ~ 11	9 ~ 40	7.5 ~ 35		16 ~ 70	2.4 ~ 11
L	26 ~ 150	∞	2.4 ~ 11	9 ~ 40	7.5 ~ 35	80 ~ 500		2.4 ~ 11
B	10 ~ 45	∞	0 ~ 0.6	4.4 ~ 19	2 ~ 8.5	70 ~ 400	6 ~ 26	

Chart #4 CDI for the WaveBlaster II 760U

If the readings are not within the limits indicated in the body of the chart, and the engine fails to operate, replace the CDI unit. Service or adjustment is not possible.

If the readings are questionable or marginal and the engine fails to operate it is possible and probable the CDI unit with **NO LOAD** could pass the resistance tests, but fail to operate the engine. In this case, if the CDI unit is doubtful, take the unit to the nearest Yamaha dealer for testing under a load with a Yamaha Ignition Tester.

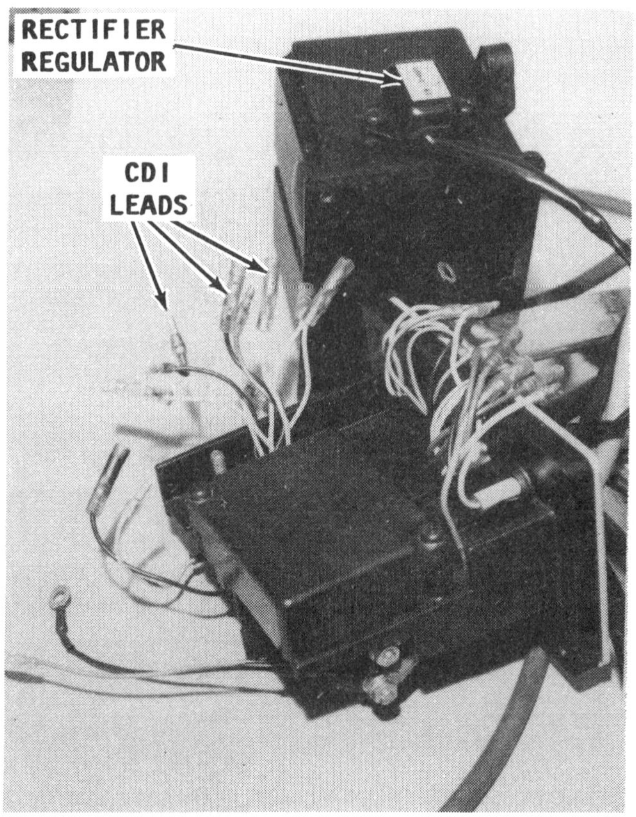

The rectifier/regulator and CDI unit ready for resistance testing, as explained in the text.

If the tests are successful, reconnect the color coded leads -- same color to same color.

If a new unit is to be installed, observe the same connections using the wiring diagram in the Appendix as a guide.

RECTIFIER/REGULATOR RESISTANCE TEST

The accompanying chart outlines testing procedures for a rectifier/regulator on a Series 700, Series 1100, or Series 1200 engine.

⊖ ⊕	R	B	G_1	G_2
R		∞	∞	∞
B	2-20		1-10	1-10
G_1	1-10	2-15		3-30
G_2	1-10	2-15	3-30	

Rectifier/Regulator Test Chart for all 700, 1100 and 1200 Models

The first column (far left) indicates rectifier/regulator leads which are to make contact with the Red **POSITIVE (+)** meter lead. The row across the top of the chart indicates rectifier/regulator leads which are to make contact with the Black **NEGATIVE (-)** meter lead. Acceptable meter readings are indicated in the body of the chart. Simply move across the chart from left to right. Where the row and column intersect gives the acceptable ohm reading in thousands.

Obtain an ohmmeter and select the 1,000 ohm scale. The rectifier/regulator is mounted on the exterior of the electrical box. Trace the

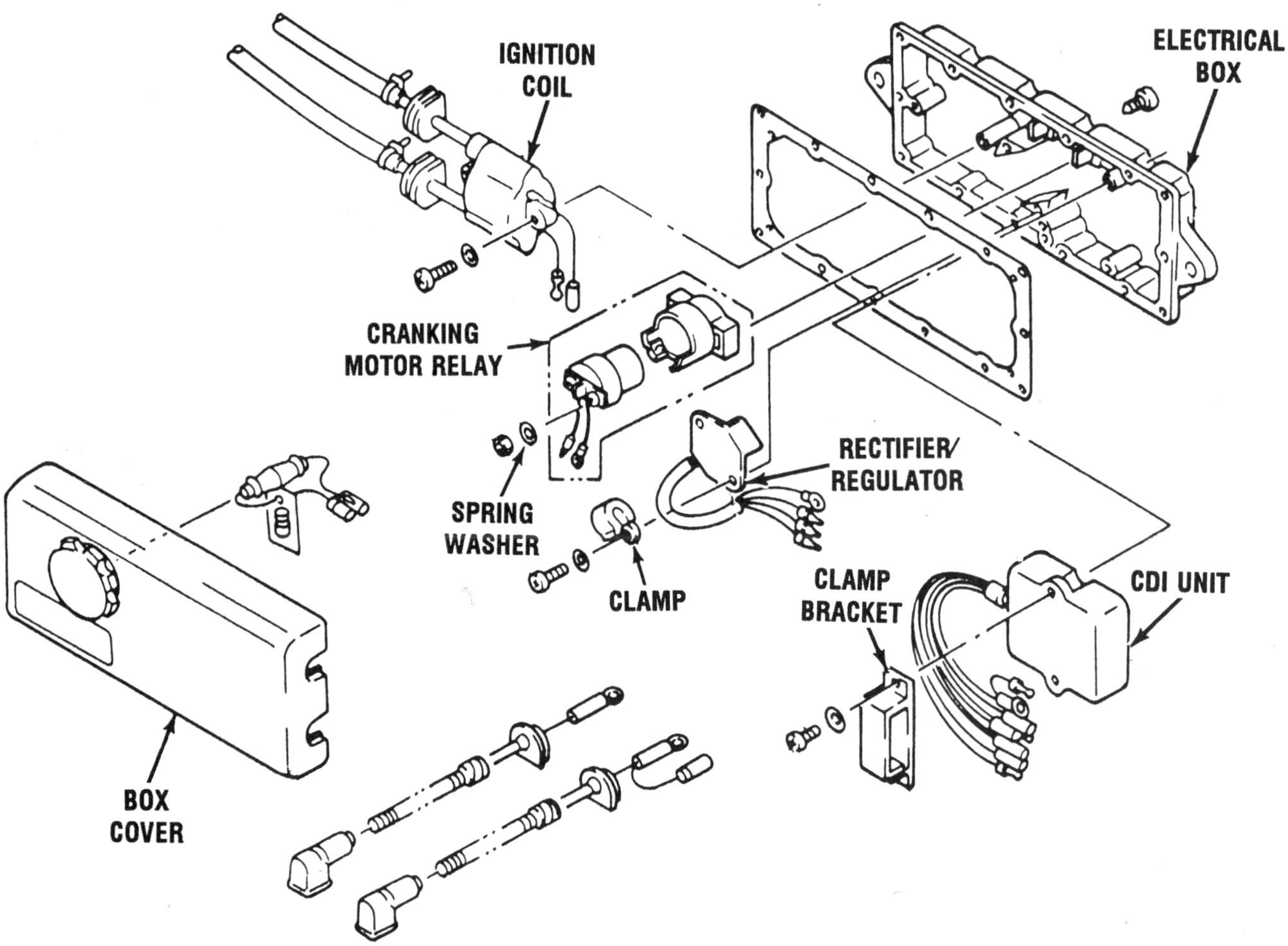

Exploded drawing of a typical electrical box installation on a Model 700 Series engine. Major parts have been identified.

rectifier/regulator harness to its quick disconnect fittings and disconnect all four leads.

If the resistance is not within the limits indicated in the chart, the battery will not charge. A fully charged battery will soon drain. The rectifier/regulator unit cannot be serviced or adjusted. Therefore, it must be replaced.

Reconnect the four leads matching color to color.

Visually check all wiring connections before installing the electrical box.

7-5 FLYWHEEL AND STATOR PLATE SERVICE

Detailed illustrated procedures to "pull" the flywheel to gain access to the stator and magneto are presented in Chapter 8. Check the table of contents. Assembling and installation steps are also included.

GOOD WORDS

If servicing a Model 1100 or 1200 Series engine, it is not necessary to "pull" the flywheel. Once the flywheel cover is removed, ignition components are exposed inside the cover.

Cleaning and inspecting the flywheel and associated ignition parts is presented in the last section of Chapter 8.

Model 1100 -- Verify all connections and wiring is in good condition before closing up the electrical box.

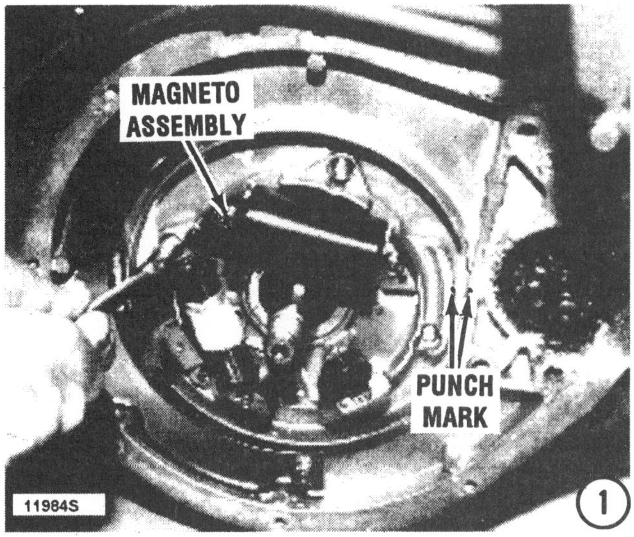

Model 650 and 700
After Flywheel Removal

Magneto Assembly Removal

For removal of the flywheel, refer to the steps outlined beginning on Page 8-4 of engine disassembly. Once the flywheel is pulled, return to this point.

1- Remove the four bolts securing the magneto assembly to the stator plate.

SPECIAL WORDS

Observe the two aligned punch marks, one on the magneto assembly and one on the stator plate. These marks serve as an aid during installation for the correct positioning of the magneto assembly on the stator plate. If, for some reason, no marks are visible, then make two aligning marks one on the stator plate and the other on the magneto assembly. The securing screws pass through elongated slots in the magneto assembly. Without the alignment marks just described, the magneto assembly

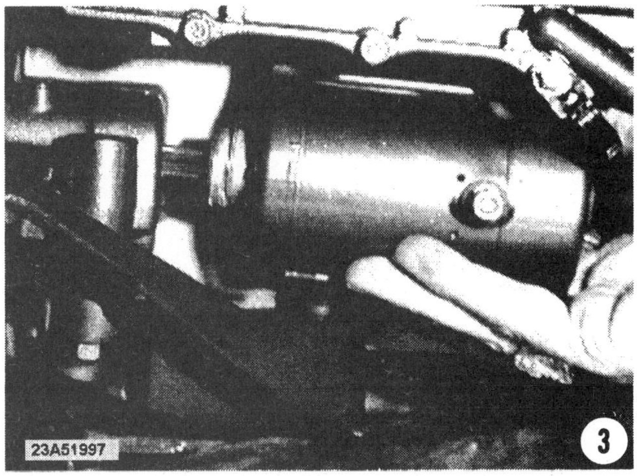

could be installed as much as 15 degrees off its original position and drastically affect the timing characteristics of the engine.

Lift the assembly up and over the crankshaft and lay it to one side until the stator harness can be released from the plate.

Note:

The next two illustrations accompanying the text, show the cranking motor being removed from a Model 1100 Series engine. The text is valid, but on a Model 650 or 700 series engine, the motor is attached to a bracket, instead of directly to the engine block.

2- Disconnect the cranking motor lead from the terminal on the motor. Remove the two bolts securing the motor to the engine.

3- Slide the cranking motor clear of the stator plate and engine.

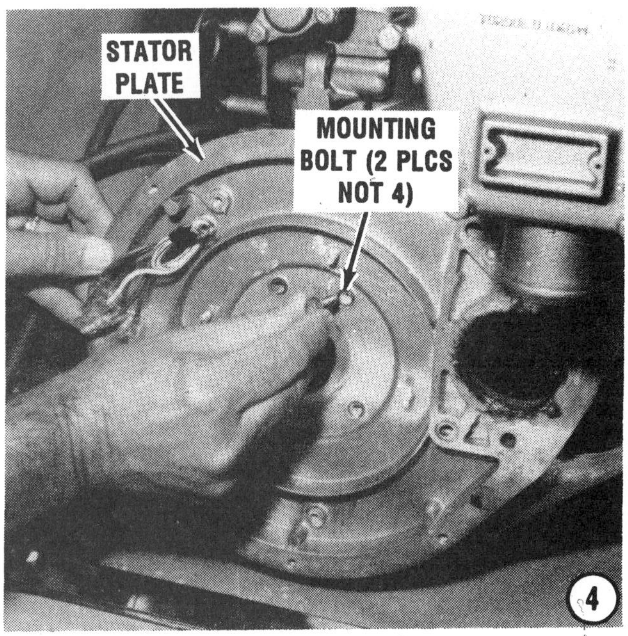

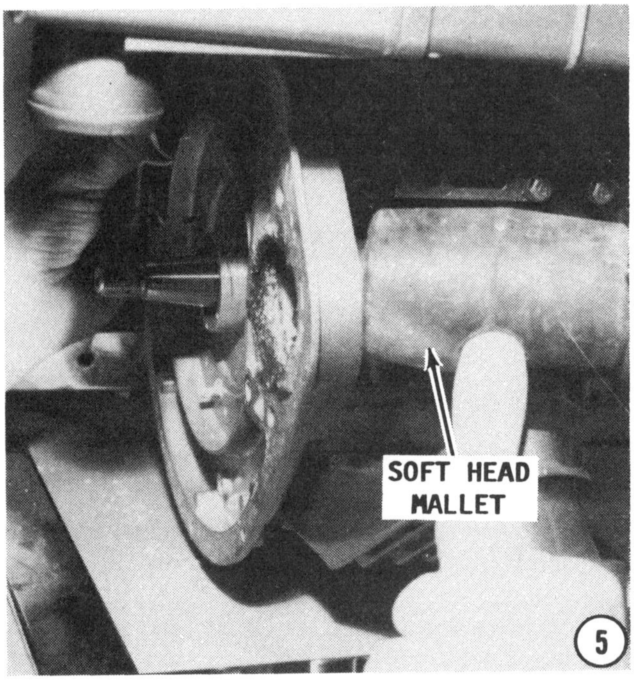

4- Remove the two bolts and washers securing the stator plate to the engine. The illustration indicates four bolts, but on late model units, the stator is secured with only two bolts.

5- Using a soft head mallet, gently tap around the perimeter of the stator plate to "break" the plate free of the crankshaft and the gasket seal under the plate.

6- Slide the stator plate up and over the crankshaft. Pry the stator harness grommet free of the crankcase. The illustration shows a gasket being used, but late model units no longer have the gasket installed at this location.

Checking action of the internal clutch of the idler gear assembly, as described in the text.

If there is evidence of oil on the stator plate, the two oil seals at the forward main bearing, inside the crankcase, may have failed. Refer to the engine chapter.

CLEANING AND INSPECTING

Inspect the flywheel for cracks or other damage, especially around the inside of the center hub. A damaged flywheel can be **EXTREMELY** dangerous. The forces exerted on the flywheel while it is spinning at high rpm are

When checking any magneto flywheel, inspect to be sure metal particles have not become stuck to the magnets.

sufficient to shatter an unbalanced damaged flywheel. Inspect the magnets to see if they are held tightly around the outer circumference of the flywheel rim. Check the surface of the magnets for fractures and grooves.

Grooves around the inner perimeter would indicate a component mounted on the stator plate is not aligned properly or the component is loose. Fractured or damaged magnets cannot be replaced. Both the magnets and flywheel share the same part number, therefore attempting to remove the magnets would be a pointless task. If magnets or the flywheel is defective, the entire flywheel must be replaced.

Check to be sure small metal particles have not become attached to the magnets. Verify each magnet has good magnetism by using a screwdriver or other suitable tool.

Thoroughly clean the inside taper of the flywheel and the taper on the crankshaft to prevent the flywheel from "walking" on the crankshaft during operation.

Test the magneto assembly to verify it is not loose. Attempt to lift each component on the plate. There should be little or no evidence of movement.

Inspect the pinion gear and the inner teeth of the idle gear assembly. If any signs of damage or excessive wear are discovered, the assembly must be replaced. Check the action of the internal clutch. If the movement of the clutch is not smooth, an internal defect exists in the clutch assembly and the idle gear assembly must be replaced.

SPECIAL WORDS ON FLYWHEEL MAGNETS

The outer ends of any magnet are called poles. One end is the north pole and the other end is called the south pole. The magnetic field surrounding a magnet is concentrated around these two poles.

Some flywheel magnets are fairly long and curved around the outer perimeter of the underside of the flywheel. Others are short and are mounted around the center hub, depending on the location of the coils mounted on the stator. Magnets are usually installed in pairs with the north pole of one adjacent to the south pole of its neighbor and so on. In this manner a continuous magnetic field surrounds the inside of the flywheel.

If a flywheel is accidentally dropped, not only could the teeth be damaged, but the impact will weaken the magnetic strength of all the magnets housed in the flywheel.

If one or more of the magnets should break or fracture, two new magnetic poles will be created. A long magnet with two poles will become two short magnets with four poles. The new poles will possess only half the magnetic strength of an original pole. The overall magnetic field will be altered. The new field of the shorter magnets will not extend to cover the area of the flywheel.

Serious consequences apply to a CDI type ignition system in the event of a flywheel magnet fracture. Pulser coils are energized by the concentrated magnetic field at the magnet poles. If new poles are suddenly created, the trigger will receive conflicting signals from the magnets and may even attempt to fire the cylinder twice in one revolution.

All these reasons require the flywheel to be handled with **CARE**.

ASSEMBLING AND INSTALLATION

1- Move the stator plate over the crankshaft and push the stator harness grommet into the groove in the crankcase. Coat the threads of the two securing bolts with Loctite #572. (Illustration indicates four bolts, late model units use only two.) Install and tighten the two bolts and washers securing the plate to the crankcase.

2- Coat the threads of the two cranking motor mounting bolts with Loctite #572. Install the two bolts securing the cranking motor to the

Text continues on Page 7-18.

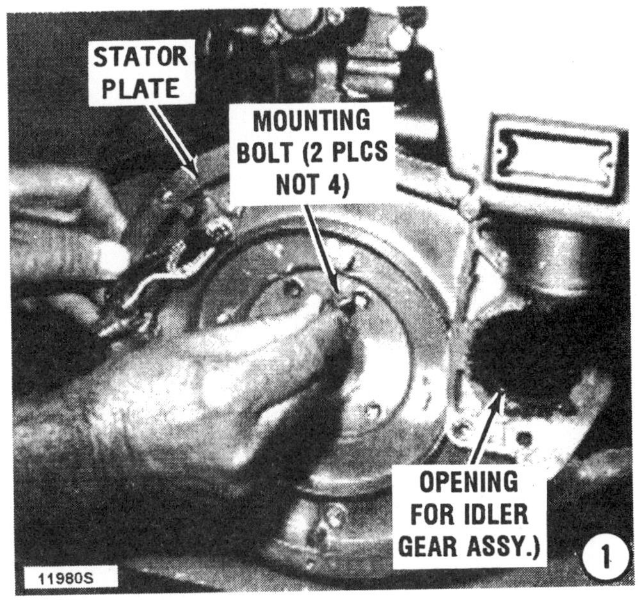

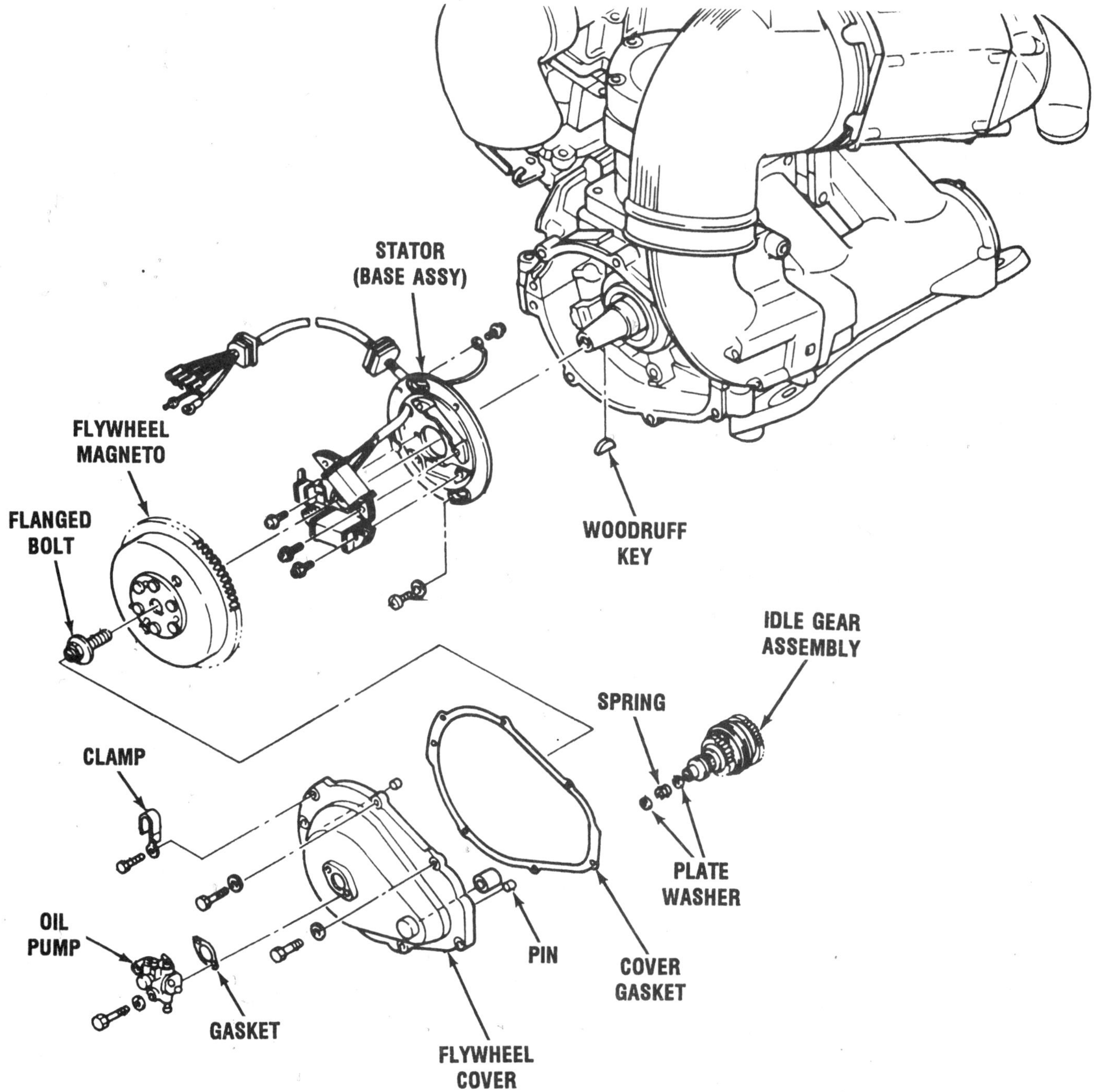

Exploded drawing of electrical components attached to the front end of a Model 650 or Model 700 Series engine. The items are covered and protected by the flywheel and flywheel cover. Major parts have been identified.

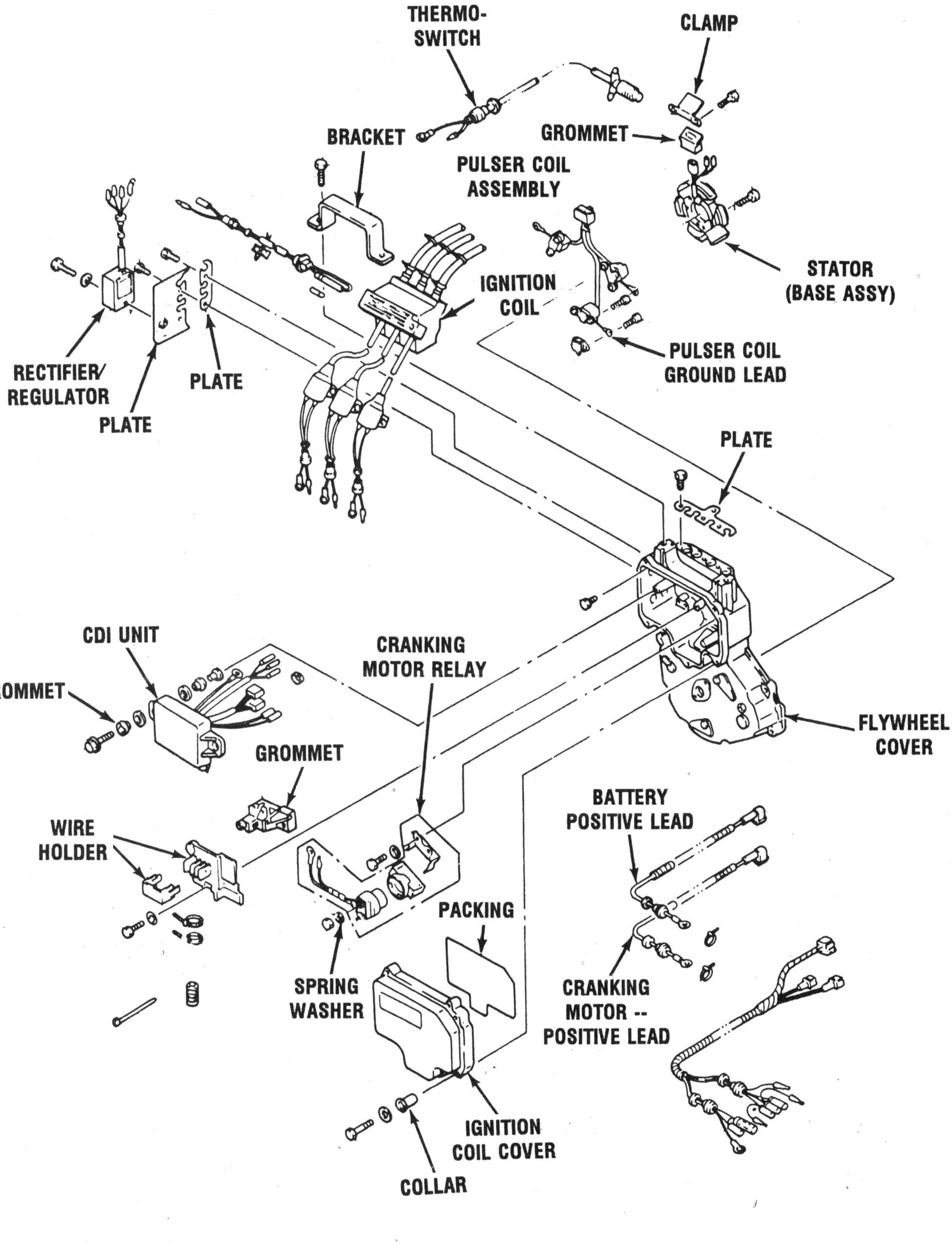

Exploded drawing of electrical parts inside or attached to the flywheel cover on a Model 1100 and 1200 Series engine. Major parts have been identified.

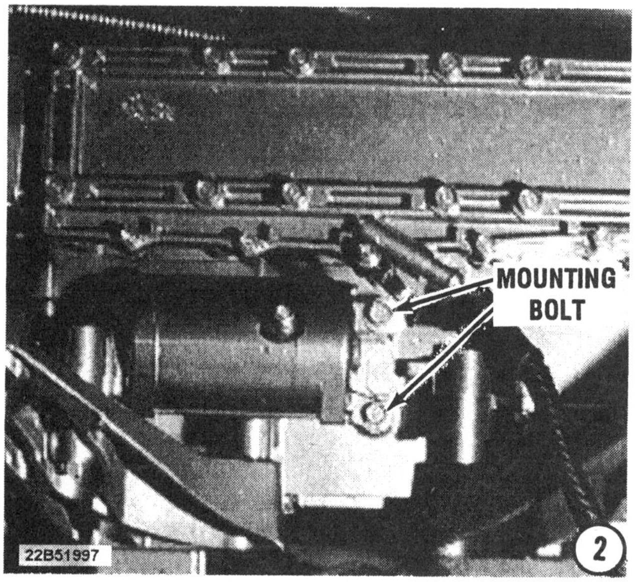

engine, or to the bracket -- whichever is the case. Tighten both bolts securely. Install the red cranking motor lead onto the motor terminal. Tighten the terminal nut to a torque value of 3 ft lb. (4Nm). Apply a "thickish" coat of water resistant multi-purpose lubricant to the shaft below the pinion gear on the cranking motor.

3- Coat the threads of the magneto attaching bolts with Loctite #242. Install the magneto assembly into the stator plate. Align the marks made during disassembly. Tighten the bolts

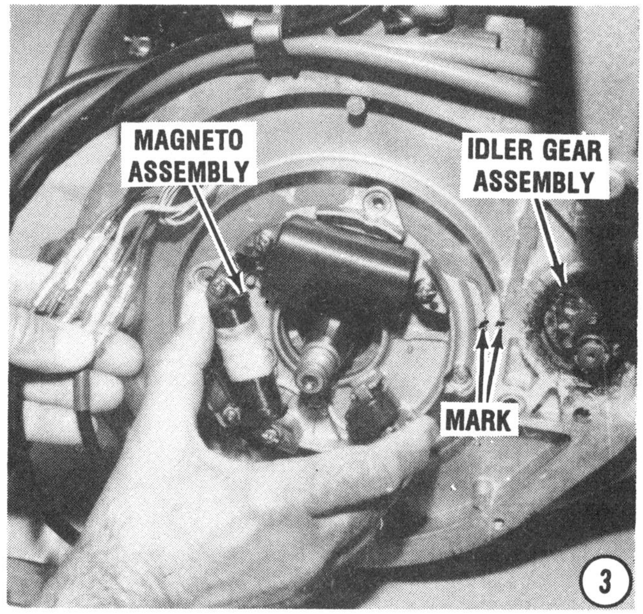

alternatively and evenly to a torque value of 5.9 ft lbs (8Nm), with the two marks still aligned.

Apply a coating of water resistant multi-purpose lubricant to the idler gear. Insert the idle gear assembly through the opening in the stator plate with the internal splines of the idler gear shaft indexed with the splines of the cranking motor shaft.

To install the flywheel and flywheel cover -- see Chapter 8, Page 8-23, for detailed illustrated procedures.

8
ENGINE

8-1 INTRODUCTION AND CHAPTER ORGANIZATION

The accompanying table lists the Yamaha names for their PWCs, the engine identifying series number and the approximate years of production. The manufacturer reserves the right to discontinue a model within a production year. By the same token, the manufacturer may introduce a new model within the year. Therefore, the term "approximate year of production" is used.

This chapter is divided into three main working sections. If differences in procedures are required, they will be clearly identified.

Section 8-2 Description and operation -- two cycle engine.
Section 8-3 Service the 650, 700, 760, 1100 and 1200 series engines.
Section 8-4 Cleaning and Inspecting -- all engines.

The carburetion and ignition principles of two-cycle engine operation **MUST** be understood in order to perform proper service work on the marine engines covered in this manual.

Repair Procedures

Service and repair procedures will vary slightly between individual models, but the basic instructions are almost identical. Any variations between models are clearly indicated. Special tools may be called out in certain instances. These tools may be purchased from the local dealer. In certain instances, an alternate tool may be obtained or fabricated.

Torque Values

All torque values must be met when they are specified. Torque values for various parts of each engine are given in the text.

A torque wrench is essential to correctly assemble the engine. **NEVER** attempt to assemble an engine without a torque wrench. Attaching bolts **MUST** be tightened

MODEL	Years Of Production
Super Jet 650	1992-1993
Super Jet 700	1994-1997
WaveRunner	1991-1992
WaveRunner III 700	1992-1997
VXR 650 & PROVXR 700	1993
WaveRunner 700	1993-1995
WaveRaider 700	1996
WaveRaider Deluxe	1994-1995
WaveRaider 1100	1995-1996
WaveBlaster 700	1994-1995
WaveBlaster 700	1996-1997
WaveBlaster II	1996-1997
WaveVenture 760	1995-1997
WaveVenture 1100	1995-1997
GP 760	1997
GP 1200	1997

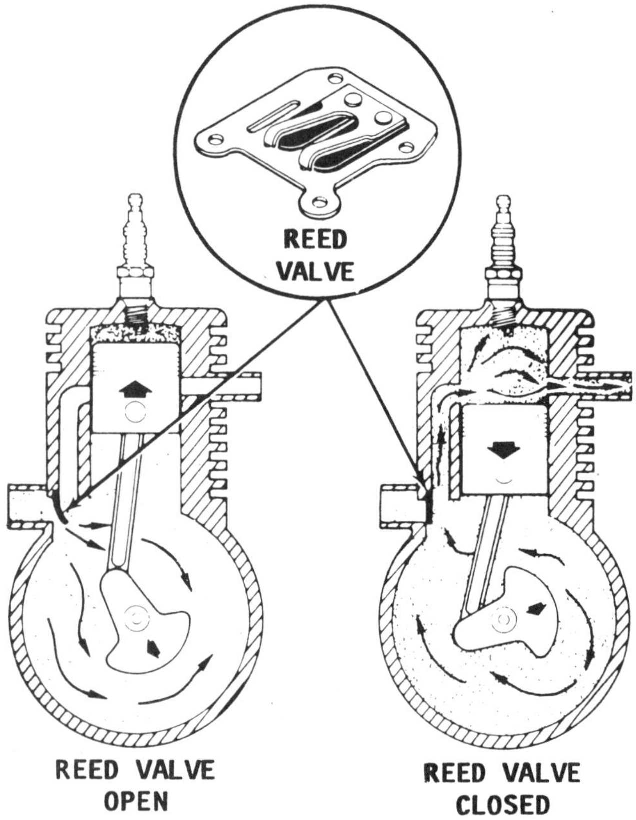

Reed valves are used to control the flow of air/fuel into the crankcase and eventually into the cylinder. As the piston moves upward in the cylinder, the resulting suction in the crankcase overcomes the spring tension of the reed. The reed is pulled free from its seat and the air/fuel mixture is drawn into the crankcase.

to the required torque value in two progressive sequences, following the specified tightening order. On the first sequence, tighten the bolts to 1/2 the torque value. On the second sequence, tighten the bolts to the full torque value.

Other Engine Components

Service procedures for the carburetor, fuel pumps, cranking motor and other components are given in separate Chapters. See the Table of Contents.

Reed Valve Service
Yamaha Only

The reeds on Yamaha engines covered in this manual are contained in an externally mounted reed valve block. Therefore, the engine need not be disassembled in order to replace a broken reed.

Cleanliness

Make a determined effort to keep parts and the work area as clean as possible. Parts **MUST** be cleaned and thoroughly inspected before they are assembled, installed, or adjusted. Use proper lubricants, or their equivalent, whenever they are recommended.

8-2 TWO-CYLCE ENGINE DESCRIPTION AND OPERATION

Intake/Exhaust

Two-cycle engines utilize an arrangement of port openings to admit fuel to the combustion chamber and to purge the exhaust gases after burning has been completed. The ports are located in a precise pattern in order for them to be opened and closed at an exact moment by the piston as it moves up and down in the cylinder. The exhaust port is located slightly higher than the fuel intake port. This arrangement opens the exhaust port first as the piston starts downward and therefore, the exhaust phase begins a fraction of a second before the intake phase.

Lubrication

A two-cycle engine is lubricated by mixing oil with the fuel. Therefore, various parts are lubricated as the fuel mixture passes through the crankcase and the cylinder.

Physical Laws

The two-cycle engine is able to function because of two very simple physical laws.

One: Gases will flow from an area of high pressure to an area of lower pressure. A tire blowout is an example of this principle. The high-pressure air escapes rapidly if the tube is punctured.

Two: If a gas is compressed into a smaller area, the pressure increases, and if a gas expands into a larger area, the pressure is decreased.

If these two laws are kept in mind, the operation of the two-cycle engine will be more easily understood.

ACTUAL OPERATION TWO-CYCLE ENGINE

Beginning with the piston approaching top dead center on the compression stroke: The intake and exhaust ports are closed by the piston; the reed valve is open; the spark plug fires; the compressed air/fuel mixture is ignited; and the power stroke begins. The reed valve was open because as the piston moved upward, the crankcase volume increased, which reduced the crankcase pressure to less than the outside atmosphere.

As the piston moves downward on the power stroke, the combustion chamber is filled with burning gases. As the exhaust port is uncovered, the gases, which are under great pressure, escape rapidly through the exhaust ports. The piston continues its downward movement. Pressure within the crankcase increases, closing the reed valves against their seats. The crankcase then becomes a sealed chamber. The air/fuel mixture is compressed ready for delivery to the combustion chamber. As the piston continues to move downward, the intake port is uncovered. A fresh air/fuel mixture rushes through the intake port into the combustion chamber striking the top of the piston where it is deflected along the cylinder wall. The reed valve remains closed until the piston moves upward again.

When the piston begins to move upward on the compression stroke, the reed valve opens because the crankcase volume has been increased, reducing crankcase pressure to less than the outside atmosphere. The intake and exhaust ports are closed and the fresh fuel charge is compressed inside the combustion chamber.

Pressure in the crankcase decreases as the piston moves upward and a fresh charge of air flows through the carburetor picking up fuel. As the piston approaches top dead center, the spark plug ignites the air/fuel mixture, the power stroke begins and one full cycle has been completed.

TIMING -- TWO-STROKE ENGINES

The exact time of spark plug firing depends on engine speed. At low speed the spark is retarded, fires later than when the piston is at or beyond top dead center. Engine timing is built into the unit at the factory. At high speed, the spark is advanced, fires earlier than when the piston is at top dead center.

Summary

More than one phase of the cycle occurs simultaneously during operation of a two-cycle engine. On the downward stroke, power occurs above the piston while the ports are closed. When the ports open, exhaust begins and intake follows. Below the piston, fresh air/fuel mixture is compressed in the crankcase.

On the upward stroke, exhaust and intake continue as long as the ports are open. Compression begins when the ports are closed and continues until the spark plug ignites the air/fuel mixture. Below the piston, a fresh air/fuel mixture is drawn into the crankcase ready to be compressed during the next cycle.

8-3 ENGINE SERVICE MODEL SERIES 650, 700, 760, 1100 and 1200

ADVICE

Before commencing any work on the engine an understanding of two-cycle engine operation will be most helpful. Therefore, it would be well worth the time to study the principles of two-cycle engines, as outlined in the previous section -- 8-2.

A polaroid, or equivalent instant-type camera is an extremely useful item, providing the means of accurately recording the arrangement of parts and wire connections **BEFORE** the disassembly work begins. Such a record is most valuable during assembling.

Preliminary Tasks

Disconnect the negative and positive leads from the battery. Disconnect the two plastic couplers, one for the starter switch and the other for the stop switch. Disconnect the thermo-sensor lead at its quick disconnect fitting.

Disconnect the fuel line; disconnect the throttle and choke cables at the carburetor and remove the carburetor/s -- see Chapter 6.

*A photograph taken with a Polaroid or similar camera is an excellent means of recording the arrangement of electrical lines, hoses, and parts, **BEFORE** the disassembly work commences.*

DO NOT remove the flywheel or stator plate until directed in the procedures. If working on the WaveRunner VXR, disconnect the fuel sender coupler and remove the sub oil tank and oil pump from the engine together with the associated oil lines. The main oil tank may remain in place.

Disconnect the exhaust hose from the muffler outer box and the cooling water hose from the base of the muffler.

Remove the coupling cover.

CRITICAL SHIM PACK WORDS

Make a note of the number of pieces of shim material used at each of the four engine mounts. Keep the four stacks of shim material separate to **ENSURE** they will be installed back into their original locations. The engine **MUST** be aligned properly with the impeller shaft to avoid vibration and coupler wear. The amount of shim material at each of the four engine mounts -- necessary for accurate alignment -- is determined at the factory or dealer/installer. The **SAME** amount must be placed under the mounts at each location to maintain alignment. Therefore, it is **ESSENTIAL** to identify the amount and location of each stack of shim material.

ENGINE REMOVAL

Remove the four engine mounting bolts. Attach an engine hoist to the lifting eye on the engine. As soon as the engine weight is taken up by the hoist, move the engine forward to disengage the rubber coupler from the jet pump coupler. If an engine hoist is not available, have an assistant help with the lifting. Two adults should have no difficulty in lifting any of the engines listed for this manual.

Remove the rubber coupler. Move the engine to a suitable work surface.

NOW, THESE WORDS

The following instructions pickup the work after the preliminary tasks listed above have been completed and the engine is in a suitable work area.

Procedural steps are given to remove and disassemble virtually all items of the engine. However, as the work moves along, if certain items, ie: bearings, bushings, seals, etc. are found to be fit for further service, simply skip the disassembly steps involved. Proceed with the required tasks to disassemble the necessary components.

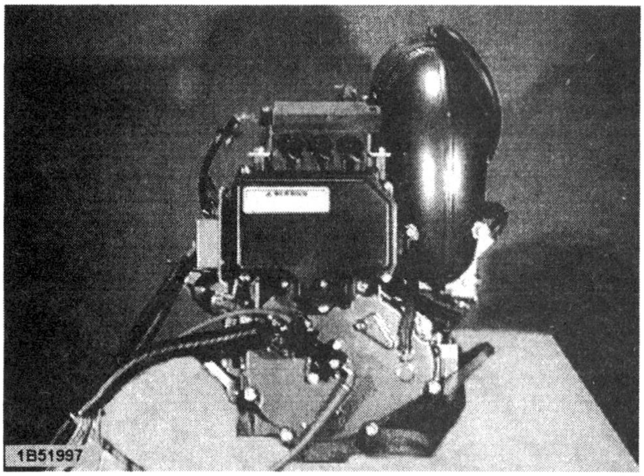

A Model 1100 Series engine removed from the watercraft, placed on a good work surface, ready for disassembly and service work.

COMPLETE and **DETAILED** procedures to clean and service all parts of the engine are outlined in the last section of this chapter, Section 8-4, beginning on Page 8-29.

DISASSEMBLING

The following procedures pickup the work after the engine has been removed and is in a suitable location.

1- Remove the two bolts securing the oil pump to the flywheel cover, and then remove the oil pump and set it aside. Notice the slot in the end of the crankshaft for the "spade" of the oil pump to index into during assembly.

2- Disconnect the electrical lead from the cranking motor terminal.

3- Remove the high tension leads from the spark plugs.

4- Withdraw the thermo-sensor from the receptacle at the inside aft end of the muffler

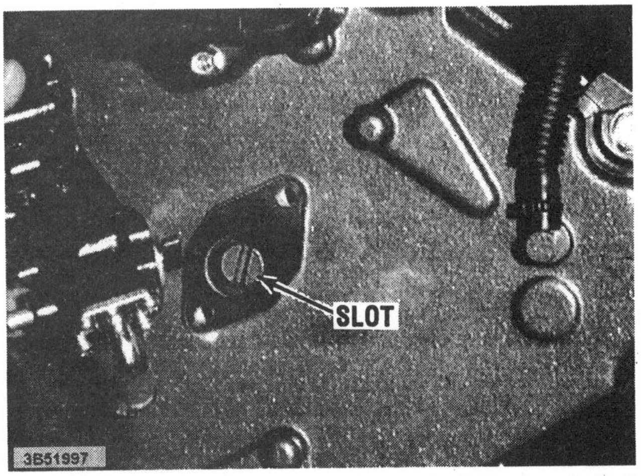

Close view of the slot in the end of the crankshaft. The "spade" of the oil pump indexes into the slot.

pipe. Loosen the tie-clip to permit the lead to clear.

Model 650 only: Remove the bolt securing the thermo-sensor to the cylinder head, and then remove the sensor.

5- Remove the bolts securing the flywheel cover to the engine block. One of the bolts on the starboard side of the cover is longer than the others. A ninth bolt is hidden behind the electrical box -- in a small bracket between the

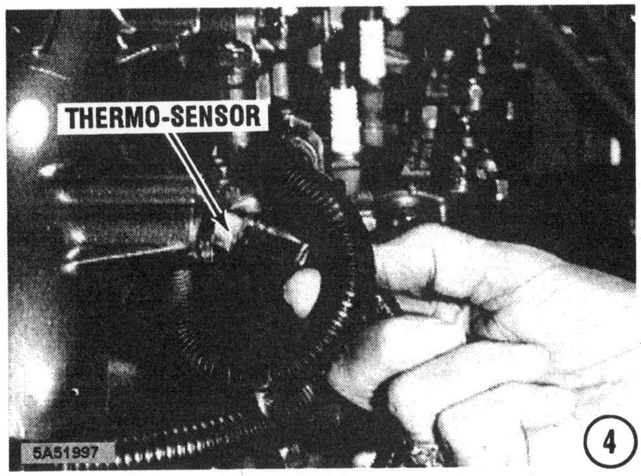

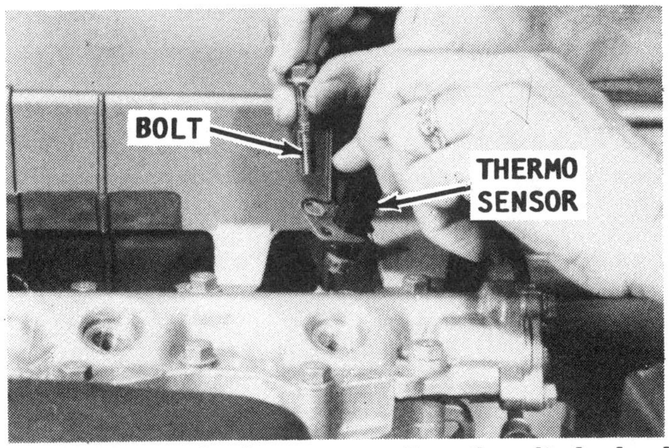

Removing the thermo-sensor from the cylinder head on a Model 650 Series engine.

box and the No. 1 cylinder. The electrical box **AND** the flywheel cover will come off together.

6- Lift the flywheel cover and the electrical box free of the block and set it aside. It is not necessary to disconnect the electrical leads from the box for an engine overhaul.

7- Check to be sure the two washers and spring for the idler shaft remained in the flywheel cover. If they did not, remove them from the idler shaft and secure them in the cover to ensure the spring and washers are not lost.

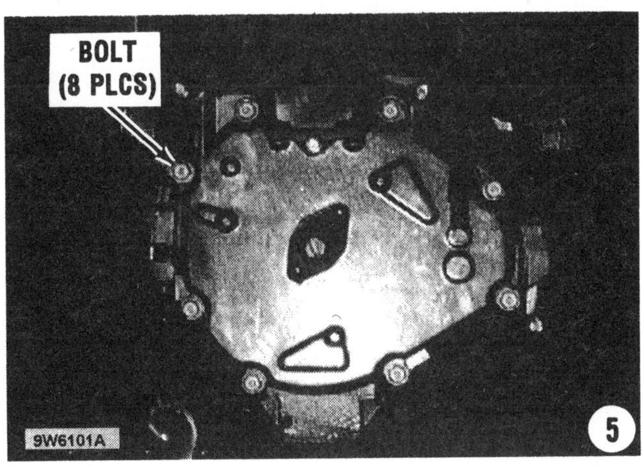

Location of the hidden flywheel cover bolt between the electrical box and the No.1 cylinder.

8- Obtain Yamaha special flywheel holding tool P/N YB-6139 for Model 650 and 700 Series engines, or P/N YB-41528 for 1100 and 1200 Series engines. Secure the holding tool to the block with the teeth in the tool indexed with the teeth in the flywheel, as shown.

Alternate Flywheel Tool

If the special tool is not available, a tool, similar to the one shown in the accompanying

illustration, may be fabricated from a metal bar and two long bolts. The longer the bar, the more leverage will be obtained.

The bolts should be long enough to allow a socket and torque wrench to be placed over the flywheel nut or bolt and yet clear the bar. Drill two holes, large enough for the bolts to pass through, at the end of the bar the same distance apart as the two holes in the flywheel. Secure the bolts to the flywheel through the bar, as shown in the accompanying illustration.

Coupler Removal

FIRST -- CRITICAL COUPLER WORDS

The coupler is made of cast material, therefore, if the special coupler tool called out in the next step is not available, be **EXTREMELY**

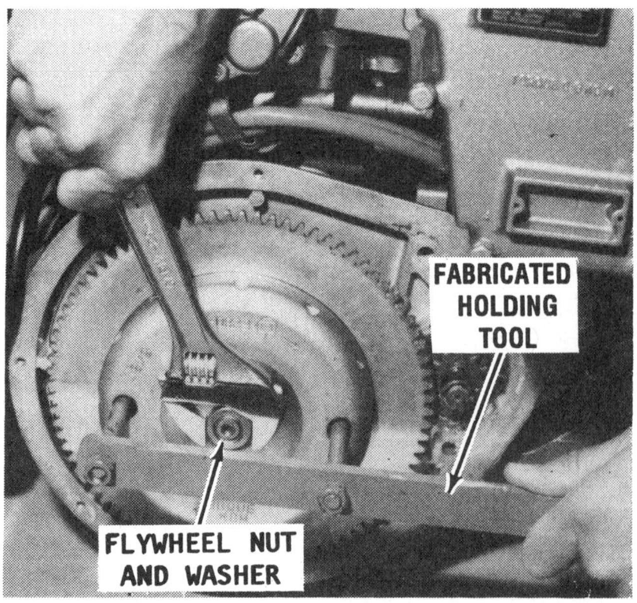

Fabricated and installed flywheel holding tool, as described in the text on this page.

careful of attempting to use a bar through the coupler slots to loosen the coupler. The coupler could very well be chipped or one of the leaves broken, causing an out-of-balance condition, resulting in unwanted vibration **AND** vibration causes expensive parts to wear rapidly.

9- Obtain special Yamaha coupler wrench P/N YW-38741 for 650 and 700 series engines, and P/N YW-06546 for 1100 and 1200 series engines. At the rear of the engine, install the wrench into the coupler, and then attach the proper size socket onto the tool nut. With the flywheel holding tool properly installed to prevent the crankshaft from rotating, loosen and then remove the coupler. An extension to the wrench handle will probably be required, because the coupler will not loosen easily.

Flywheel Removal

10- Loosen and remove the flywheel nut -- Model 650 series, or flanged bolt -- all others -- using the proper size wrench. The nut or bolt may be difficult to loosen requiring some type of extension on the wrench handle for added leverage.

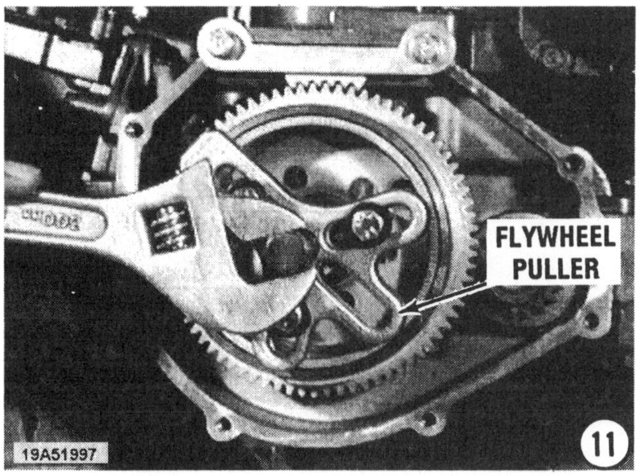

11- Obtain flywheel puller tool, Yamaha P/N YB-6117. If this particular puller is not available, a similar puller may be used **PROVIDED** it will pull from the bolt holes in the flywheel and **NOT** on the perimeter of the flywheel.

NEVER attempt to use a puller which pulls on the outside edge of the flywheel.

Install the puller onto the flywheel. If the flywheel holding tool is installed, the flywheel puller is ready to be installed. If the special holding tool is not available, have an assistant use adequate means of preventing the flywheel from rotating. Now, using the puller tool, take a strain on the puller with the proper size wrench. Continue to tighten on the special tool and at the same time, "**SHOCK**" the crankshaft with a gentle to moderate tap with a hammer on the end of the special tool. This "shock" will assist in "breaking" the flywheel loose from the crankshaft. Remove the flywheel.

SPECIAL WORDS ON FLYWHEEL MAGNETS AND FLYWHEEL HANDLING

The outer ends of any magnet are called "poles". One end is the north pole and the other end is the south pole. The magnetic field surrounding a magnet is concentrated around these two poles.

Magnets are usually installed in pairs with the north pole of one adjacent to the south pole of its neighbor and so on. In this manner, a continuous magnetic field surrounds the inside of the flywheel.

If a flywheel is accidently dropped, not only could the teeth be damaged, but the impact will weaken the magnetic strength of all the magnets housed in the flywheel.

If one or more of the magnets should break or fracture, two new magnetic poles would be

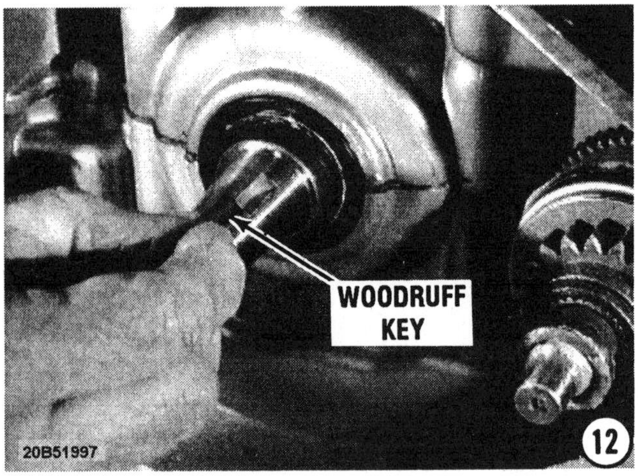

created. A long magnet with two poles will become two short magnets with four poles. The new poles will possess only half the magnetic strength of an original pole. The overall magnetic field will be altered. The new field of the shorter magnets will not extend to cover the area of the flywheel.

Serious consequences apply to a CD type ignition system in the event of a flywheel magnet fracture. Pulser coils are energized by the concentrated magnetic field at the magnetic poles. If new poles are suddenly created, the trigger will receive conflicting signals from the magnets and may even attempt to fire the cylinder twice in one revolution.

All these reasons require the flywheel to be handled with CARE.

12- Remove and save the Woodruff key from the recess in the crankshaft.

Model 650 and 700 Series Only
Next Two Steps

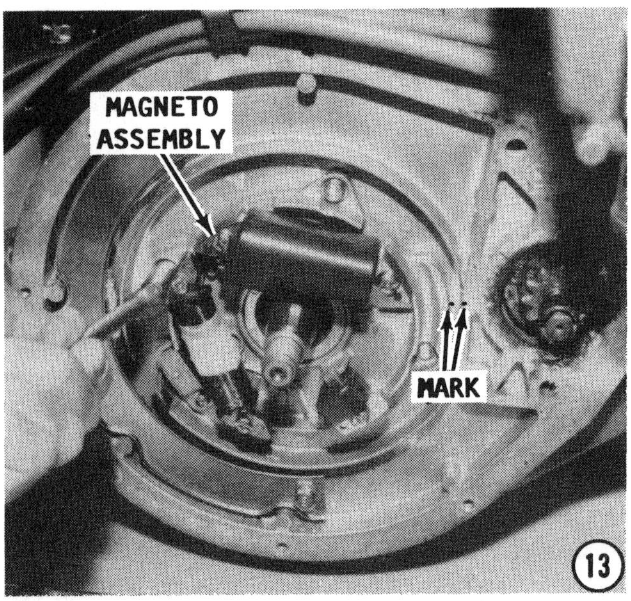

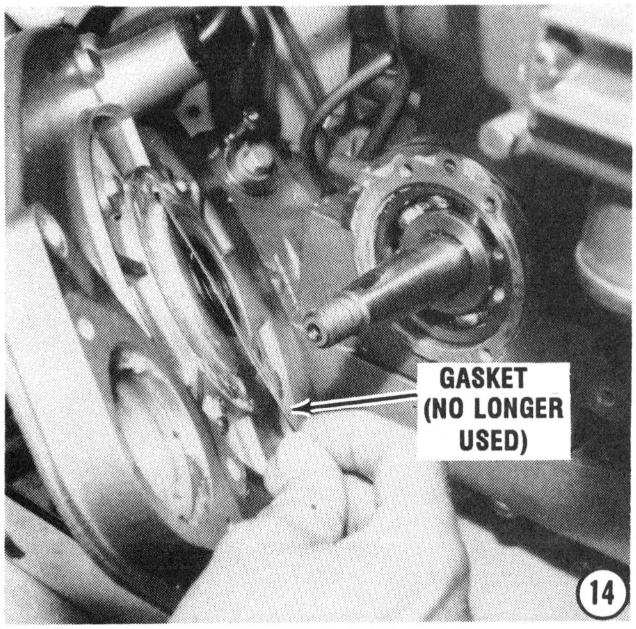

Magneto and Stator Removal

13- Observe the two aligned punch marks, one on the magneto assembly and one on the stator plate. These marks serve as an aid during installation for the correct positioning of the magneto assembly on the stator plate. If, for some reason, no marks are visible, then make two aligning marks, one on the stator plate and the other on the magneto assembly. The securing screws pass through elongated slots in the magneto assembly. Without the alignment marks just described, the magneto assembly could be installed as much as 15° off its original position and drastically affect the timing characteristics of the engine.

Remove the four bolts securing the magneto assembly to the stator plate. Lift the magneto assembly up and over the crankshaft and lay it to one side until the stator harness can be released from the plate.

14- Remove the two bolts and washers securing the stator plate to the engine. **GENTLY** tap around the perimeter of the stator plate with a soft head mallet to "break" the plate free of the crankshaft and the gasket seal under the plate. Slide the stator plate up and over the crankshaft. (The illustration shows a gasket, but this is no longer used on 650 Series engines). Pry the stator harness grommet free of the crankcase.

Oil Seal Words

If there is any evidence of oil on the stator plate, the two oil seals at the forward main bearing, inside the crankcase, may have failed. Check these seals during later disassembling.

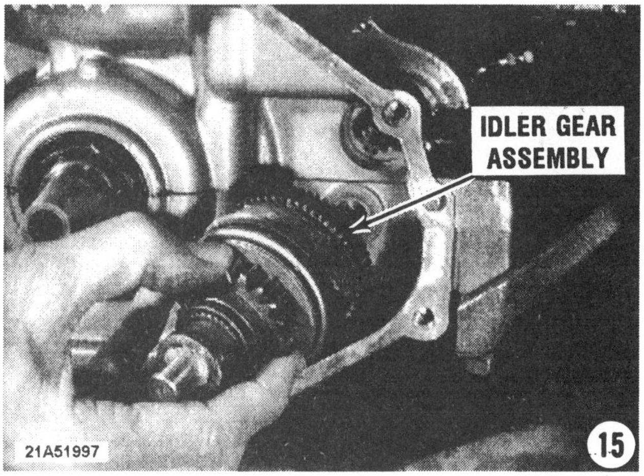

ALL MODEL ENGINES

15- Withdraw the idler gear assembly from the splined cranking motor shaft. The shim material on the block behind the assembly should have stayed in place on the block. If it did not, **TAKE CARE** to remove it from the assembly, and identify its location for assembling.

16- Remove the two bolts securing the cranking motor to the block, and then lift the cranking motor free.

ADVICE FROM EXPERIENCE

The exhaust and muffler systems should always be removed during an engine overhaul. Many times water in the engine is caused by a leaking cover gasket or plate.

Muffler and Exhaust System Removal

Model 650 and 700 Series
Next Seven Steps

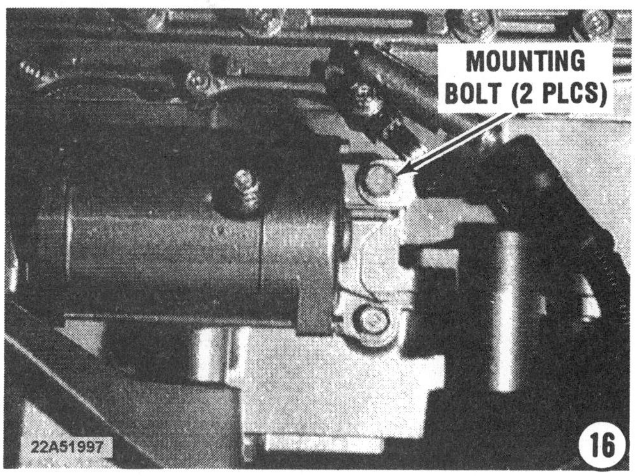

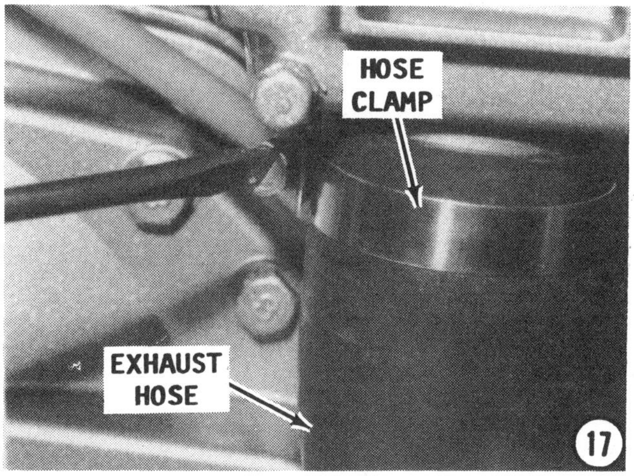

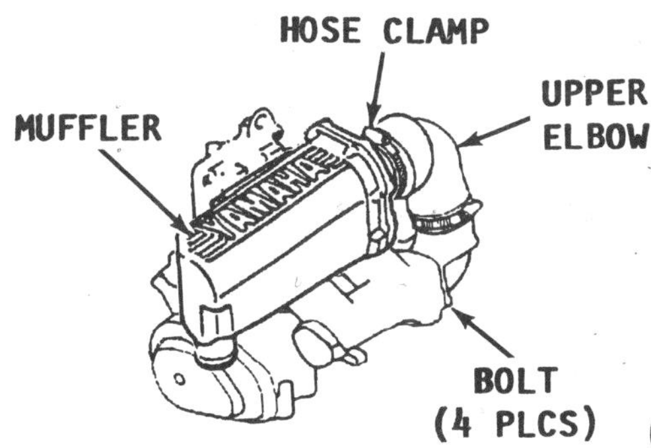

18

Model 1100 and 1200 Series
Proceed Directly to Step 24

17- Loosen the hose clamp around the large exhaust hose and ease the hose off the muffler.

18- Disconnect the small hose from the fitting on the lower exhaust elbow. Loosen the hose clamp closest to the muffler box on the upper elbow and then remove the four bolts securing the lower elbow to the exhaust manifold/muffler. Remove and discard the gasket.

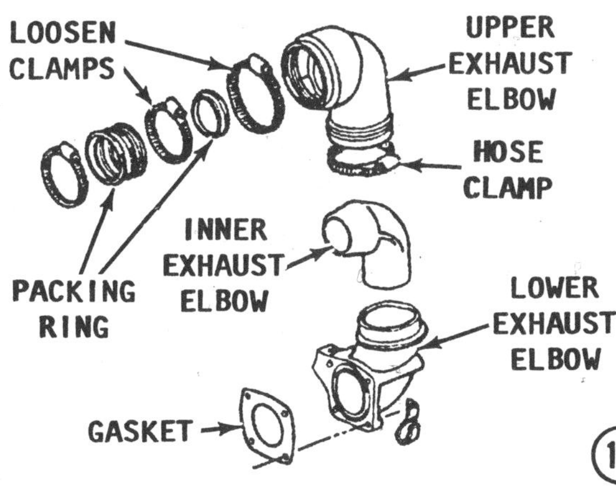

19

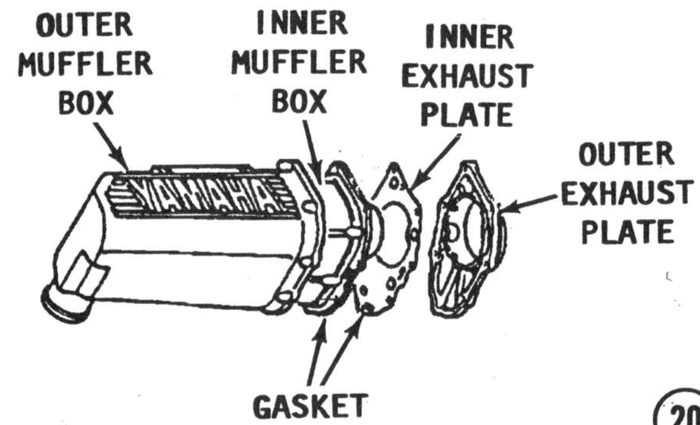

20

19- If further disassembling is required, loosen the hose clamp between the two elbows, and then pull them apart. The upper exhaust elbow will slide off to reveal an inner exhaust elbow. Loosen the two remaining hose clamps on the upper elbow. Remove the large and small packing rings.

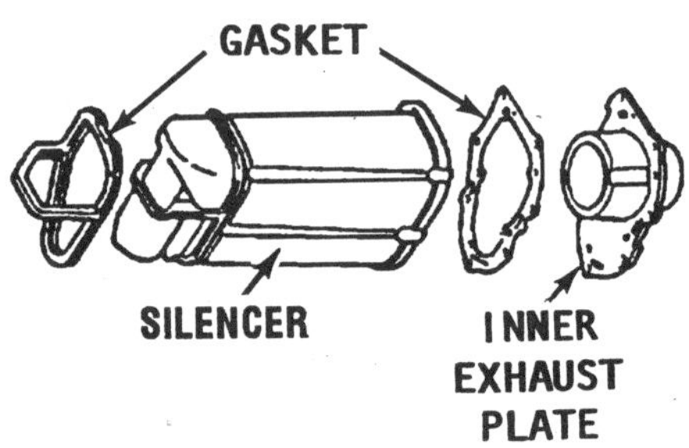

21

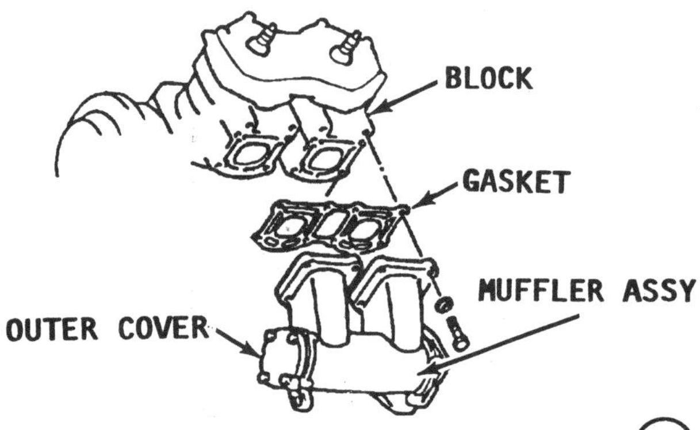

22

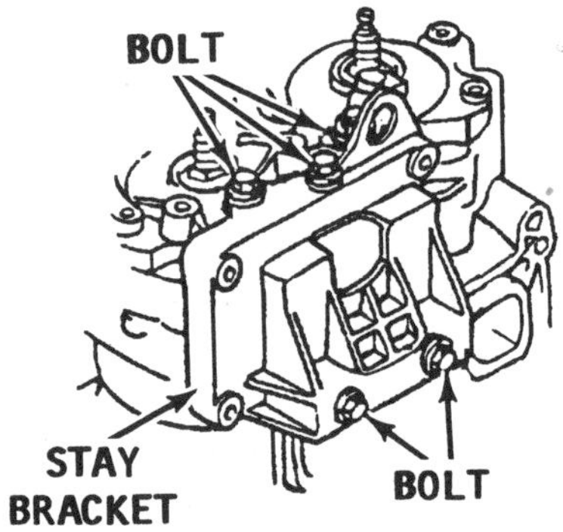

23

20- Remove the bolts securing the outer exhaust plate to the muffler outer box. **CAREFULLY** pry the plate free of the muffler. Remove and discard the gasket.

21- Remove the bolts securing the silencer cover plate to the silencer. Pry the plate free. Remove and discard the gasket.

Withdraw the silencer from the outer box. Remove and discard the seal located at the forward end of the silencer. Remove the three bolts securing the muffler outer box to the stay bracket and block. Lift the muffler outer box free of the engine.

22- Remove the eight bolts securing the exhaust manifold/muffler assembly to the block. Remove all traces of gasket material from the contact surfaces.

If the muffler is to be disassembled further, first remove the four bolts and washers from the end of the manifold/muffler. Next, remove the following items in the order given: An outer cover plate, a gasket, an inner cover plate, and finally another gasket.

23- Now, remove the stay bracket from the cylinder head and block. Three bolts secure the bracket to the head and two bolts secure it to the block.

Muffler and Exhaust System Removal Model 1100 and 1200 Series

24- Remove the two main bolts from the stay bracket.

25- Remove the twelve bolts securing the exhaust manifold to the engine.

26- Disconnect the cooling hoses from the fore and aft locations on the cylinder head.

27- Lift the muffler and exhaust system assembly free of the engine.

ALL ENGINE MODELS SPECIAL WORDS ON REED VALVES

Take great care in the next step when handling reed valve assemblies. Once the assembly is removed, keep it away from sunlight, moisture, dust, and dirt. Sunlight can deteriorate valve seat rubber seals. Moisture can easily rust stoppers overnight.

Dust and dirt -- especially sand or other gritty material -- can break reed petals, if caught between stoppers and reed petals.

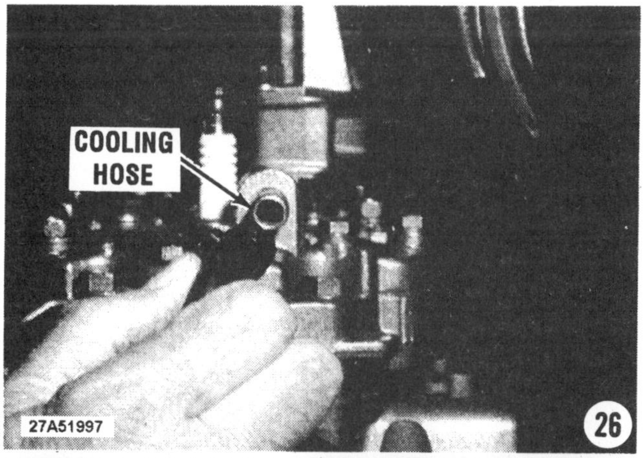

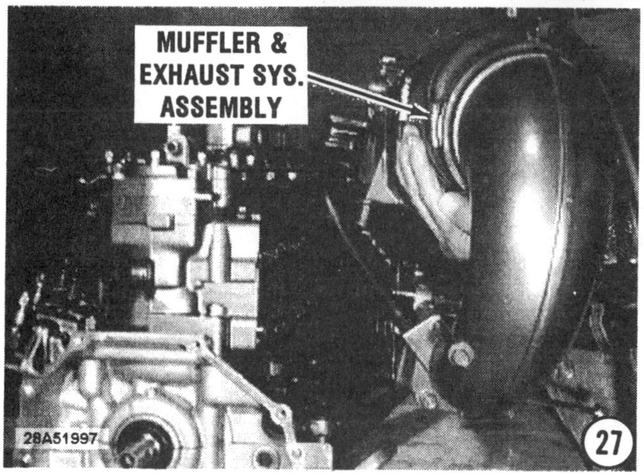

Make special arrangements to store the reed valves to keep them isolated from the elements while further work is being performed on the engine.

Intake Manifold Removal

28- Remove the stay bracket from the cylinder head.

29 Remove the bolts securing the intake manifold and reed block assemblies to the engine. Remove and discard the gasket.

Model 650 only: After the intake manifold is removed, remove the inner manifold plate with reed blocks attached. Remove and discard the second gasket.

MORE SPECIAL WORDS

Many components are difficult to remove -- separate -- due to hardened sealant between contact surfaces. Yamaha engineers have thoughtfully incorporated prying tabs at strategic locations to assist in separating surfaces. **ALWAYS** pry only at these tab locations. Prying elsewhere could very likely damage an aluminum sealing surface.

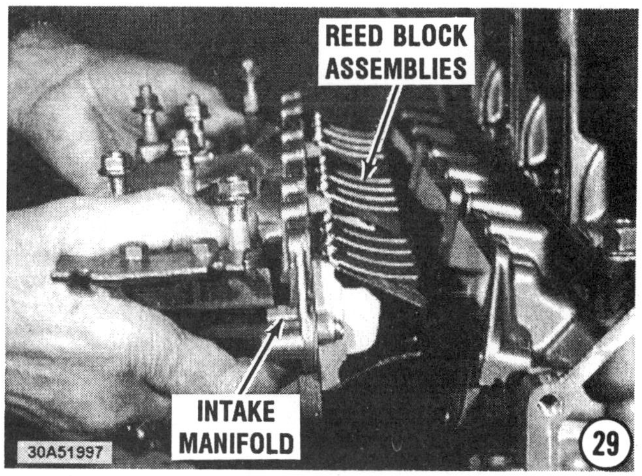

Cylinder Head Removal

30- Remove the remaining head bolts. Pry the head loose, using the prying tabs provided. **TAKE CARE** not to damage the smooth machined mating surfaces of the block and head.

31- Lift the head free of the block. Discard the gasket.

32- If the one anode in the block -- 650/700 Series or two in the 1100/1200 Series are disintegrated to less than 2/3 their original size, remove the screw securing the anode to the water jacket and remove the anode. For piece

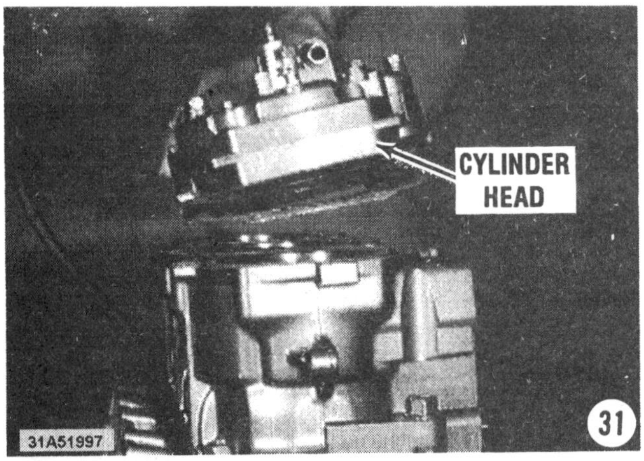

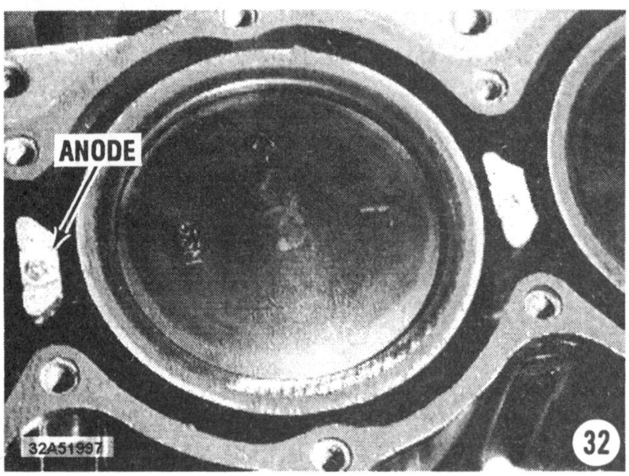

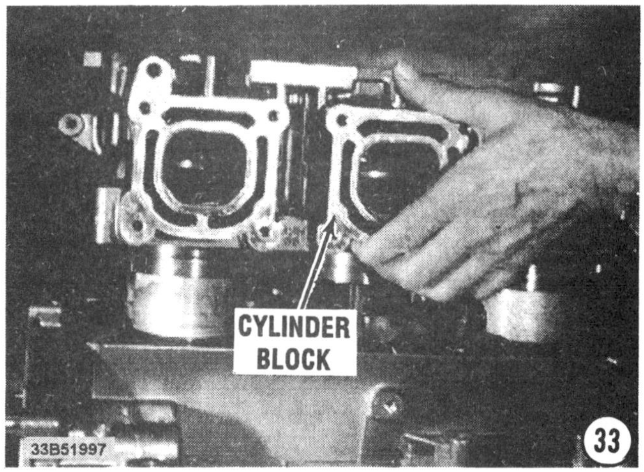

of mind, it might be best to remove the anode/s regardless, and install a new one.

33- Remove the bolts securing the cylinder block to the crankcase, and then lift the cylinder block free. The pistons are still attached to the rods and will remain in place, as shown.

SPECIAL PISTON WORDS

The pistons will **NOT** pass through the upper crankcase. Therefore, the pistons **MUST** be removed from the connecting rods, at this time, before the crankcase halves are separated.

34- Scribe a mark on the inside of the piston skirt to identify the No. 1, No. 2 or No. 3 piston **BEFORE** removal from the connecting rod, as described in following text.

SAFETY WORDS

The piston pin **C**-lockrings are made of spring steel and may pop out of the groove with considerable force. Therefore, warn other people in the area and **WEAR** eye protection glasses or shield while removing the piston pin lockrings.

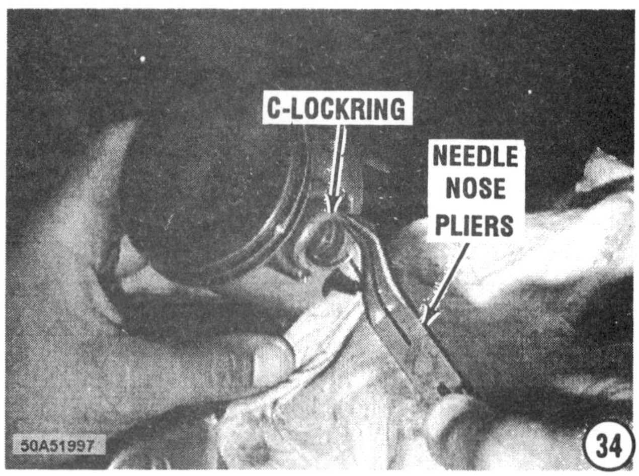

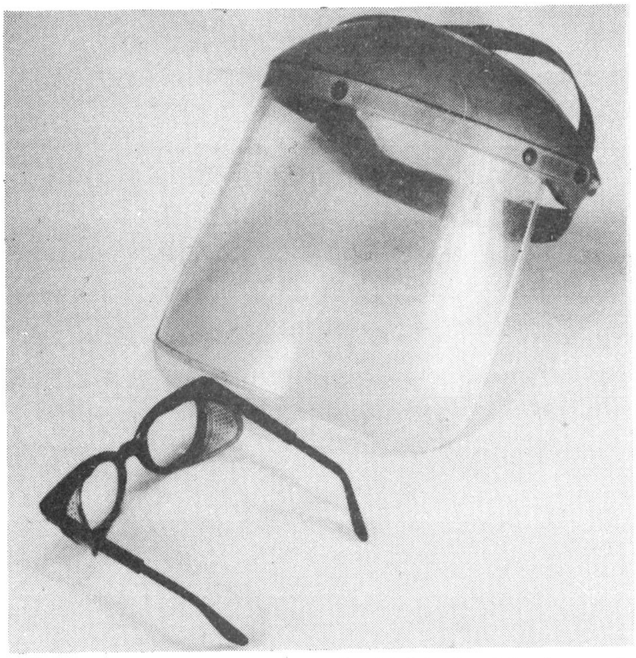

Safety glasses or a safety shield should always be worn when working with C-lockrings. The rings are made of spring steel and may pop out of the groove quite suddenly and with tremendous force.

Remove the **C**-lockring from both ends of the piston pin using a small blade screwdriver inserted into the small groove next to the piston pin opening. Discard the **C**-lockrings. These rings stretch during removal and must **NEVER** be used a second time.

Push the piston pin out -- free of the piston. Remove the caged needle bearing from the small end of the connecting rod. Save the two washers (spacers).

GOOD WORDS

Good shop practice dictates to replace the rings during an engine overhaul. However, if the rings are to be used again, expand them **ONLY** enough to clear the piston and the grooves, because used rings are brittle and break very easily.

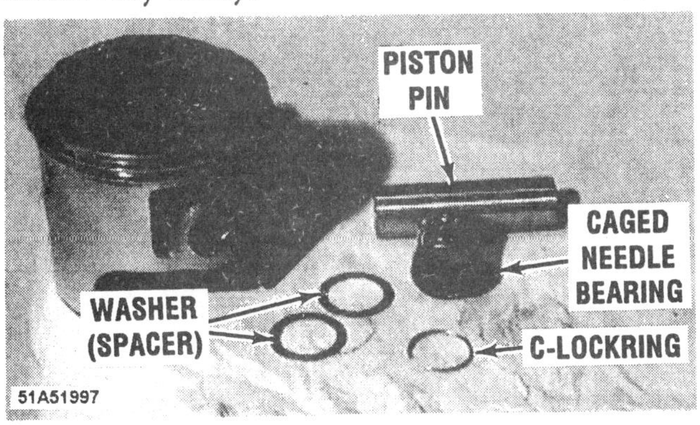

Piston and associated parts after the piston has been separated from the rod. The rings are yet to be removed.

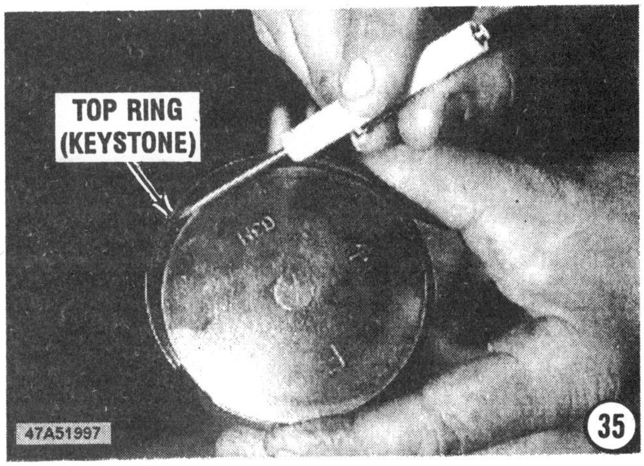

35- No special tool is required to remove the piston rings. **GENTLY** spread the top piston ring enough to pry it out and up over the top of the piston. Remove the lower ring in a similar manner. These rings are **EXTREMELY** brittle and must be handled with **CARE**, if they are intended for further service.

ADVICE ON NEEDLE BEARINGS

New needle bearings should be installed in the connecting rods, even though they may appear to be in serviceable condition. New bearings will ensure lasting service after the overhaul work is completed. If it is necessary to install the used bearings, keep them separate and identified to **ENSURE** they will be installed back into the same connecting rod from which they were removed.

CRITICAL WORDS

The rod is an integral part of the crankshaft. The two are manufactured together and **CANNOT** be separated.

Slowly rotate the three bearings races. If rough spots are felt, a new crankshaft must be

installed. The bearings are installed at the factory and are **NOT** replaceable.

Separate Cylinder Block From Upper Crankcase

36- Turn the two halves of the crankcase over with the bottom portion facing **UP**. Remove the two engine mount brackets. One bracket is secured with three bolts and the other is secured with four bolts. The mount bolts are tightened very securely with locking compound. Therefore, it will take extra effort to loosen and remove the bolts. Note how the bolts will vary in size. Attempt to remember their location as an aid during assembling.

37- Remove the bolts securing the two crankcase halves together. Insert a slotted screwdriver between the prying tabs on the lower crankcase half and the upper crankcase half. Pry the two surfaces apart. **NEVER** pry at gasket sealing surfaces. Such action would very likely damage the sealing surface of an aluminum engine. Separate the two crankcase halves, and then lift the lower half up and free of the upper half.

TAKE CARE not to lose the two locating pins. These pins may remain in either half when the crankcase is separated.

38- CAREFULLY tap the tapered end of the crankshaft, with a soft head mallet, to jar it free of the block. **SLOWLY** lift the crankshaft assembly straight up and out of the block.

Slide the two oil seal carriers from the aft (threaded), end of the crankshaft. Slide the single oil seal carrier with two oil seals inside from the forward (tapered with internal threads), end of the crankshaft. If the oil seals are no longer fit for further service, pry the seals out with a screwdriver.

CLEANING AND INSPECTING

COMPLETE and **DETAILED** procedures to clean and inspect virtually **ALL** parts of the engine, including the block and head will be found in the last section of this chapter, Section 8-4, beginning on Page 8-29.

ASSEMBLING AND INSTALLATION

Detailed procedures are given to assemble and install virtually all parts of the engine. Therefore, if certain parts were not removed or disassembled because a part was found to be fit for further service, simply skip the particular step involved and continue with the required tasks to return the engine to operating condition.

The following instructions pickup the work after all parts of the engine have been thoroughly cleaned and inspected according to the procedures outlined in Section 8-5, the last section in this chapter **AND** replacement parts have been purchased and are on hand.

CRITICAL WORDS

The pistons cannot be assembled onto the connecting rods at this time, because they will not pass through the upper half of the crankcase.

Crankcase Assembling

1- Coat the lips of the four new oil seals with multi-purpose water resistant marine lubricant. Install two oil seals **BACK-TO-BACK** inside the single oil seal carrier. Slide the carrier over the tapered end of the crankshaft. Install the other two oil seals into their respective carriers and install the two carriers onto the threaded end of the crankshaft with **BOTH** lips facing **AWAY**

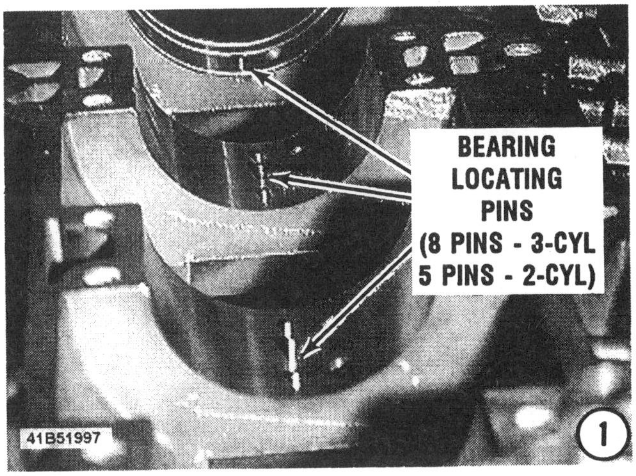

from the block. Fit the bearing locating pins into the recesses in the lower crankcase.

Five pins are used on a 2-cylinder engine (three in the center and one at each end). Eight pins are used on a 3-cylinder engine (three in the center two and one at each end). In the accompanying illustration, seven of the eight pins are visible for a 3-cylinder engine.

2- Apply a thin bead of Yamaha Gasket Maker by Loctite P/N 90890-74001-00 around

Applying a coating of Yamaha Gasket Maker to the mating surface of the lower crankcase. Keep the work moving to prevent the material from "setting" (hardening).

Spreading gasket sealing compound on the mating surface of the lower crankcase.

Lowering the crankshaft into the lower crankcase. One of the locating pins for the upper crankcase is clearly visible.

both crankcase surfaces. Keep the work moving to prevent the gasket maker from setting. Lower the crankshaft assembly into the lower crankcase.

Rotate the bearings until their locating pins fit into the recesses in the lower crankcase. Check to be sure the two locating dowel pins are in place -- one at the forward end, starboard side -- the other at the aft end, port side.

Mate the upper crankcase to the lower crankcase. Coat the bolt threads with Loctite #572. Install and tighten the crankcase bolts to the torque value listed in the Appendix in the sequence shown in the accompanying illustration for the Model 700 Series engine, on the next page. For other model engines, begin in the center and work alternately across and towards both ends, as indicated in the illustration for the 700.

3- Install the engine mount brackets. One bracket uses three bolts with washers and the other mount four bolts with washers. Tighten the bolts -- in two sequences -- to a torque value of 20 ft lbs (28Nm).

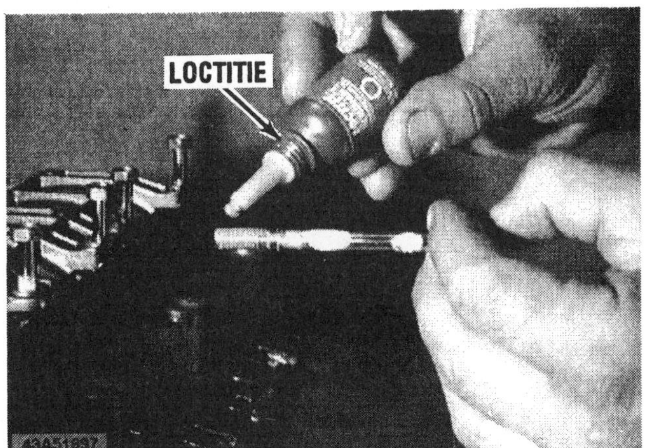

Coating the threads of the crankcase bolts with Loctite to ensure they do not work loose.

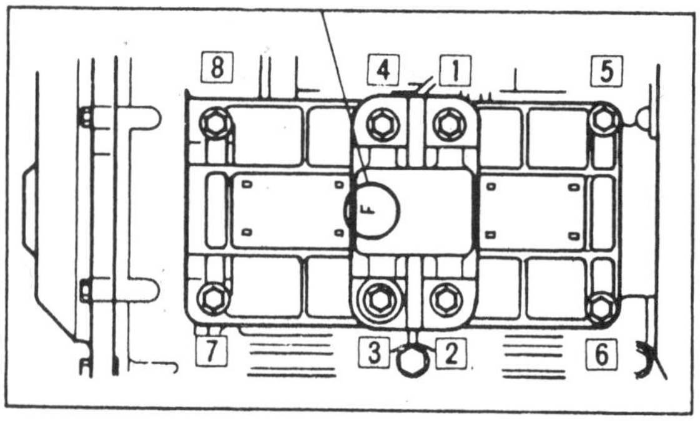

Crankcase bolt tightening sequence for a 2-cylinder engine. Sequence for a 3-cylinder engine follows the same pattern -- start in the center -- work alternately across towards both ends.

4- Turn the assembled crankcase over -- resting on its engine mounts, ready for the pistons to be installed on the rods.

Pistons, Rings, and Rods

5- No special tool is necessary for installation of the rings. **HOWEVER**, much care must be exercised to spread the ring only enough to clear the top of the piston. The rings are **EXTREMELY** brittle and will snap if spread be-

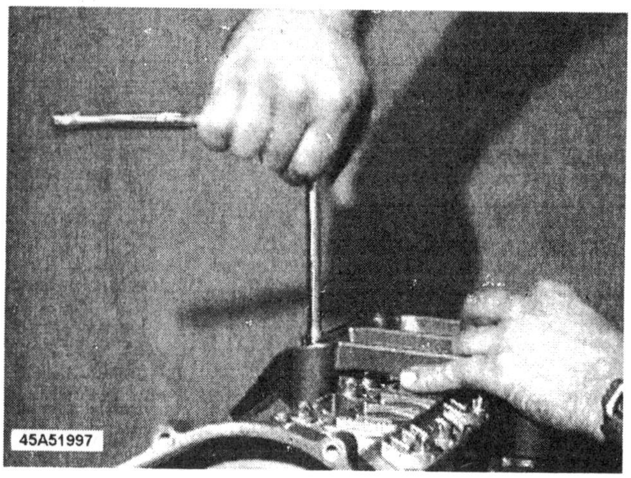

Tightening the engine mount bolts to the required torque value.

yond their limit. The top ring is a keystone ring and the bottom ring is a standard plain ring. Observe the cross-sectional drawing in the insert in the accompanying illustration. Install the bottom ring first. A plain ring may be installed with either surface facing up, **UNLESS** a letter or dot is embossed on one side of the ring. A lettered or embossed ring must be installed with the letter or dot facing **UP**.

CAREFULLY work the ring over the top of the piston, and into the ring groove with the end gap of the ring straddling the locating pin in the groove. The top (Keystone) ring **MUST** be installed with the tapered surface facing **UP**.

6- Coat the inner circumference of the small end of the No. 1 connecting rod with two-stroke engine oil. Dip the caged needle bearing in two-stroke oil and insert the bearing into the small end of the connecting rod. Insert a washer (spacer) into each side of the rod against the bearing, as indicated in the accompanying illustration, on the next page.

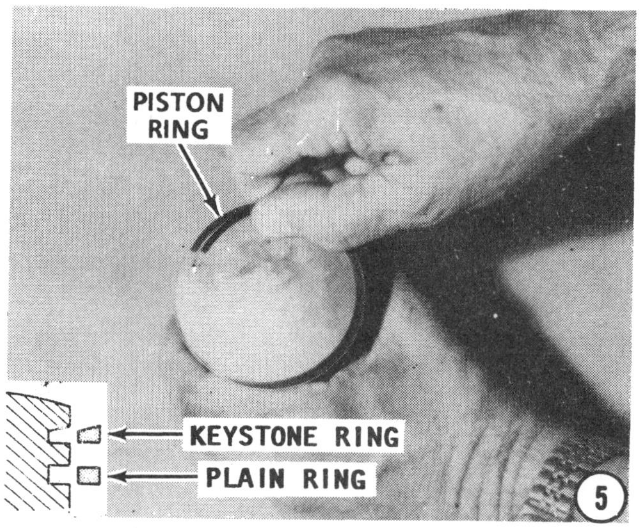

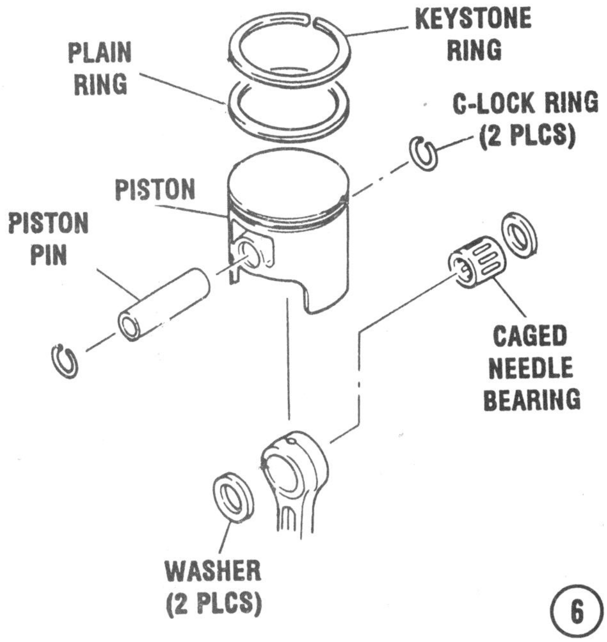

Position the end of the rod with needle bearings in place in the piston. The arrow on the piston crown **MUST** face **TOWARD** the exhaust side of the engine. Slide the piston pin through the piston and connecting rod. Continue to push the pin through. Center the pin in the piston. Install a washer (spacer) onto each end of the piston pin.

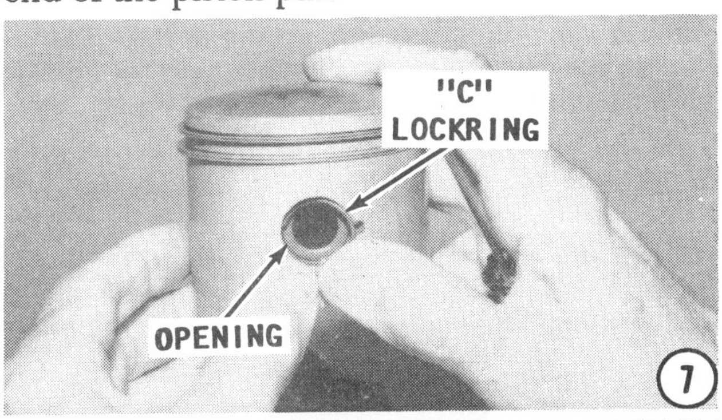

Complete piston assemblies properly installed onto the rods -- ready for cylinder block installation. A check should be made to ***ENSURE*** *each ring straddles the locating pin in the ring groove.*

SAFETY WORDS

The piston pin **C**-lockrings are made of spring steel and may slip out of the groove with considerable force. Therefore, warn other persons in the area and **WEAR** eye protection, as described and illustrated in the disassembling section, while installing the piston pin lockrings.

7- Install a **C**-lockring at each end of the piston pin. The lockrings may be worked in by hand, as shown. Position the end gap at the 12 o'clock position or at the 6 o'clock position. In other words -- the end gap of the lockring should face straight up or straight down.

Perform Steps 5 thru 7 for the other piston/s.

GOOD WORDS

Make one more check of the piston installations. The arrow **MUST** face **TOWARD** the exhaust side of the engine. If necessary, realign the ring gap over the locating pin. The purpose of the pin is to prevent the ring from rotating in the ring groove. The ring end gap must travel up and down a portion of the cylinder wall where there is no port opening. If the ring was free to rotate, the end might catch on the port opening and break the ring.

NOTE

The services of an assistant might prove very helpful in starting the pistons into the cylinder bores as the cylinder block is lowered onto the crankcase, in this next step.

8- Coat the upper sides of each piston and the rings with two-stroke engine oil. **SLOWLY** lower the cylinder block as each piston -- one-at-a-time is started into the appropriate cylinder.

The services of an assistant will prove most helpful to feed the pistons into the cylinders, as the cylinder block is lowered onto the upper crankcase half.

Squeeze in the rings around the locating pin as the block is lowered and the piston enters the bore.

CRITICAL WORDS

If difficulty is experienced in fitting the piston into the cylinder, **DO NOT** use force. Such action might result in a broken piston ring. Make sure the ring end gap is aligned with the locating pin.

Check The Work Thus Far

Rotate the crankshaft by hand to be sure the crankshaft does not bind.

BAD NEWS

If binding is felt, it will be necessary to remove the crankcase and reseat the crankshaft. It will also be necessary to check the positioning of the bearing locating pins. If binding is still a problem after the crankcase has been installed a second time, the cause might very well be a broken piston ring.

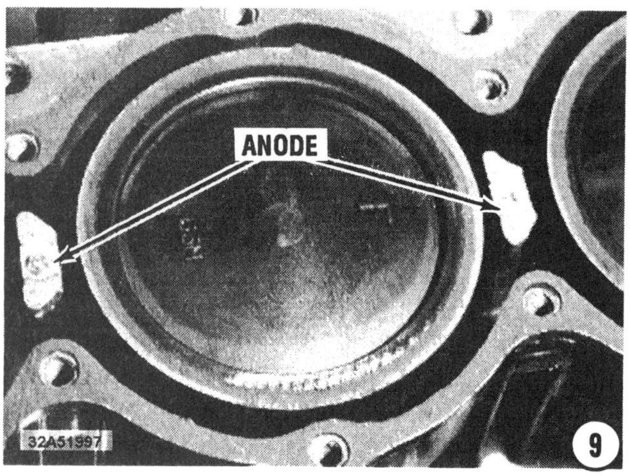

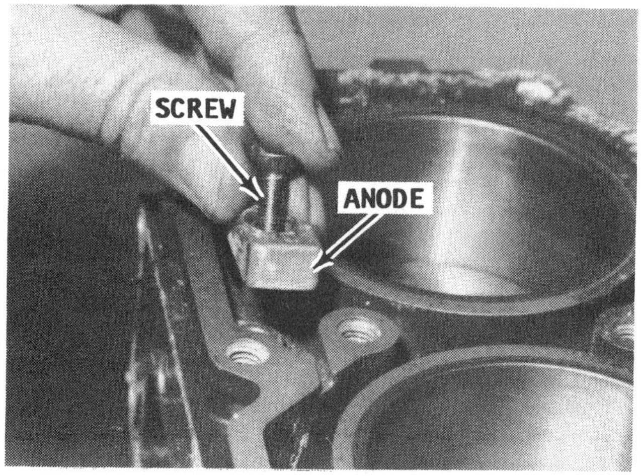

Installing an anode into the cylinder block of a 2-cylinder engine. To give "peace of mind" to the owner it is best to install new anodes during an engine overhaul.

Check to be sure the embossed "F" is facing forward -- toward the flywheel end **-- AND** the embossed arrow is directed toward the exhaust manifold. Failure to have the pistons correctly positioned, as just described, would probably result in premature failure of the piston.

9- Regardless of the condition of the old anode/s, install new anode/s into the water jacket, to give "peace of mind" to the owner. Model 650 and 700 Series engines have one anode, but the 1100 and 1200 Series engines have two -- one on each side of the center cylinder. Coat the threads of the attaching screw with Loctite #572, or equivalent. Secure the anode with the screw.

Head Installation

10- Position a new head gasket and the cylinder head in place on the block.

SPECIAL WORDS

The manufacturer recommends **NO** sealing agent be used on either side of the head gasket.

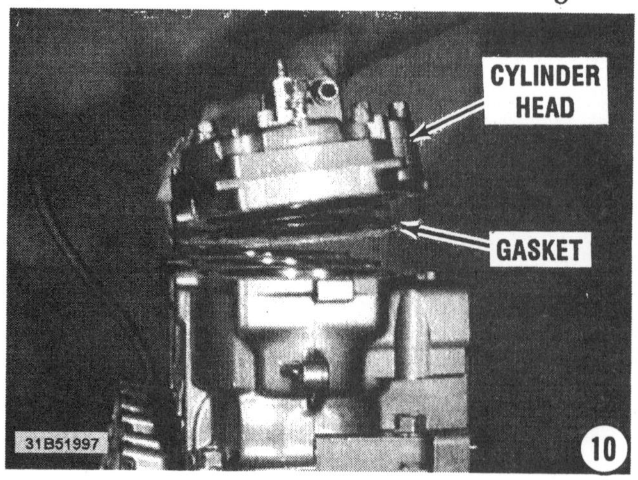

Sealing Surface Words

Because of the high temperatures and pressures developed, the sealing surfaces of the cylinder head and the cylinder block are the most prone to water leaks. No sealing agent is recommended BECAUSE it is almost impossible to apply an even coat of sealer. An even coat would be essential to ensure an air/water tight seal.

Some head gaskets are supplied with a tacky coating on both surfaces applied at the time of manufacture. This tacky substance will provide an even coating all around. Therefore, no further sealing agent is required.

HOWEVER, if a slight water leak should be noticed following completed assembly work and engine start up, DO NOT, and again let it be said, DO NOT attempt to stop the leak by tightening the head bolts beyond the recommended torque value. Such action will only aggravate the problem and most likely distort the head.

FURTHERMORE, tightening the head bolts, which are case hardened aluminum, may force the bolt beyond its elastic limit and cause the bolt to FRACTURE. BAD NEWS, very BAD NEWS indeed. A fractured bolt must usually be drilled out and the hole re-tapped to accommodate an oversize bolt, etc. Avoid such a situation, with the extra time and work involved.

Probable causes and remedies of a new head gasket leaking after the engine is installed and operating are:

a. Sealing surfaces not thoroughly cleaned of old gasket material. Disassemble and remove ALL traces of old gasket material.

b. Damage to the machined surface of the head or the block. The remedy for this damage is the same as for the next item.

c. Permanently distorted head or block. Spray a light EVEN coat of any type metallic spray paint on both sides of a new head gasket. Use only metallic paint - any color will do. Regular spray paint does not have the particle content required to provide the extra sealing properties this procedure requires. Assemble the block and head with the gasket while the paint is still TACKY. Install the head bolts and tighten them in the sequence, indicated by the numbers cast into the head and to the proper torque value, but NO more!

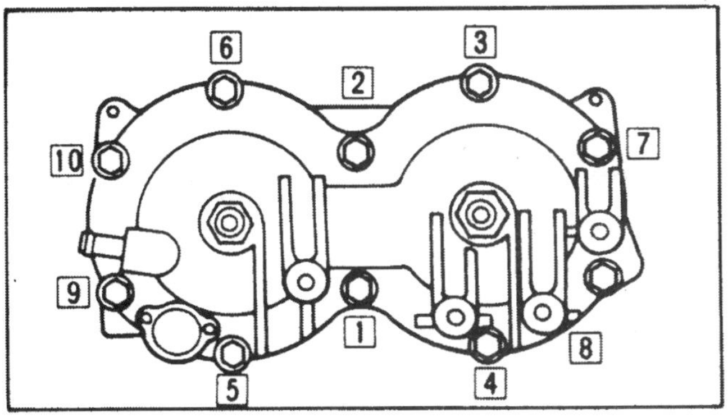

Head bolt tightening sequence -- 2-cylinder engine.

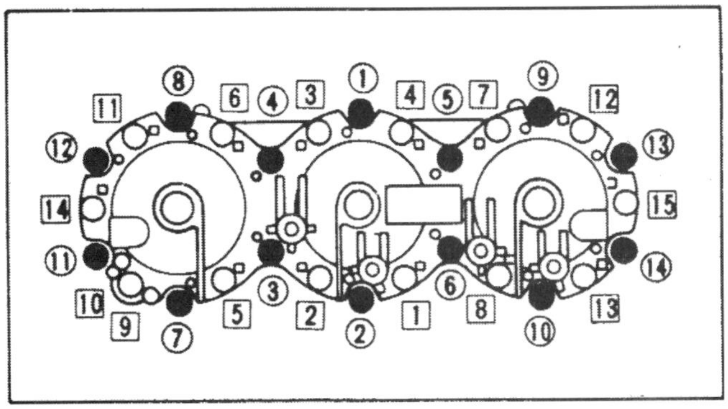

Head bolt tightening sequence -- 3-cylinder engine.

Allow the paint to set for at least 24 hours before starting the engine. Consider this procedure as a temporary "band aid" type solution until a new head may be purchased or other permanent measures can be performed.

Under normal circumstances, if procedures have been followed to the letter, the head gasket will not leak.

1. Coat the threads of all the head bolts with Loctite #572, or equivalent. The tightening sequence numbers are cast into the head beside each bolt hole. The accompanying illustration indicates the tightening sequence for the engines covered in this section.

2. Tighten the head bolts in the sequence indicated by the numbers on the head to 11 ft. lbs. (15 Nm) on the 1st pass and 26 ft. lbs. (35 Nm) on the 2nd and final sequence.

Muffler And Exhaust System Assembling Model 650 and 700 Series Next Seven Steps

(12)

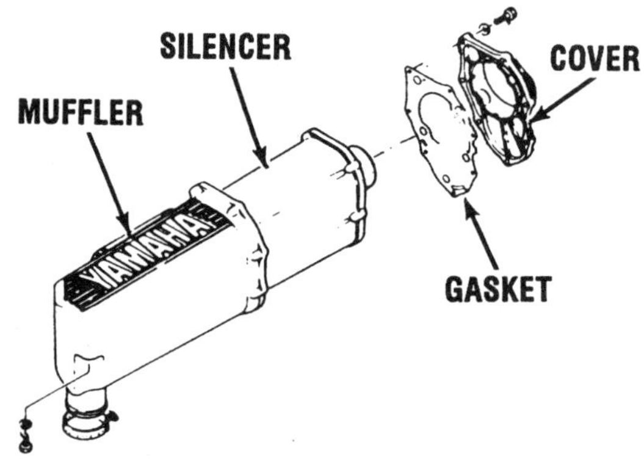

(15)

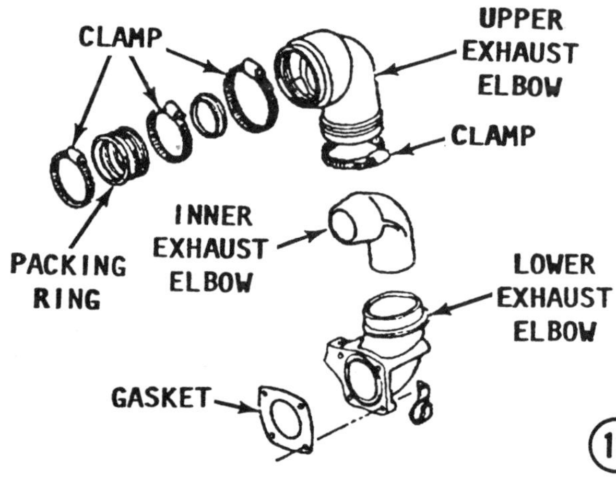

(16)

Model 1100 and 1200 Series
Proceed Directly to Step 19

12- Install the stay bracket to the cylinder head and block by first coating the threads of the attaching bolts with Loctite #572, or equivalent. Three bolts secure the bracket to the head and two bolts secure the bracket to the block. Tighten all five bolts to a torque value of 2.9 ft lb (4Nm) on the first sequence and 29 ft lbs (40Nm) on the second and final sequence. (This is quite a jump in ft lbs, but the manufacturer's word is law.)

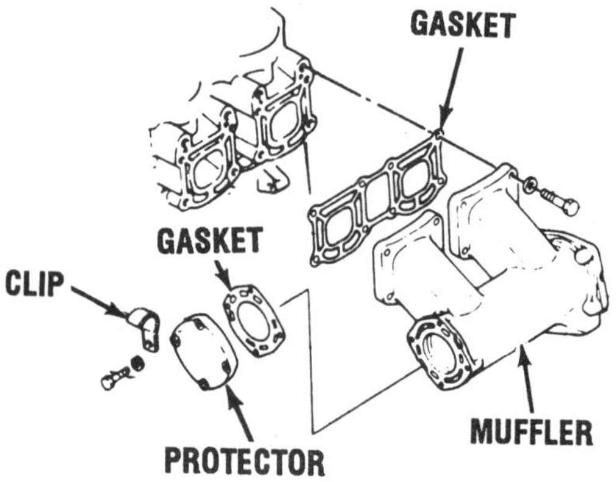

(13)

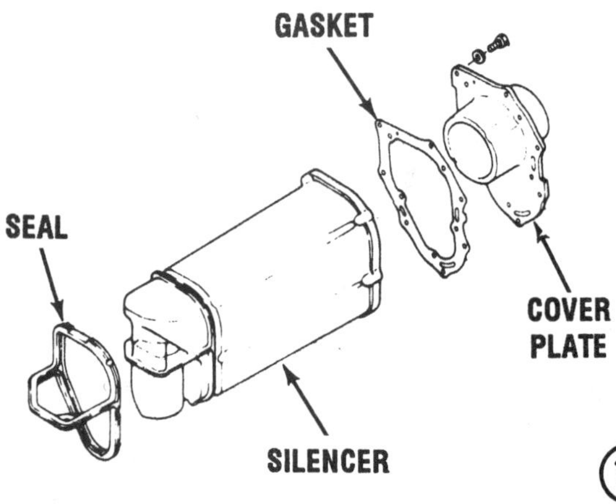

(14)

13- Coat the threads of the eight muffler attaching bolts with Loctite #572, or equivalent. Position a new gasket against the block and then move the muffler into place and secure it with the attaching bolts and washers. Tighten the bolts to a torque value of 13 ft lbs (18Nm). If the muffler was disassembled, replace the protector and gasket with the attaching hardware. Note the small clamp bracket is secured with one of the bolts.

14- Assemble the silencer by first applying water resistant lubricant to the seal and then positioning it in place over the smaller end. Install the diffuser into the larger end with a new gasket. Secure the diffuser with the bolts and washers.

15- Insert the assembled silencer into the muffler. Install the cover -- with a new gasket -- and secure it in place with the bolts and washers. Tighten the bolts securely.

Assemble Exhaust
Elbow Manifolds

16- If the exhaust elbows were removed and disassembled, begin by securing the small packing ring to the top of the upper elbow with a hose clamp. Next, secure the large packing ring

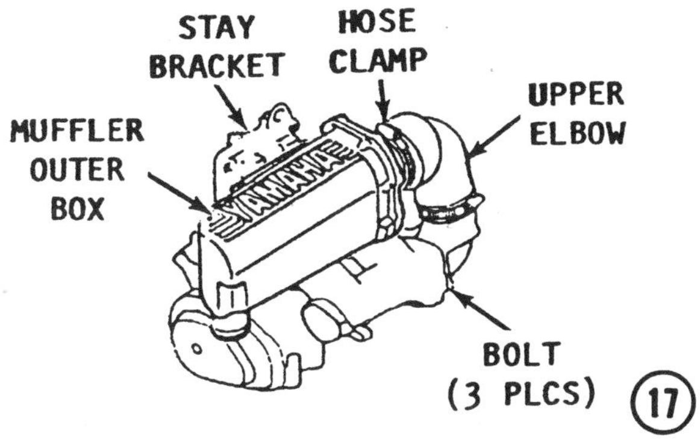

to the small packing ring with another hose clamp. Slide the upper elbow over the inner elbow with the cooling fins. Attach the lower exhaust elbow to the upper elbow with a hose clamp. Now, secure the elbow assembly to the exhaust manifold/muffler with the four bolts and washers.

The lower outside bolt also secures a wire harness retainer. Tighten the bolts alternately and evenly to a torque value of 5.6 ft lbs (7.8Nm). Secure the large packing ring at the end of the upper elbow to the exhaust fitting on the end of the muffler box housing. Tighten all four hose clamp screws securely.

17-- Coat the threads of the muffler bolts with Loctite #572, or equivalent. Secure the muffler outer box to the stay bracket and block with the three bolts and washers. Tighten the upper forward bolt first; the lower forward bolt second; and the single rear bolt last. Tighten the bolts to a torque value of 18 ft lbs (25Nm) on the first sequence and to 36 ft lbs (50Nm) on the second and final sequence. Secure the lower exhaust elbow to the exhaust manifold with the attaching bolts. Tighten the bolts securely.

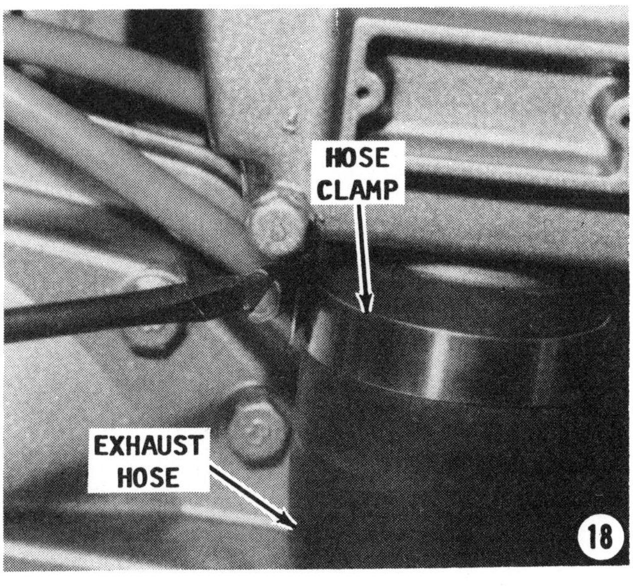

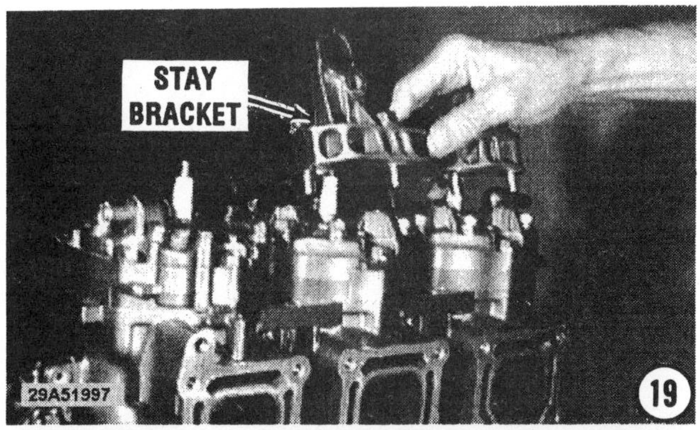

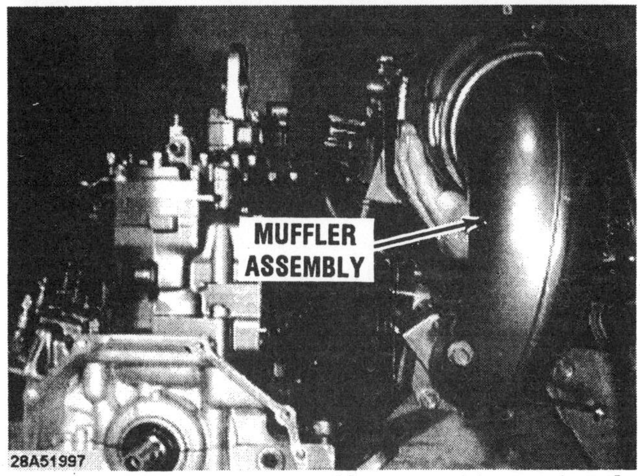

Moving the exhaust assembly into position against the engine block.

18- Work the large exhaust hose onto the muffler and then secure it in place with the hose clamp.

Muffler and Exhaust System Installation Model 1100 and 1200 Series

19- Install the stay bracket. Move the muffler and exhaust system assembly into place against the block.

20- Install and tighten the two main bolts securing the exhaust system to the stay bracket to a torque value of 22 ft lbs (30Nm).

21- Apply a coating of Loctite 271, or equivalent to the twelve bolts to secure the exhaust assembly to the side of the engine. Install and tighten the bolts in two sequences to a torque value of 22 ft lbs (30Nm).

22- Connect the cooling hoses to the fore and aft locations on the cylinder head.

Cranking Motor Installation

23- Apply a "thickish" coating of water resistant multi-purpose lubricant to the shaft below

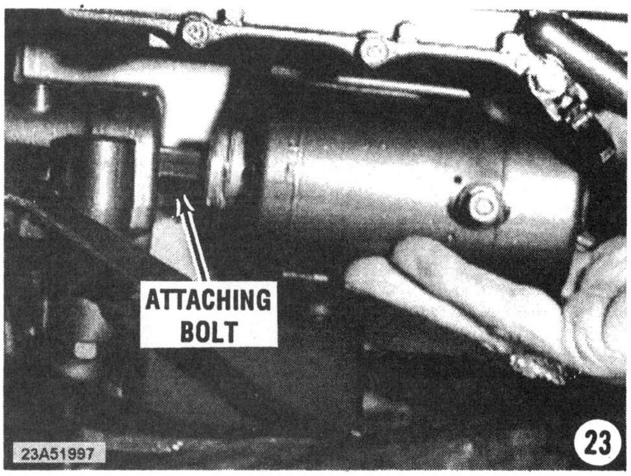

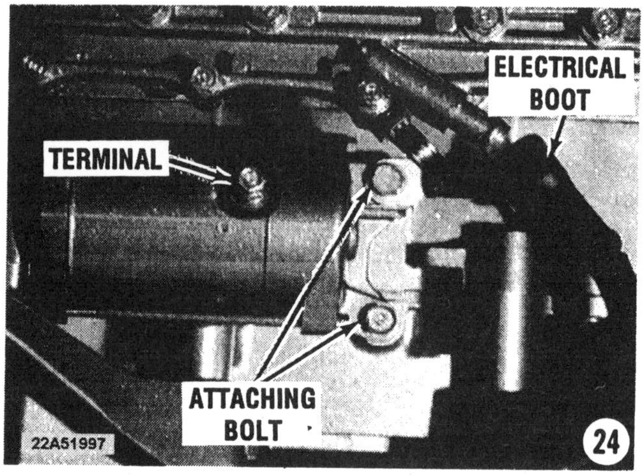

the pinion gear on the cranking motor. Move the cranking motor into place, with the armature shaft extending through the opening in the block. The idler assembly will be installed later.

24- Secure the cranking motor with the two bolts -- coated with Loctite and washers. Tighten the bolts securely. The accompanying illustration shows the cranking motor being installed on a Model 1100 series engine. The cranking motor on Model 650 and 700 Series is secured with two bolts passing through a bracket on the block in a fore-and-aft direction. Connect the electrical lead to the terminal on the cranking motor. Coat the connection with some type of dialectric grease, and then slide the boot over the connection.

25- Insert the idler gear shaft through the opening and index the splines of idler gear shaft with the splines of the cranking motor armature shaft.

Stator Plate Installation Model 650 Series and Early 700 Series

26- Slide the stator plate over the crankshaft and push the stator harness grommet into the

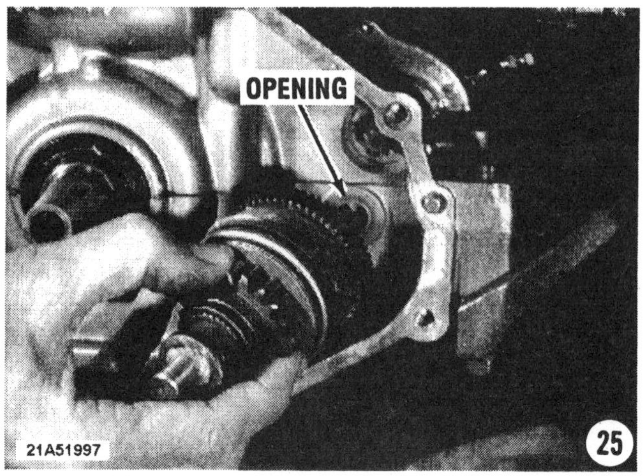

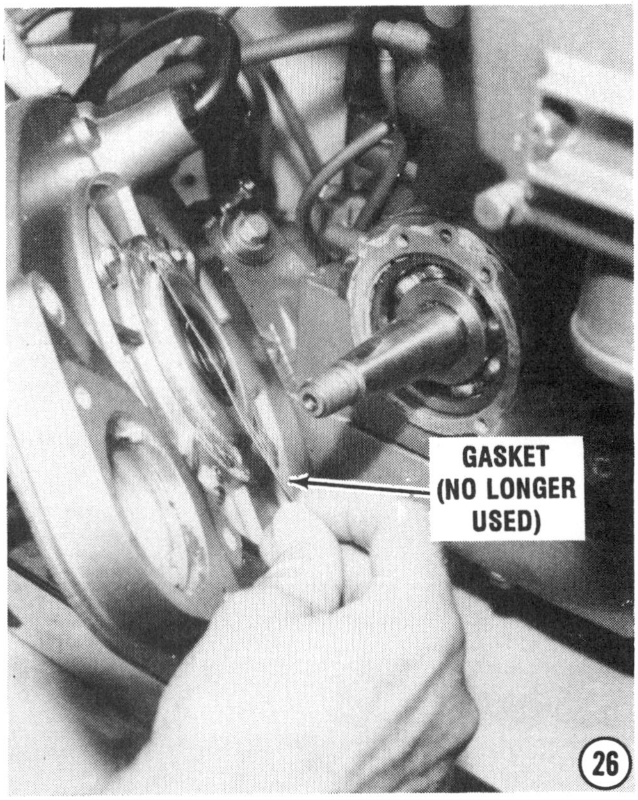

groove in the crankcase. Late model units no longer use the gasket, as shown.

27- Coat the threads of the two securing bolts with Loctite #572, or equivalent. The illustration indicates four bolts, but only two are used on late model engines. Install and tighten the bolts with washers, alternately and evenly to a torque value of 5.9 ft lbs (8Nm).

On newer models, the magneto is an integral part of the flywheel and the stator is housed inside the flywheel cover.

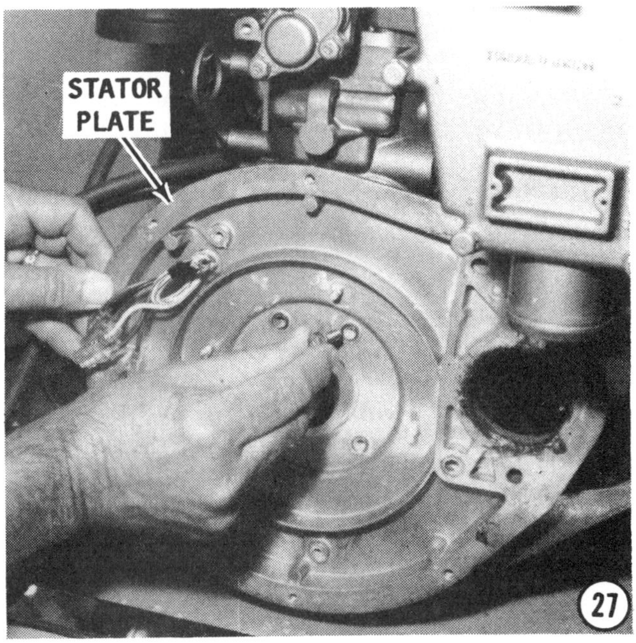

Stator Plate Installation
700, 760, 1100
and 1200 Series Engines

The stator on these model engines is installed within and is a part of the flywheel cover.

Flywheel Installation
All Models

28- Place a dab of thick lubricant onto the curved surface of the Woodruff key to hold it in place while the flywheel is being installed. Press the Woodruff key into place in the crankshaft recess. Wipe away any excess lubricant to prevent the flywheel from "walking" during engine operation.

29- Check the flywheel magnets to ensure they are free of any metal particles. Double check the taper in the flywheel hub and the taper on the crankshaft to verify they are clean and free of any oil.

Now, slide the flywheel onto the crankshaft with the keyway in the flywheel aligned with the Woodruff key in place on the crankshaft. Move the flywheel completely onto the crankshaft with the keyway in the flywheel indexed over the Woodruff key.

Take time to rotate the flywheel **COUNTERCLOCKWISE** to be sure it does not contact any part of the stator plate or wiring.

Thread the special flanged bolt onto the crankshaft -- just fingertight -- at this time.

30- Obtain special flywheel holding tool Yamaha P/N YB-6139 or the alternative tool made during disassembly. Install the tool with the bolts into the block and with the teeth of the holding tool indexed with the flywheel teeth or the bolts secured through the alternate tool into the flywheel. Tighten the flywheel bolt to a torque value of 50 ft lbs (68Nm).

Leave the flywheel holding tool or the fabricated tool in place for installation of the coupler at the rear of the engine in the next step.

Early Model 650 and 700 Series

31- At the rear of the engine, slide the washer onto the crankshaft.

All Other Models

FIRST -- CRITICAL COUPLER WORDS

The coupler is made of cast material, therefore, if the special coupler tool is not available, be **EXTREMELY** careful of attempting to use a bar through the coupler slots to tighten the coupler. The coupler could very well be chipped or one of the leaves broken, causing an out-of-balance condition, resulting in unwanted vibration **AND** vibration causes expensive parts to wear rapidly.

31-Continues

Obtain coupler tool P/N YW-6365. With the flywheel holding tool still installed, as in the previous step, to prevent the flywheel/crankshaft from rotating, install the special coupler tool.

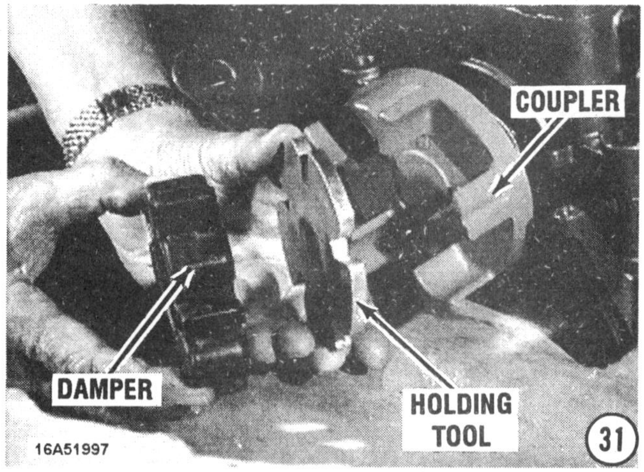

The illustration shows the rubber dampener ready to be installed, but this is not done until the coupler is tightened to the required torque value.

32- Using the proper size wrench with a long handle, tighten the coupler to a torque value of 27 ft lbs (37Nm). After the coupler is installed, remove the special tool and install the rubber dampener.

Flywheel Cover Installation

33- Replace the plastic cover to protect the electrical connections, if it was removed.

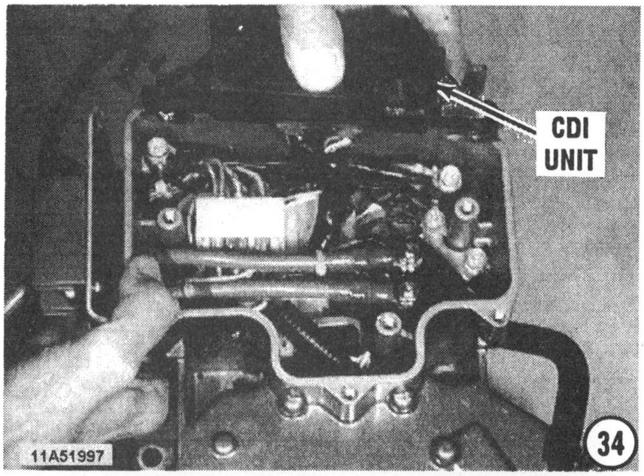

34- Install the CDI unit and secure it in place with the attaching hardware.

35- Pack the spring for the idler assembly shaft with water resistant multi-purpose lubricant. Place one washer, then the spring, followed by another washer, into the recess of the flywheel cover.

36- Coat the threads of the cover attaching bolts with Loctite #572, or equivalent. Position a new gasket around the rim of the stator plate. Move the flywheel cover into place over the

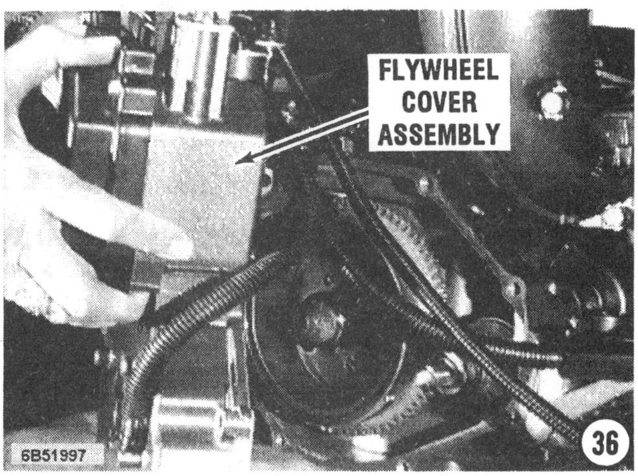

crankshaft. Install the attaching bolts. One bolt is longer than the others and will be installed in the next step.

37- Install the "hidden" bolt into the small bracket behind the cover plate assembly and just forward of the No. 1 cylinder. Tighten all cover bolts to a torque value of 5.8 ft lbs (8Nm).

Model 650 and 700 Series

38- Coat the threads of the thermo-sensor attaching bolt with Loctite #572, or equivalent. Install the thermo-sensor into the head. Secure it in place with the bracket and bolt. Tighten the bolt securely.

Model 1100 and 1200 Series

Insert the thermo-sensor into the receptacle at the aft end of the muffler pipe -- inside.

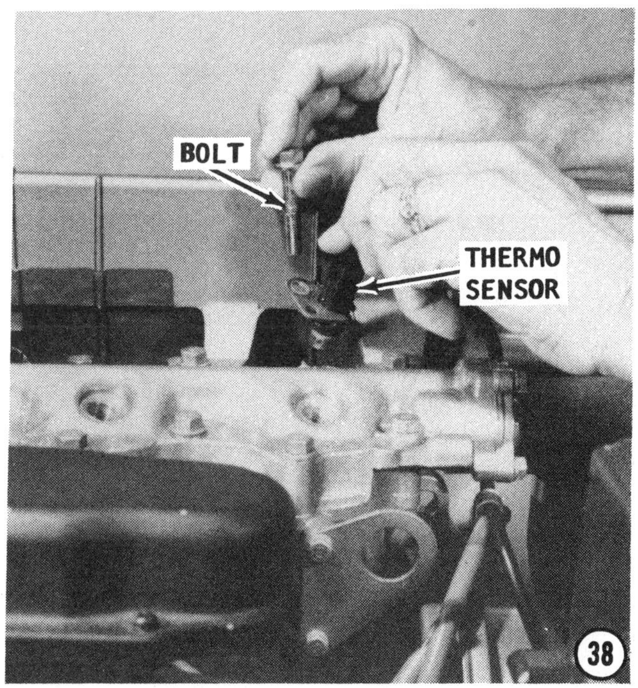

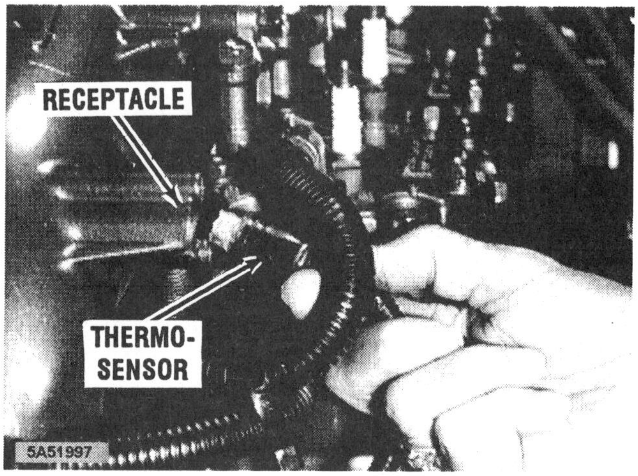

Inserting the thermo-sensor into the receptacle at the aft end of the muffler pipe -- on the inside.

Oil Pump Installation

39- Apply a coating of Loctite to the threads of the oil pump mounting bolts. Install the oil pump to the front of the flywheel cover with the "spade" in the pump indexed into the slot in the forward end of the crankshaft.

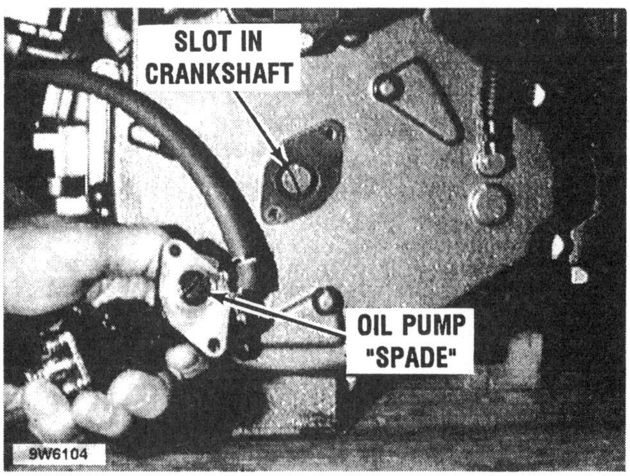

*Close view to show the oil pump "spade" which **MUST** index into the slot at the end of the crankshaft.*

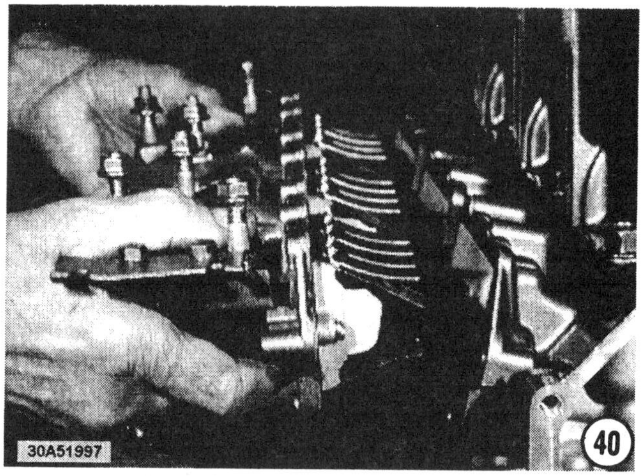

Intake Manifold

40- CAREFULLY install the intake manifold to prevent damage to the reeds. Coat the manifold bolts with Loctite. Secure the manifold in place with the sixteen bolts for a Model 1100 or 1200, or eleven bolts for a Model 650 or 700. Bring the bolts up just "snug".

41- Tighten the intake manifold bolts to a torque value of 5.8 ft lbs (8Nm), in the sequence indicated in the accompanying illustrations.

DO NOT install the carburetor/s at this time.

ENGINE INSTALLATION

First These Words

Check to be sure the rubber mount dampener is glued to the craft hull just forward of the engine mounts. Obtain special gauge block for use with a 650 Series engine. If the special tool is not

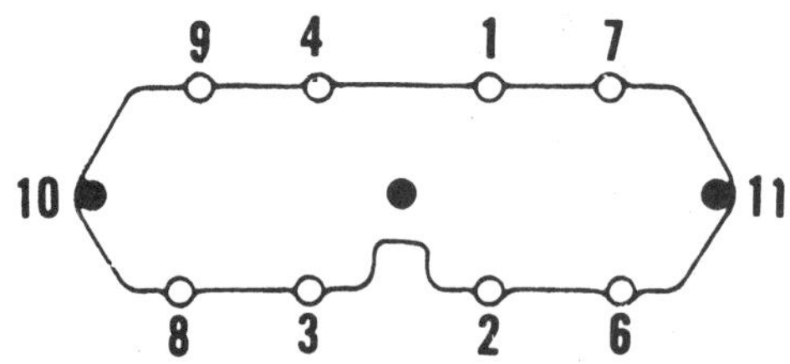

INTAKE MANIFOLD BOLT TIGHTENING SEQUENCE FOR 2-CYLINDER ENGINE

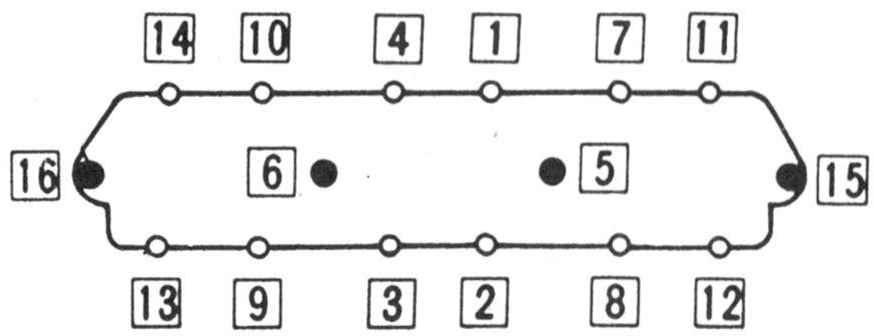

INTAKE MANIFOLD BOLT TIGHTENING SEQUENCE FOR 3-CYLINDER ENGINE

41

available, obtain a piece of hard wood with the following thickness in place of the special tool: 1-7/8" (48.0mm). Set the gauge block with the stamped mark facing **UP** on the craft hull, just forward of the engine mounts. This position would be under the flywheel cover after the engine is installed.

Slide the rubber coupler into the jet pump coupler with the flat side of the coupler facing toward the jet pump. Use an engine hoist, or enlist the aid of an assistant, and move the engine into the craft slightly forward of the mounts. Lower the engine **SLOWLY** onto the mounts and at the same time, push the engine aft to engage the engine coupler with the rubber coupler on the jet pump.

Coat the threads of the engine mount bolts with Loctite #242, or equivalent, and then temporarily thread the bolts, just a few turns, into the fixed engine mounts.

SPECIAL WORDS

During engine removal, the instructions called for the shim material under each engine mount to be identified and kept separate to assist in engine alignment. If these groups of shim material are installed back in their original locations, engine alignment should require very little adjustment.

Install the marked groups of shim material back into the original location from which they were removed between the fixed engine mounts and the engine support brackets.

Engine Alignment

Thread the motor mount bolts (6 x 25mm) into each outer threaded hole on the engine support brackets.

Obtain a short straight edge ruler. Measure the vertical clearance between the two metal couplers identified as dimension **"A"** on the accompanying illustration. This clearance must be between 0.079-0.157" (2-4mm). Measure the horizontal clearance between the two metal couplers, identified as dimension **"B"**. This clearance must be between 0.0-0.024" (0-0.6mm). Measure each clearance twice, one measurement taken at 180° to the other. Check to be sure each engine bolt makes contact with the fixed engine mount. If the amount of shim material at a particular location is too high, the engine mount bolt will not contact the fixed engine mount.

Tighten or loosen the mount bolts until the correct clearances are obtained. Fill in the

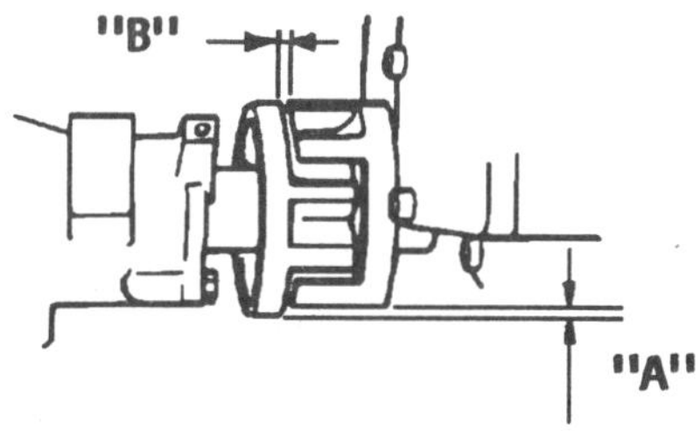

Simple line drawing to depict coupler alignment described in the text. Clearances "A" and "B" must be exact, as listed in the text, for correct crankshaft to impeller shaft alignment.

space between the engine support bracket and fixed engine mount with shim material. Tighten the four mounting bolts to a torque value of 12 ft lbs (17Nm).

Closing Tasks

Position the cover over the coupler. Coat the threads of the two attaching bolts with Loctite #242, or equivalent. Install and tighten the bolts securely.

Install the carburetor/s, associated hoses, throttle and choke cables, see Chapter 6.

Install the electrical box, see Chapter 7. Connect the starter switch and stop switch lead at their quick disconnect couplers. Connect the thermo-sensor leads at their quick disconnect fitting.

Connect the fuel sender coupler and install the oil injection components, if the engine is so

The hoses and linkage should have been identified during preparation for engine removal, before the carburetors were removed. Remember, on a triple carburetor installation, only the No. 1 and No.2 carburetors are equipped with the integral fuel pump. Actually the carburetors should have been identified as to their position.

equipped, following the illustration on Page 6-29. The oil injection system **MUST** be bled while operating the engine on a premix, as directed in Section 6-11. Connect the positive and negative cables to the battery.

Move the craft to a test tank, or to a body of water, or connect a flush attachment to the jet pump.

REMEMBER the engine will **NOT** start without the emergency tether in place behind the kill switch knob.

CAUTION

Water must circulate through the jet pump -- to and from the engine, anytime the engine is operating. Lack of circulating water will surely cause overheating and serious expensive damage to the moving engine parts and possibly to an engine seizure.

Attempt to start and operate the engine without the engine cover in place. Without the cover a check can be made for water or fuel leaks.

After the engine is operating properly, install the engine cover. Following the break-in procedures with a load on the jet pump.

Break-in Procedures

As soon as the engine starts, **CHECK** to be sure a fine stream of water is discharged from the exhaust relief opening.

DO NOT operate the engine at full throttle except for **VERY** short periods, until after 10 hours of operation as follows:

a- Operate at 1/2 throttle, approximately 2500 to 3500 rpm, for two hours.

b- Operate at any speed after two hours **BUT NOT** at sustained full throttle until another eight hours of operation.

c- Mix gasoline and oil during the break-in period -- total of 10 hours, at a ratio of 25:1.

d- While the engine is operating during the initial period, check the fuel, exhaust, and water systems for leaks.

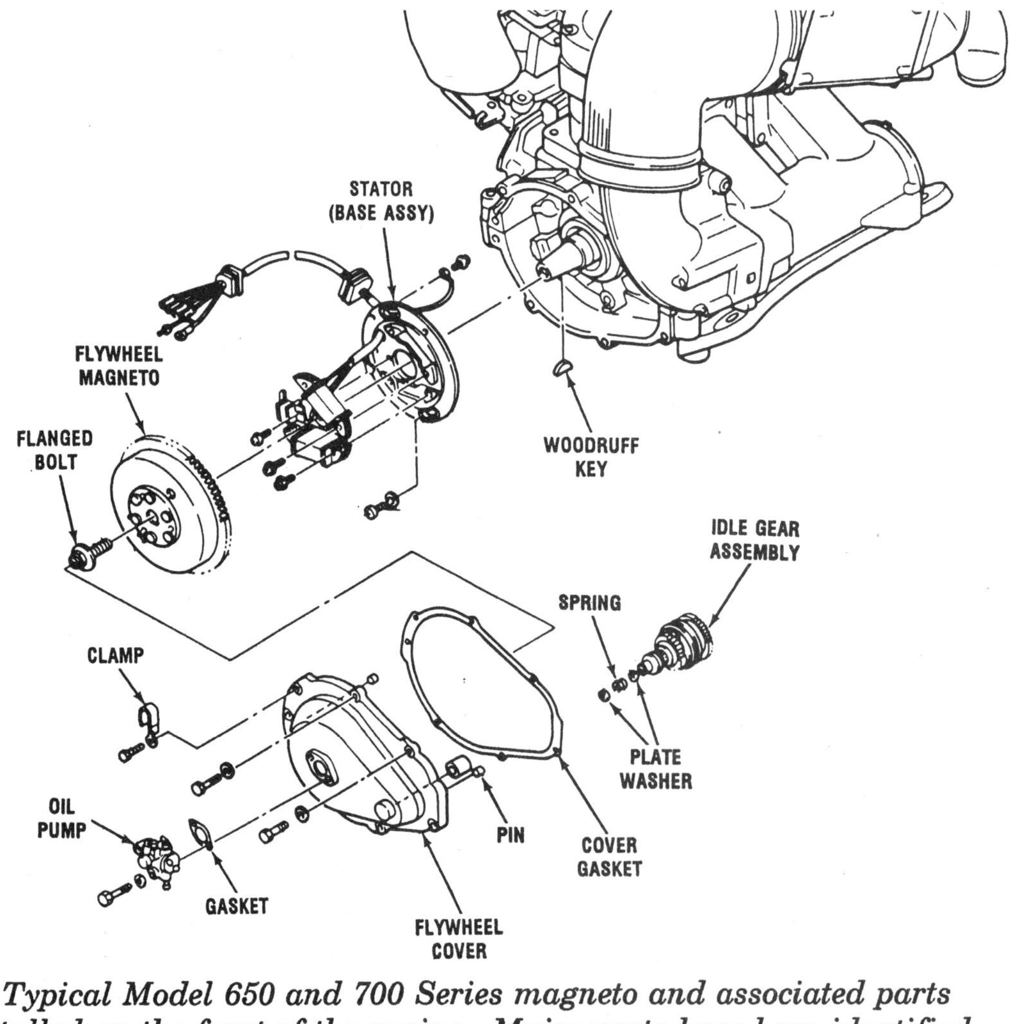

Typical Model 650 and 700 Series magneto and associated parts installed on the front of the engine. Major parts have been identified.

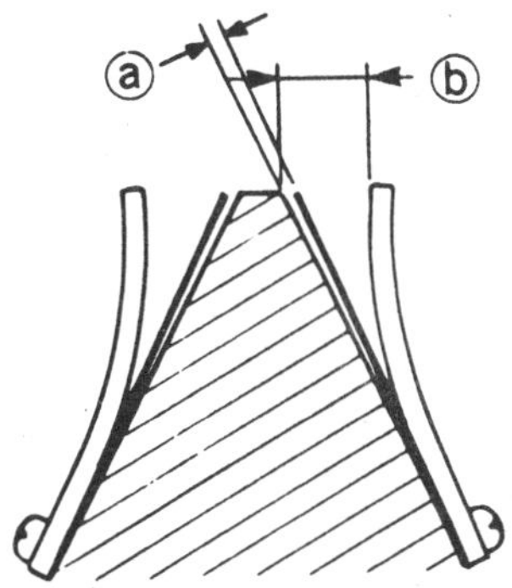

Simple line drawing to depict the limits for petal bending and petal stopper height. The "A" and "B" dimensions are identified in the table in the adjacent column.

8-4 CLEANING AND INSPECTING ALL ENGINES

The success of the overhaul work is largely dependent on how well the cleaning and inspecting tasks are completed. If some parts are not thoroughly cleaned, or if an unsatisfactory unit is allowed to be returned to service through negligent inspection, the time and expense involved in the work will not be justified with peak engine performance and long operating life. Therefore, the procedures in the following sections should be followed closely and the work performed with patience and attention to detail.

Reed Block Service

Disassemble the reed block housing by first removing the screws securing the reed stoppers and reed petals to the housing. After the screws are removed, lift the stoppers and petals from the housing.

Clean the gasket surfaces of the housing. Check the surfaces for deep grooves, cracks or any distortion which could cause leakage.

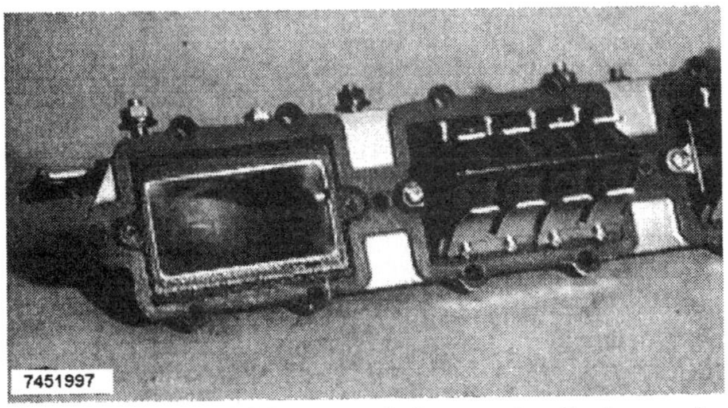

Intake manifold removed from a 3-cylinder engine showing the reed block side of the manifold. One of the reed blocks has been removed, exposing the opening through which the fuel from the carburetor passes before reaching the reed block. The opening from the carburetor is clearly visible.

Model	**Petal Bending Limit Identified as "A"**
650 series --	0.008in. (0.2mm)
700 series --	0.008in. (0.2mm)
1100/1200 series --	0.008in. (0.2mm)

Model	**Petal Stopper Height Identified as "B"**
650 series --	**WRA650R/RA Series**
	0.406 - 0.421in. 10.3 - 10.7mm
	WRB650 Series
	FN8: 0.382 - 0.398in. (9.7 - 10.1mm)
	GD0: 0.421 - 0.437in. (10.7 - 11.1mm)
700 series --	**WRB700R/RA Series**
	FN8: 0.382 - 0.398in. (9.7 - 10.1mm)
	GD0: 0.421 - 0.437in.
	WVT700, WB760U Series
	0.35 +- 0.01in. (9.0 +- 0.2mm)
	All Others
	0.421 - 0.437in. (10.7 - 11.1mm)
1100/1200 series --	0.35 +- 0.01 in (9.0 +- 0.35mm)

Replace the reed block housing if it is damaged. The reed petals should fit flush against their seats, and not be pre-loaded against their seats. The limits listed above in this column are recommended by the manufacturer.

If the reed petal is distorted beyond its bending limit, rarely, if ever can the petal be successfully straightened. **THEREFORE**, it must be replaced.

The valve stopper clearance is the distance between the bottom edge of the stopper and the top of the reed petal. This measurement **MUST** be within the limits listed in the above table.

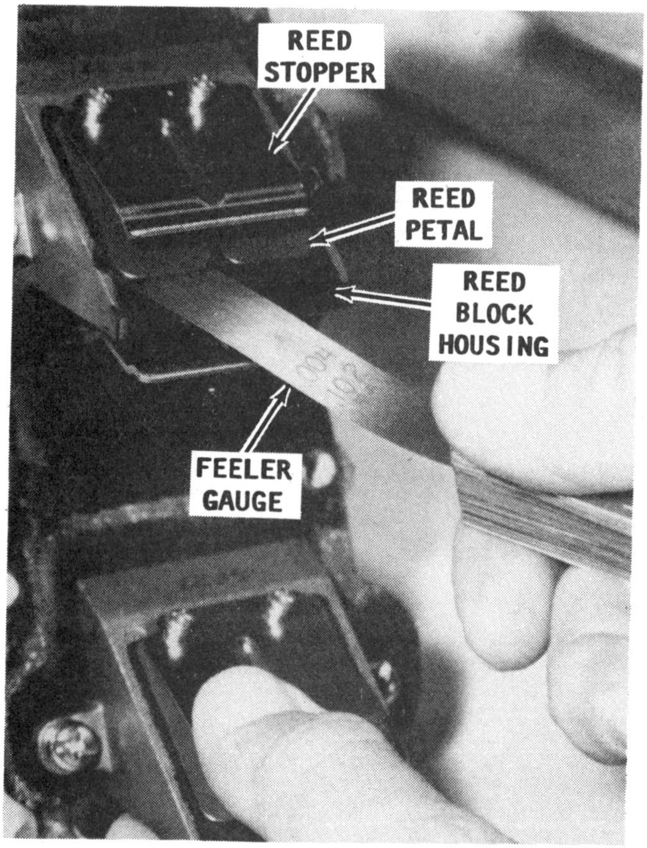

Example of measuring the reed petal clearance with a feeler gauge, as explained in the text.

The valve stopper can sometimes be successfully bent to achieve the required clearance, if not, it **MUST** be replaced.

Do not remove the reed valves unless they, or the stoppers, are to be replaced. The reeds **MUST** be replaced in sets.

Apply Loctite to the threads of the reed retaining screws. Tighten each screw gradually, starting in the center and working outward across the reed block. Tighten the screws to a torque value of 3.5 ft lbs (5Nm).

Exhaust Cover
All Models

The exhaust covers are one of the most neglected items on any marine engine. Seldom are they checked and serviced. Many times an engine may be overhauled and returned to service without the exhaust covers ever having been removed.

One reason the exhaust covers are not removed is because the attaching bolts usually become corroded in place. This means they are very difficult to remove, but the work should be done. Heat applied to the bolt head and around the exhaust cover will help in removal. However, some bolts may still be broken. If the bolt is broken it must be drilled out and the hole tapped with new threads.

The exhaust covers are installed over the exhaust ports to allow the exhaust to leave the engine and be transferred to the muffler. If the cover was the only item over the exhaust ports, they would be severely burned if they came in contact with the cover.

Therefore, an inner plate is installed to help dissipate the exhaust heat. Two gaskets are installed -- one on either side of the inner plate. Water is channeled to circulate between the exhaust cover and the inner plate. This circulating water cools the exhaust cover and prevents it from becoming a hazard.

A thorough cleaning of the upper plate behind the exhaust covers should be performed during a major engine overhaul. If the integrity of the exhaust cover assembly is in doubt, replace the inner plate.

Bleed System

Check the condition of both rubber bleed hoses. Replace a hose if it shows signs of deterioration or leakage. Check the operation of the two check valves. The air/fuel mixture should be able to pass through the valve in only **ONE** direction. The check valves and hoses connect the upper main bearing to the lower main bearing.

Defective check valves cannot be serviced. If defective, they **MUST** be replaced.

Crankshaft Service
All Models

Clean the crankshaft with solvent and wipe the journals dry with a lint free cloth. Inspect the main journals and connecting rod journals for cracks, scratches, grooves, or scores. Inspect the crankshaft oil seal surface for nicks, sharp edges or burrs which might damage the oil seal during installation or might cause premature seal wear. **ALWAYS** handle the crankshaft carefully to avoid damaging the highly finished journal surfaces. Blow out all oil passages with compressed air. The oil passageway leads from the rod to the main bearing journal. **TAKE CARE** not to blow dirt into the main bearing journal bore.

Inspect the threads at both ends for signs of abnormal wear. Check the crankshaft for runout by supporting it on two "V" blocks at the main bearing surfaces.

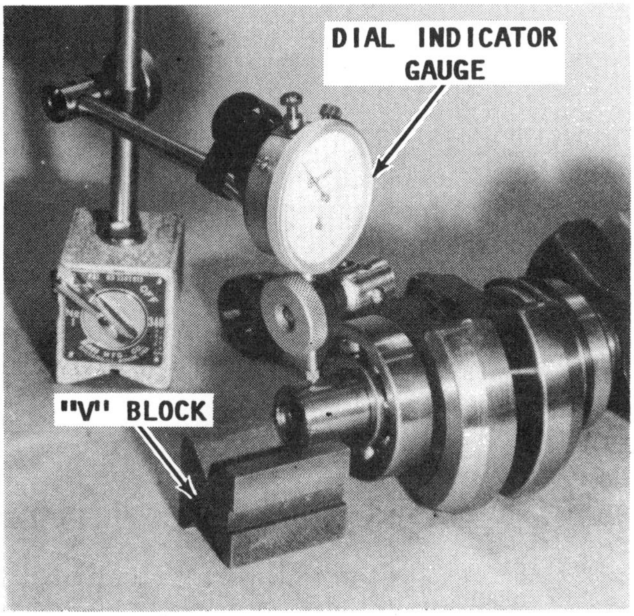

Typical setup of a crankshaft with "V" blocks and dial indicator to measure main bearing journals on an assembled two-stroke crankshaft. The bearings and connecting rod will not affect the reading.

Install a dial indicator gauge above the main bearing journals. Rotate the crankshaft and measure the runout (or the out-of-round) and the taper at both ends (and in the center journal on all two-cylinder models).

The crankshaft runout and taper limit for the Yamaha 650 series is 0.0012" (0.03mm). The crankshaft runout limit for the 700 and 1100 series is 0.002" (0.05mm).

If "V" blocks or a dial indicator are not available, a micrometer may be used to measure the diameter of the journal. Make a second measurement at right angles to the first. Check

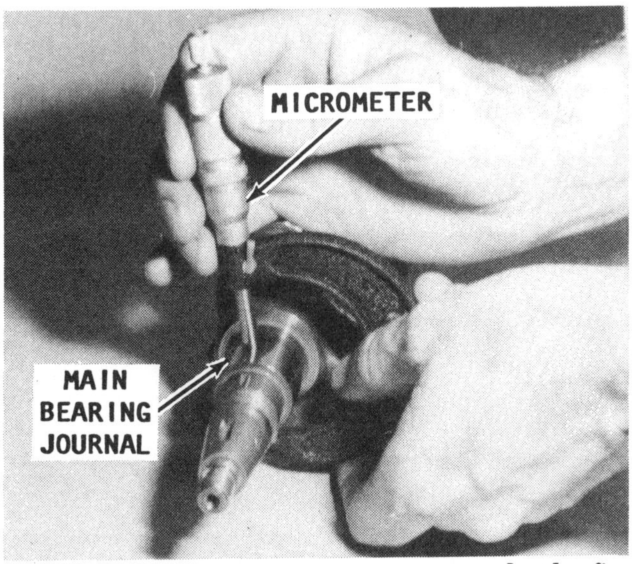

Method of using a micrometer to take the first measurement of a crankshaft main journal for out-of-round and taper.

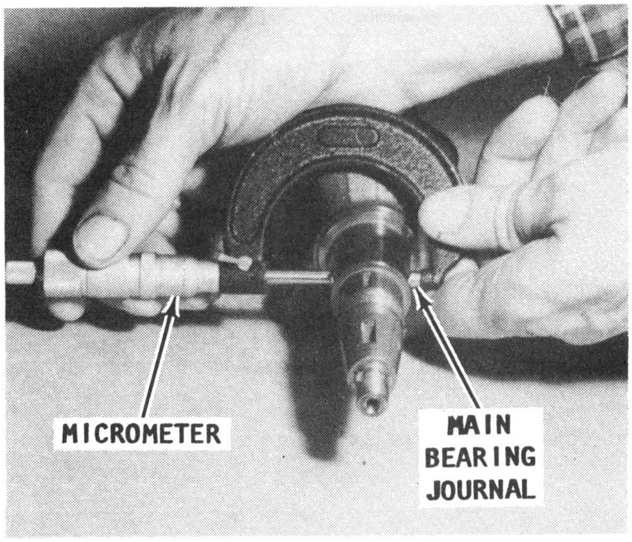

Taking a second measurement on a crankshaft main bearing journal 90° to the first measurement.

the difference between the first and second measurement for out-of-round condition. If the journals are tapered, ridged, or out-of-round by more than the specification allows, the journals should be reground, or the crankshaft replaced.

Any out-of-round or taper shortens bearing life. Good shop practice dictates new main bearings be installed with a new or reground crankshaft.

Normally the connecting rods would **ONLY** be pressed from the crankshaft if either the crankshaft and/or the connecting rods were to be replaced. Therefore, the connecting rod axial "play" is checked at the piston end to determine the amount of wear at the crankshaft end of the connecting rod. Checking the "play" is described in the following paragraph.

Setup the crankshaft in the "V" blocks. Setup a dial indicator to touch the flat surface of the piston end of the rod. Now, hold the crankshaft steady in the "V" blocks and at the same time, rock the piston end of the rod along the same axis as the crankshaft. If the dial indicator needle moves through more than 0.08" (2mm) for all engines covered in this manual, the "play" is considered excessive. The rod must be pressed from the crankshaft, the journal checked and a determination made as to whether the crankshaft and/or the rod must be replaced. A new rod may be purchased, **BUT** it must be pressed onto the crankshaft throw with a hydraulic press.

To check the connecting rod side clearance at the crankshaft, first insert a feeler gauge between the connecting rod and the counterweight of the crankshaft. Acceptable clearances are listed in the table on the next page.

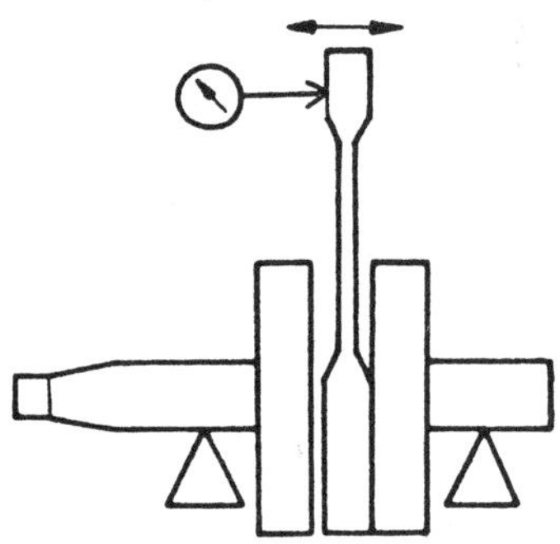

Crankshaft and piston rod setup to check for axial rod "play", as explained in the text.

Model	Connecting Rod Big End Side Clearance
650 series --	0.012" - 0.028" (0.3 - 0.7mm)
700 series --	0.010" - 0.030" (0.25 - 0.75mm)
1100/1200 series --	0.010" - 0.030" (0.25 - 0.75mm)

If the measurement is not within the limits listed, measure the distance from the outside edge of one counterweight for the throw of the connecting rod involved. This measurement will give an indication if the counterweight is "walking" on the crankpin or if the clearance is due to worn parts. The connecting rod would wear before the edge of the counterweight because the rod is manufactured from a much softer material. The distance measured -- from outside edge to outside edge -- should be as follows:

Model	Crank Width
650 series --	2.439 - 2.441" (61.95 - 62.00mm)
700 series --	2.439 - 2.441" (61.95 - 62.00mm)
1100/1200 series --	2.439 - 2.441" (61.95 - 62.00mm)

Inspect the crankshaft oil seal surfaces to be sure they are not grooved, pitted, or scratched. Replace the crankshaft if it is severely damaged or worn. Check all watermarks, chatter marks, uneven wear or overheating. Clean the crankshaft surfaces with 320-grit carborundum cloth. **NEVER** spin-dry a crankshaft ball bearing with compressed air.

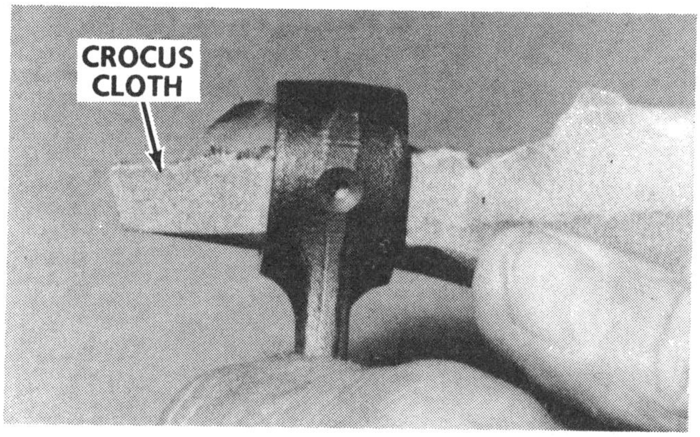

Cleaning the piston end of a connecting rod with crocus cloth.

Clean the crankshaft and crankshaft ball bearing with solvent. Dry the parts, but not the ball bearing, with compressed air. Check the crankshaft surfaces a second time. Replace the crankshaft if the surfaces cannot be cleaned properly for satisfactory service. If the crankshaft is to be installed for service, lubricate the surfaces with light oil. **DO NOT** lubricate the crankshaft ball bearing at this time.

After the crankshaft has been cleaned, grasp the outer race of the crankshaft ball bearing installed on the lower end of the crankshaft, and attempt to work the race back-and-forth. There should not be excessive "play". A very slight amount of side "play" is acceptable because there is only about 0.001" (0.255mm) clearance in the bearing.

Lubricate the ball bearing with light oil. Check the action of the bearing by rotating the outer bearing race. The bearing should have a smooth action and no rust stains. If the ball bearing sounds or feels rough or catches, the bearing should be removed and discarded.

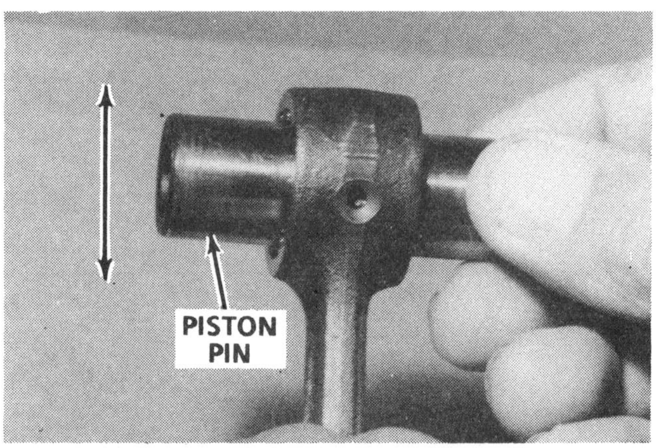

Check the piston end of a connecting rod for vertical free "play" using a piston pin.

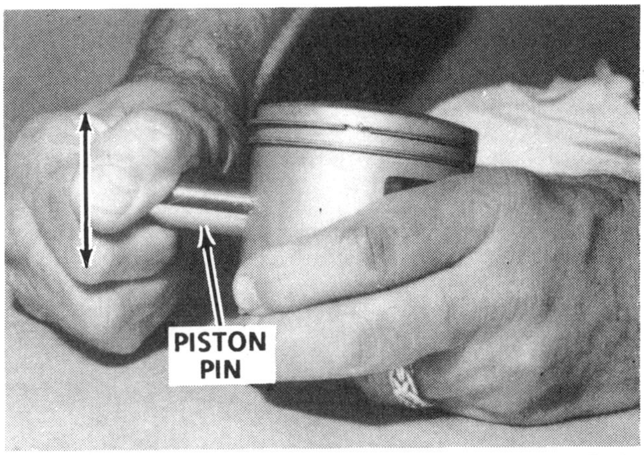

Check free "play" between the piston pin and the piston boss. There should be NO "play".

Connecting Rod Service

Inspect the connecting rod bearings for rust or signs of bearing failure. **NEVER** intermix new and used bearings. If even one bearing in a set needs to be replaced, all bearings at that location **MUST** be replaced.

Clean the connecting rod **ONLY** enough to remove marks. **DO NOT** continue, once the marks have disappeared.

Assemble the piston end of the connecting rod with loose needle bearings, caged needle bearings, or no needle bearing, depending on the model being serviced. Insert the piston pin and check for vertical "play". The piston pin should have **NO** noticeable vertical "play".

If the pin is loose or there is vertical "play" check for and replace the worn part/s.

Inspect the piston pin and matching rod end for signs of heat discoloration. Overheating is identified as a bluish bearing surface color

It is believed, this crown seized with the cylinder wall when the unit was operated at high rpm and the timing was not adjusted properly. At the same instant, the rod apparently pulled the lower part of the piston downward, severing it from the crown.

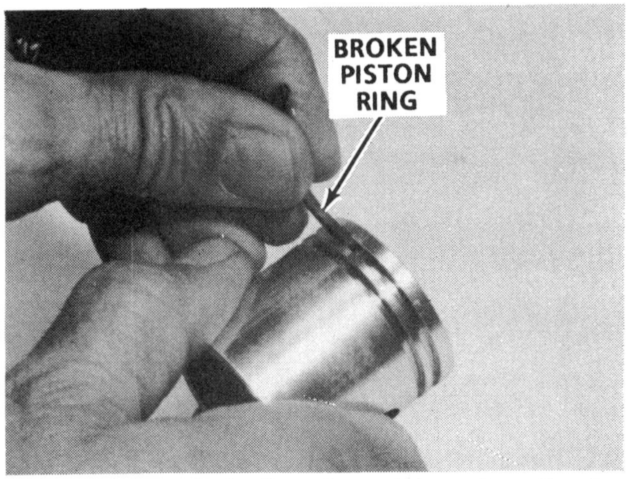

*Using part of a broken piston ring to clean the ring groove. Exercise **CARE** not to disturb the locating pin in each groove.*

and is caused by inadequate lubrication or by operating the engine at excessive high rpm.

Piston Service

Inspect each piston for evidence of scoring, cracks, metal damage, cracked piston pin boss, or worn pin boss. Be especially critical during inspection if the craft and engine has been submerged. If the piston pin is bent, the piston and pin **MUST** be replaced as a set for two reasons. First, a bent pin will damage the boss when it is removed. Secondly, a piston pin is not sold as a separate item.

The pitted damage to this piston crown was probably caused by a broken piston ring working its way into the combustion chamber. The little "hills" then became "hot" spots on the crown, contributing to "dieseling" after the engine was shut down.

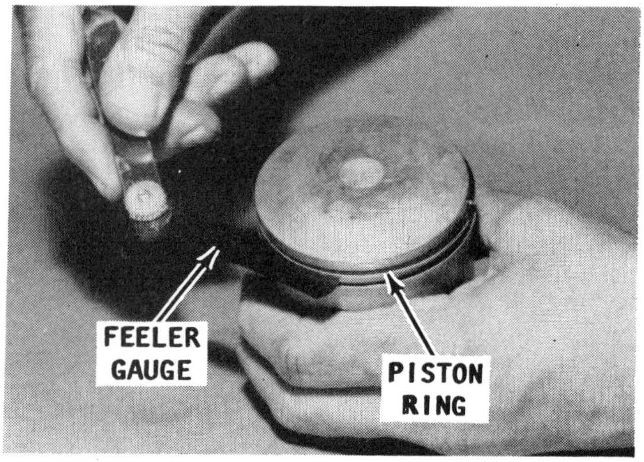

Method of measuring the side piston ring clearance. Insert the feeler gauge between the underside of the ring and the piston groove, especially for a keystone ring.

Check the piston ring grooves for wear, burns, distortion, or loose locating pins. During an overhaul, the rings should be replaced to ensure lasting repair and proper powerhead performance after the work is completed. Clean the piston crown, ring grooves and the piston skirt. Clean carbon deposits from the ring grooves using the recessed end of a broken piston ring.

NEVER use a rectangular ring to clean the groove for a tapered ring, or use a tapered ring to clean the groove for a rectangular ring.

NEVER use an automobile-type ring groove cleaner, because such a tool may loosen the piston ring locating pins.

Stock piston diameters are as follows:

Model	Stock Piston Diameter
650 series --	3.030" (77.0mm)
700 series --	3.186 - 3.187" (80.925 - 80.950mm)
1100/1200 series --	3.184 - 3.185" (80.885 - 80.890mm)

Model	Piston To Cylinder Wall Clearance
650 series --	0.0031 - 0.0033" (0.080 - 0.085mm)
700 series --	0.0031 - 0.0033" (0.080 - 0.085mm)
1100/1200 series --	0.0043 - 0.0045" (0.110 - 0.115mm)

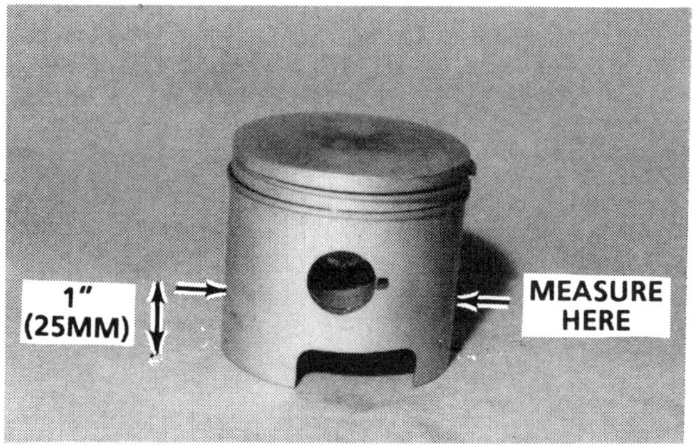

Measure the piston diameter approximately 1" above the bottom of the "skirt", as shown.

Clean carbon deposits from the top of the piston using a soft wire brush, carbon removal solution or by sand blasting. If a wire brush is used, **TAKE CARE** not to burr or round machined edges. Clean the piston skirt with crocus cloth.

Install the piston pin through the first boss only. Check for vertical free "play". There should be **NO** vertical free "play". The presence of "play" is an indication the piston boss is worn. The piston is manufactured from a softer material than the piston pins. Therefore, the piston boss will wear more quickly than the pin.

Excessive piston skirt wear **CANNOT** be visually detected. Therefore, good shop practice dictates, the piston skirt diameter be measured with a micrometer.

Piston skirt diameter should be measured at right angles to the piston pin axis at a point 1" (25mm) above the bottom edge of the piston.

The rings on this piston became stuck due to lack of adequate lubrication, incorrect timing, or overheating.

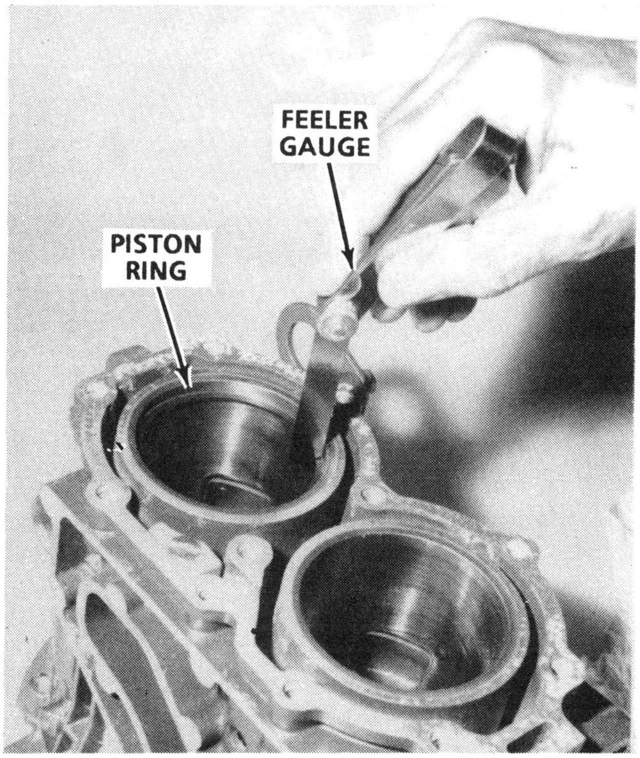

Only accurate method of measuring piston ring end gap is with the ring in the cylinder and using a feeler gauge, as described in the text.

Ring End Gap

Before the piston rings are installed onto the piston, the ring end gap clearance for each ring must be determined. The purpose of the piston rings is to prevent the blowby of gases in the combustion chamber. This cannot be achieved unless the correct oil film thickness is left on the cylinder wall.

The rings on this piston were broken, possibly during installation, and then caused extensive damage to the piston crown.

Locating pins prevent the rings from rotating and catching on a port in the cylinder wall.

This thin coating of oil acts as a seal between the cylinder wall and the face of the piston ring.

Model	End Gap
650 series --	0.008 - 0.016" (0.2 - 0.4mm)
700 series --	0.008 - 0.016" (0.2 - 0.4mm)
1100/1200 series --	0.008 - 0.016" (0.2 - 0.4mm)

An excessive end gap will allow blowby and the cylinder will lose compression. An inadequate end gap will scrape too much oil from the cylinder wall and limit lubrication. Lack of adequate lubrication will cause excessive heat and wear.

IDEALLY the ring end gap measurement should be taken **AFTER** the cylinder bore has been measured for wear and taper **AND** after any corrective work, such as boring or honing, has been completed.

IF the ring end gap is measured with a taper to the cylinder wall, the diameter at the lower limit of ring travel will be smaller than the diameter at the top of the cylinder.

IF the ring is fitted to the upper part of a cylinder with a taper, the ring end gap will not be great enough at the lower limit of ring travel. Such a condition could result in a broken ring and/or damage to the piston and/or damage to the cylinder head.

IF the cylinder is to be only honed, not bored, **OR** if only cleaned, not honed, the ring end gap should be measured at the lower limit of ring travel.

The ring should be inserted into the cylinder just above the ports to perform this measurement, using the piston crown. Be sure the ring is parallel to the surface of the block, then measure the ring end gap with a feeler gauge.

If the end gap is greater than the amount listed, replace the entire ring set.

If the end gap is less than the amount listed, replace the entire ring set.

If the end gap is less than the amount listed, carefully file the ends of the ring -- just a little at a time -- until the correct end gap is obtained.

Inspect the piston ring locating pins to be sure they are tight. There is one locating pin in each ring groove. If the locating pins are loose, the piston **MUST** be replaced.

Piston Ring Side Clearance

After the rings are installed on the piston, the clearance in the grooves needs to be checked with a feeler gauge. Check the clearance between the ring and the upper "land" and compare your measurement with the specifications listed in the following table. Ring wear forms a step at the inner portion of the upper "land". If the piston grooves have worn to the extent to cause high steps on the upper "land", the step will interfere with the operation of new rings and the ring clearance will be too much. Therefore, if steps exist in any of the upper "lands", the piston should be replaced.

On a plain ring this clearance may be measured either above or below the ring. On a Keystone ring -- one with a taper at the top -- the clearance **MUST** be measured below the ring.

Model	Ring Side Clearance
650 series --	0.0012 - 0.0020" (0.03 - 0.05mm)
700 series --	0.0010 - 0.0020" (0.02 - 0.06mm)
1100/1200 series --	0.0010 - 0.0020"

Cylinder Block Service

Inspect the cylinder block and cylinder bores for cracks or other damage. Remove carbon with a fine wire brush on a shaft attached to an electric drill or use a carbon remover solution.

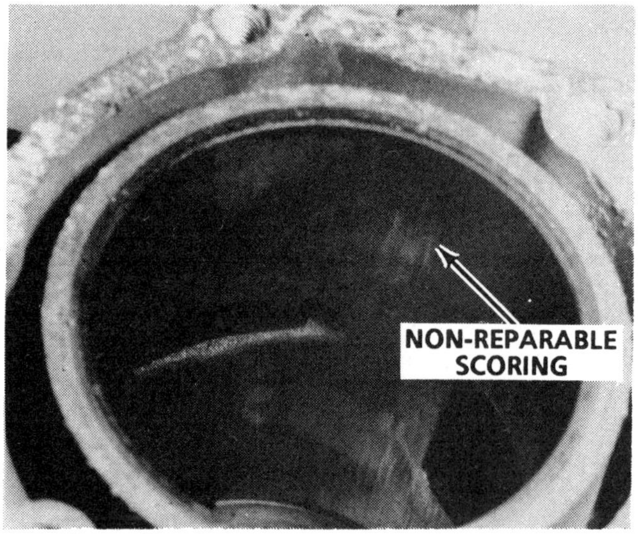

The walls of this cylinder were damaged beyond repair when a piston ring broke and worked its way into the combustion chamber.

STOP: If the cylinder block is to be submerged in a carbon removal solution, the crankcase bleed system **MUST** be removed from the block to prevent damage to hoses and check valves.

Use an inside micrometer or telescopic gauge and micrometer to check the cylinders

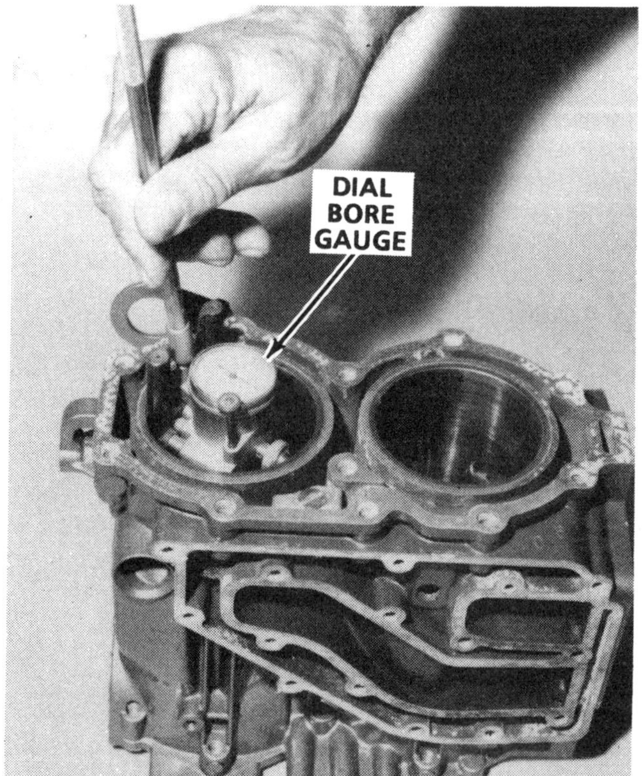

Effective method of checking the cylinder for taper using an inside micrometer. One measurement should be taken near the top and another near the bottom of the cylinder. The difference between the two measurements is the amount of taper.

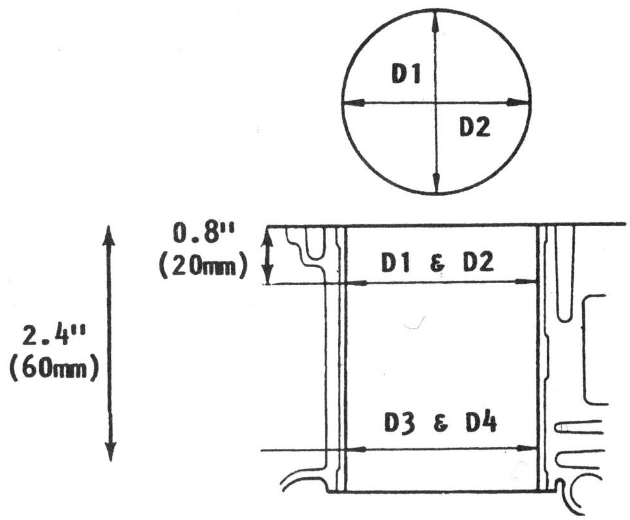

Top view diagram and cross-section of a typical cylinder to indicate where measurements are to be taken for wear limit, taper, and out-of-round limits.

for wear. Check the bore for out-of-round and/or oversize bore. If the bore is tapered, out-of-round or worn more than the wear limit specified by the manufacturer, the cylinders should be re-bored -- provided oversize pistons and rings are available.

Check with the dealer **PRIOR** to re-boring. If oversize pistons and matching rings are not available, the block **MUST** be replaced.

GOOD WORDS

Oversize piston weight is approximately the same as a standard size piston. Therefore, it is **NOT** necessary to re-bore all cylinders in a block just because one cylinder requires re-boring.

Cylinder sleeves are an integral part of the die cast cylinder block and **CANNOT** be replaced. In other words, the cylinder cannot be "re-sleeved".

Four inside cylinder bore measurements must be taken for each cylinder to determine an out-of-round condition, the maximum taper, and the maximum bore diameter.

Out-of-Round

Measure the cylinder diameter at D1 and D2. The manufacturer requires the difference between the two measurements should be less than 0.002" (0.050mm) for **ALL** models.

Maximum Taper

Measure the cylinder diameter at D1, D2, D3, and D4. Take the largest of the D1 or D2 measurements and subtract the smallest measurement at D3 or D4. The answer to the subtraction -- the cylinder taper -- should be less than 0.003" (0.08mm) for **ALL** models.

Bore Wear Limit

The maximum cylinder diameter D1, D2, D3 and D4 must not exceed the bore wear limits indicated in the following table **BEFORE** the bore is re-bored for the **FIRST** time. These limits are only imposed on original parts because the sealing ability of the rings would be

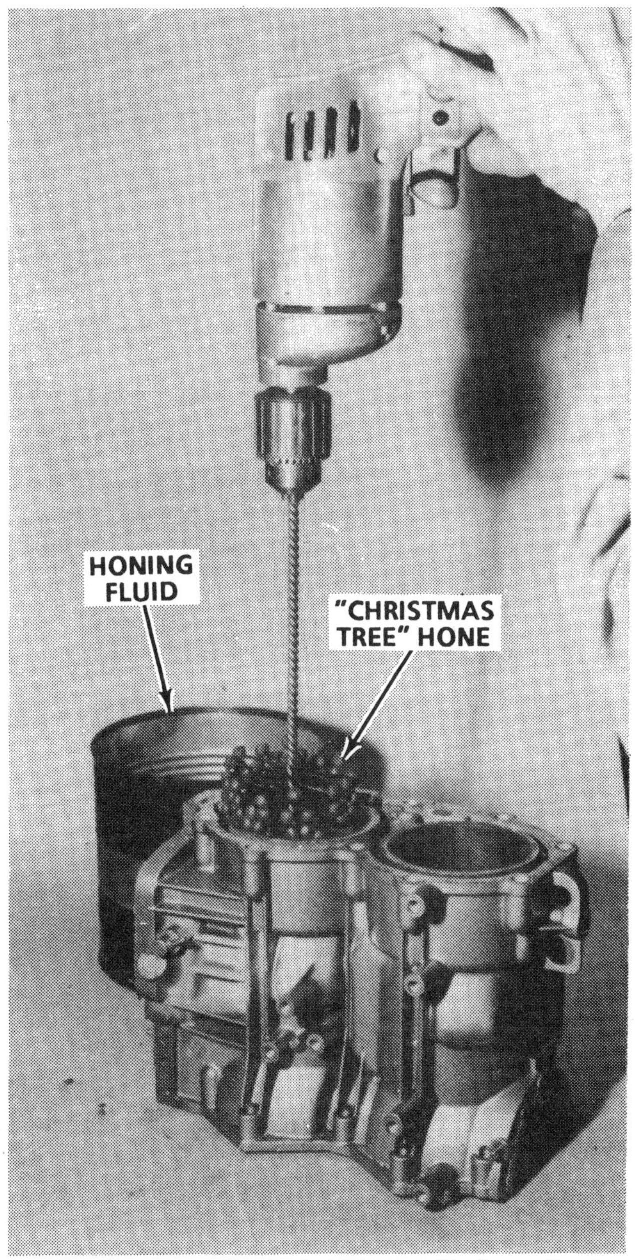

*Excellent example of refinishing a cylinder wall using an electric drill and \"Christmas Tree" hone. **ALWAYS** keep the tool moving in long even strokes the entire cylinder depth. Use a continuous **LIBERAL** amount of honing fluid.*

*All traces of gasket material **MUST** be removed to ensure a good seal with a new gasket. If checking for warpage, even the smallest trace of foreign material would give a false reading.*

lost, resulting in power loss, increased engine noise, unnecessary vibration, piston slap, and excessive oil consumption.

The limits indicated are usually 0.003 to 0.005" (0.83 to 0.127mm) above the standard bore. Therefore, if the bore is resized, it may sustain another 0.003 to 0.005" (0.83 to 0.127m) wear before a second re-boring is required -- provided the oversize pistons and matching rings are available.

Model	Std. Cyl. Bore	Wear Lmt.
650 series --	3.03"	3.034"
	(77.0mm)	(77.1mm)
700 series --	3.189 - 3.190"	3.193"
	(81.00 - 81.02mm)	(81.10mm)
1100/ series -	3.189 - 3.190"	3.193"
1200	(81.00 - 81.02mm)	(81.10mm)

Piston Clearance

Piston clearance is the difference between a maximum piston diameter and a minimum cylinder bore diameter. If this clearance is excessive, the engine will develop the same symptoms as for excessive cylinder bore wear -- loss of power, increased engine noise, unnecessary vibration, and excessive oil consumption.

Maximum piston diameter was described earlier in this section. Minimum cylinder bore diameter is usually determined by measurement D3 or D4 also described earlier in this section, on the previous page.

If the piston clearance exceeds the limits outlined in the following table, either the piston or the cylinder block **MUST** be replaced.

Calculate the piston clearance by subtracting the maximum piston skirt diameter from the maximum cylinder bore measurement and compare the results for the model being serviced.

Model	Piston Clearance
650 series --	0.0031 - 0.0033"
	(0.08 - 0.085mm)
700 series --	0.0031 - 0.0033"
	(0.08 - 0.085mm)
1100/1200 series --	0.0043 - 0.0045"
	(0.110 - 0.115mm)

HONING CYLINDER WALLS

Hone the cylinder walls lightly to seat the new piston rings, as outlined in this section. If the cylinders have been scored, but are not out-of-round or the bore is rough, clean the surface

This cylinder head was removed from the same engine as the pitted piston shown on Page 8-33. In order to return this head to a serviceable condition, the combustion chamber surface must be refinished to a smooth surface using a stone. If left in its present condition, the sharp corners of the gouges will become "hot" spots resulting in pre-ignition and possible "dieseling" after the engine is shut down.

of the cylinder with a cylinder hone as described in the following procedures.

SPECIAL WORDS

If overheating has occurred, check and resurface the spark plug end of the cylinder block, if necessary. This can be accomplished with 240-grit sandpaper and a small flat block of wood.

To ensure satisfactory engine performance and long life following the overhaul work, the honing work should be performed with patience, skill, and in the following sequence:

a- Follow the hone manufacturer's recommendations for use of the hone and for cleaning and lubricating during the honing operation. A "Christmas tree" hone may also be used.

b- Pump a continuous flow of honing oil into the work area. If pumping is not practical, use an oil can. Apply the oil generously and frequently on both the stones and work surface.

c- Begin the stroking at the smallest diameter. Maintain a firm stone pressure against the cylinder wall to assure fast stock removal and accurate results.

d- Expand the stones as necessary to compensate for stock removal and stone wear. The best cross-hatch pattern is obtained using a stroke rate of 30 complete cycles per minute. Again, use the honing oil generously.

e- Hone the cylinder walls **ONLY** enough to de-glaze the walls.

f- After the honing operation has been completed, clean the cylinder bores with hot water and detergent. Scrub the walls with a stiff bristle brush and rinse thoroughly with hot water. The cylinders **MUST** be thoroughly cleaned to prevent any abrasive material from remaining in the cylinder bore. Such material will cause rapid wear of new piston rings, the cylinder bore, and the bearings.

g- After cleaning, swab the bores several times with engine oil and a clean cloth, and then wipe them dry with a clean cloth. **NEVER** use kerosene or gasoline to clean the cylinders.

h- Clean the remainder of the cylinder block to remove any excess material spread during the honing operation.

Block and Cylinder Head Warpage

First, check to be sure all old gasket material has been removed from the contact surfaces of the block and the cylinder head. Clean both surfaces down to shiny metal, to ensure a true measurement.

Next, place a straight edge across the gasket surface. Check under the straight edge with a 0.004" (0.m) feeler gauge. Move the straight edge to at least eight different locations. If the feeler gauge can pass under the straight edge --

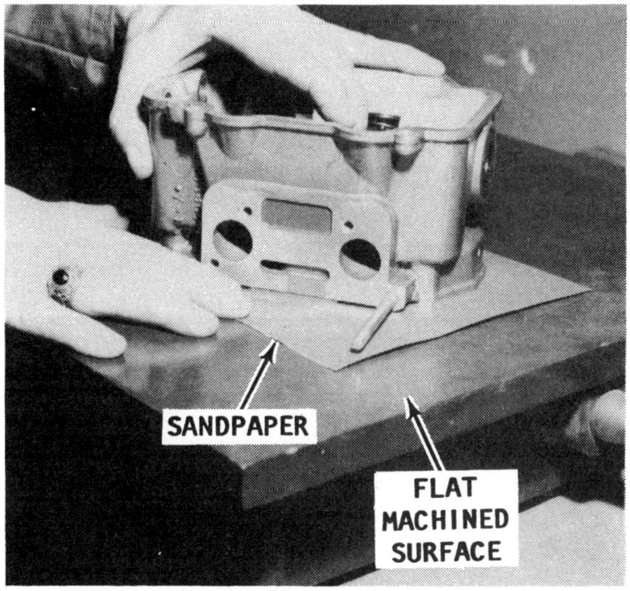

*A machined surface and wet sandpaper may be used to resurface a cylinder head,. as explained in the text. A piece of glass or mirror may also be used, but do **NOT** attempt this task on a workbench.*

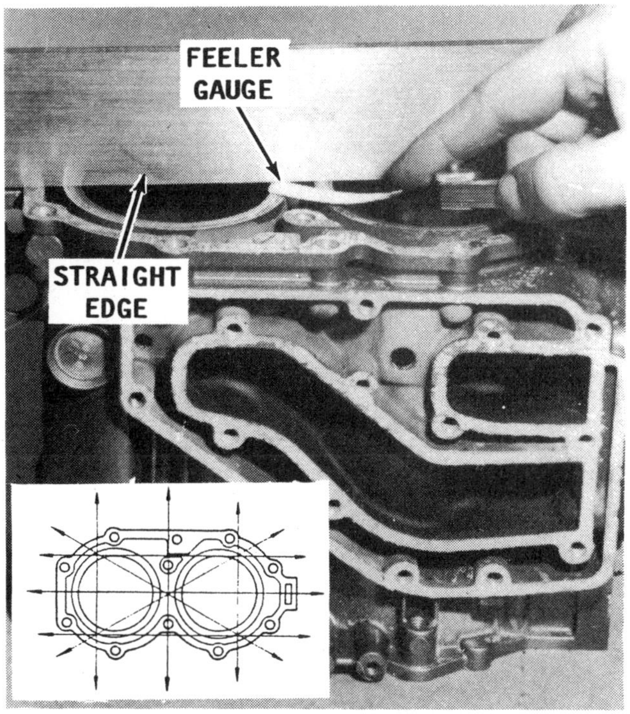

A straight edge and feeler gauge must be used to check engine-to-head mating surface on any block for warpage. Move the straight edge to at least eight different positions, as indicated in the superimposed drawing.

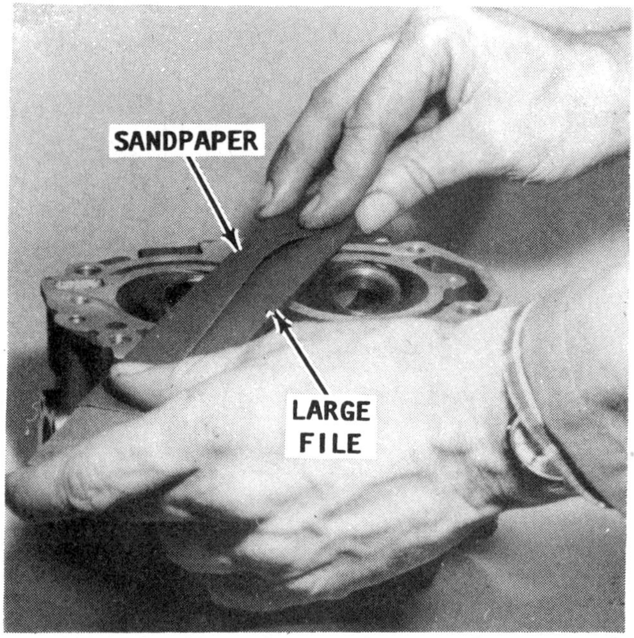

*A **LARGE** file and piece of wet sandpaper may be used to resurface a head or cylinder block when a suitable flat surface is not available.*

anywhere contact with the other is made -- the surface will have to be resurfaced.

The block or the cylinder head may be resurfaced by placing the warped surface on

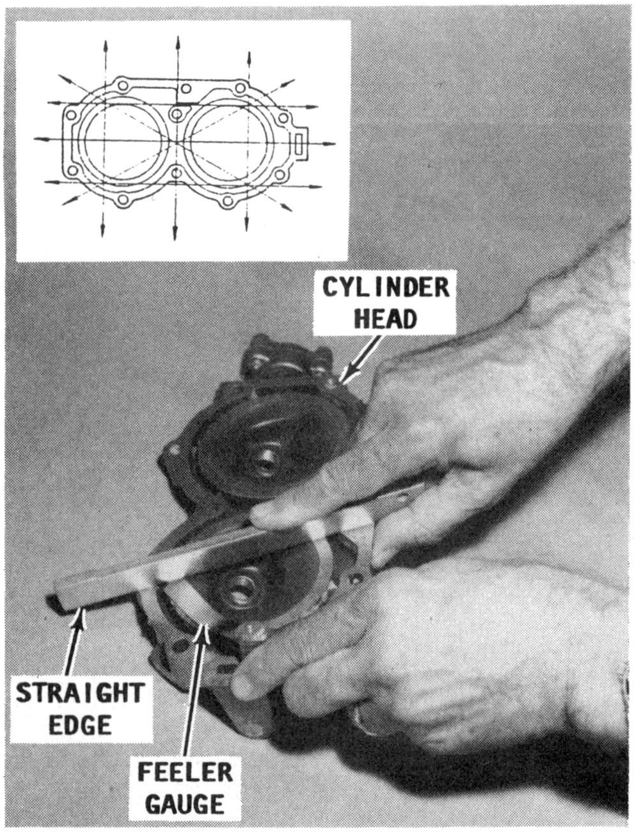

Using a straight edge and feeler gauge to check a cylinder head surface for warpage. Move the straight edge to at least eight different positions, as indicated in the superimposed drawing.

400-600 grit **WET** sandpaper, with the sandpaper resting on a **FLAT MACHINED** surface. If a machined surface is not available, a large piece of glass or mirror may be used. **DO NOT** attempt to use a workbench or similar surface for this task. A workbench is never perfectly flat and the block or cylinder head will pickup the imperfections of the surface and the warpage will be made worse.

Sand -- work -- the warped surface on the wet sandpaper using large figure "8" motions. Rotate the block, or head, through 180 degrees (turn it end-for-end) and spend an equal amount of time in each position to avoid removing too much material from one side.

If a suitable flat surface is not available, the next best method is to wrap 400-600 grit wet sandpaper around a **LARGE** file. Draw the file as evenly as possible in one sweep across the surface. Do not file in one place. Draw the file in many, many directions to get as even a finish as possible.

As the work moves along, check the progress with the straight edge and feeler gauge. Once the 0.004" (0.m) feeler gauge will no longer slide under the straight edge, consider the work completed.

If the warpage cannot be reduced using one of the described methods, the block or cylinder head should be replaced.

ONE LAST CHANCE

If the warpage cannot be reduced and it is not possible to obtain new items -- and the warped part must be assembled for further use -- there is a strong possibility of a water leak at the head gasket. In an effort to prevent a water leak, follow the instructions outlined in Assembly for **650, 700, 1100 and 1200 series** engines on Page 8-18.

8-6 SEALANTS, ADHESIVES, LUBRICANTS, AND FUEL STRAINERS

Sealants and Adhesives

Four sealants are recommended and they are **NOT** interchangeable. Each is designed to perform under a different set of conditions.

VHT[r] (very high temperature) Quick Gasket compound is a silicone rubber based adhesive recommended for use where rubber gaskets are required next to a metal surface at high temperature. This sealant is used on the exhaust manifold cover gaskets. This substance has a milky white color.

9 ELECTRICAL

9-1 INTRODUCTION

The battery, charging system, and the cranking system are considered subsystems of the electrical system. Each of these units will be covered in detail in this chapter beginning with the battery.

9-2 BATTERIES

The battery is one of the most important parts of the electrical system. Because of its job and the consequences, (failure to perform when needed), the best advice is to purchase a well-known brand, with an extended warranty period, from a reputable dealer.

Personal Watercraft Batteries

The battery developed for use in a personal watercraft is the same kind used for many years on motorcycles. Personal watercraft batteries are required to perform under the most rigorous conditions.

Personal watercraft batteries have a much heavier exterior case than the usual automobile battery to withstand the violent pounding and shocks imposed on it as the craft moves through rough water. The battery case must also be vibration and seepage resistant. Therefore, a personal watercraft battery should always be the best the owner can afford.

The caps of marine batteries are "spill proof" to prevent acid from spilling into the bilges when the craft is subjected to violent maneuvers. These special caps are designed to vent gases regardless of the battery position, even when upside down.

Because of these features, the personal watercraft battery will recover from a low charge condition and give satisfactory service over a much longer period of time.

Battery Construction

A battery consists of a number of positive and negative plates immersed in a solution of diluted sulfuric acid. The plates contain dissimilar active materials and are kept apart by separators. The plates are grouped into what are termed elements. Plate straps on top of each element connect all of the positive plates and all of the negative plates into groups.

The battery is divided into cells which hold a number of the elements apart from the others. The entire arrangement is con-

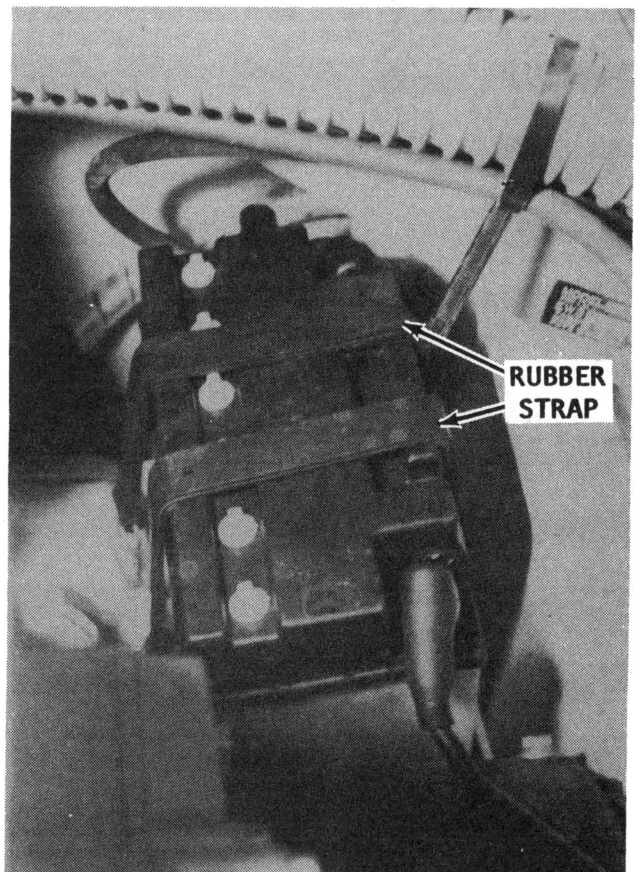

Usually two heavy-duty rubber straps secure the battery in place on a personal watercraft.

tained within a hard plastic case. The top is a one-piece cover and contains the filler caps for each cell. The terminal posts protrude through the top where the battery connections for the craft are made. Each of the cells is connected to its neighbor in a positive-to-negative manner with a heavy strap called the cell connector.

Battery Ratings

Four different methods are used to measure and indicate battery electrical capacity:

1- Ampere-hour rating
2- Cold cranking performance
3- Reserve capacity
4- Watt-hour rating

The **ampere-hour** rating of a battery refers to the battery's ability to provide a set amount of amperes for a given amount of time under test conditions at a constant temperature of 80° (27°C). Amperes x hours equals ampere-hour rating. Therefore, if the battery is capable of supplying 3 amperes of current for 5 consecutive hours, the battery is rated as a 15 ampere-hour battery.

The ampere-hour rating is useful for some service operations, such as slow charging or battery testing.

The recommended ampere-hour rating for a personal watercraft battery is 15-19 ampere-hours.

Cold cranking performance is measured by cooling a fully charged battery to 0°F (-18°C) and then testing it for 5 seconds to determine the maximum current flow. In this manner the cold cranking amperes rating is the number of amperes available to be drawn from the battery before the voltage drops below 9.8 volts. A typical cold cranking ampere rating for a personal watercraft battery is 240 amps.

Reserve capacity of a battery is considered the length of time -- in minutes -- at 80°F (27°C) a 25 ampere current can be maintained before the voltage drops below 10.5 volts. This test is intended to provide an approximation of how long the engine, including electrical accessories such as bilge pump, could operate satisfactorily if the stator assembly or lighting coil did not produce sufficient current. A typical rating is 25 minutes.

Watt-hour is a very useful rating of battery power. It is determined by multiplying the number of ampere hours times the voltage. Therefore, a 12-volt battery rated at 16 ampere-hours would be rated at 192 watt-hours (16 x 12 = 192).

If possible, the new battery should have a power rating equal to or higher than the unit it is replacing.

Battery Installation

Every battery installed in a personal watercraft must be secured in a well-protected ventilated area. If the battery area lacks adequate ventilation, hydrogen gas which is given off during charging could become very explosive. This is especially true if the gas is concentrated and confined.

Battery Service

The battery requires periodic servicing and a definite maintenance program will ensure extended life. If the battery should test satisfactorily, but still fails to perform properly, one of five problems could be the cause.

1- Slow speed engine operation for long periods of time resulting in an undercharged condition.

2- A defect in the charging system. A faulty stator assembly or lighting coil, defective rectifier, or high resistance somewhere in the system could cause the battery to become undercharged.

3- Failure to maintain the battery in good order. This might include a low level of electrolyte in the cells; loose or dirty cable connections at the battery terminals; or possibly an excessively dirty battery top.

Remove the battery from the engine compartment for service. Inspect and service the battery, cables and connections. Check for signs of corrosion. Inspect the battery case for cracks or bulges, dirt, acid, and electrolyte leakage.

Make sure the breather pipe is attached to the battery and not pinched by any part of the engine compartment.

Cleaning

Dirt and corrosion should be cleaned from the battery just as soon as it is dis-

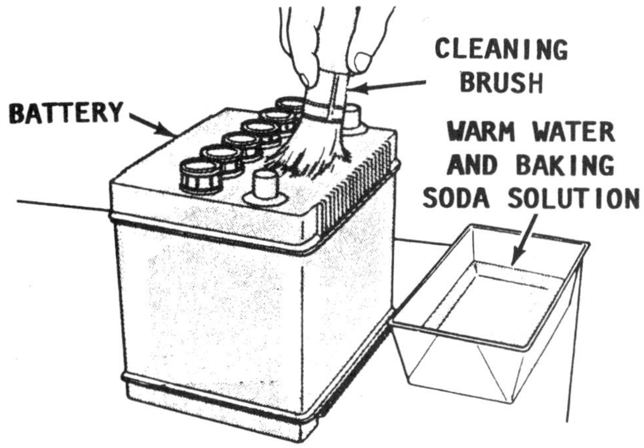

The battery top should be kept clean. A water and baking soda solution applied with a brush will neutralize battery electrolyte and clean the top nicely.

covered. Any accumulation of acid film or dirt will permit current to flow between the terminals. Such a current flow will drain the battery over a period of time. In time an acid film on top of the battery will rot the two rubber hold down straps.

Clean the exterior of the battery with a solution of diluted ammonia or a soda solution to neutralize any acid which may be present. Flush the cleaning solution off with clean water. **TAKE CARE** to prevent any of the neutralizing solution from entering the cells, by keeping the caps tight.

A poor contact at the terminals will add resistance to the charging circuit. This resistance will cause the voltage regulator to register a fully charged battery, and thus cut down on the stator assembly or lighting coil output adding to the low battery charge problem.

Scrape the battery posts clean with a suitable tool or with a stiff wire brush. Clean the inside of the cable clamps to be sure they do not cause any resistance in the circuit.

Battery Sulfation

Battery sulfation can be identified by the formation of white crystals forming on top of exposed battery plates. This usually occurs when a battery has been stored in a discharged condition over a period of time and the electrolyte has evaporated leaving the tops of the plates exposed to the air. This condition may also occur if the battery is not serviced at regular intervals during the season and the electrolyte not replenished when low.

Once white crystals form, the plates are permanently damaged and the battery will never hold a charge. It must be replaced.

Filling the Battery

Remove each filler cap using a pair of pliers. Fill each cell to the proper level with distilled water. The level of electrolyte should be between the upper and lower level marks during operation. When filling the battery, **WITHOUT CHARGING,** fill to the upper line and allow the battery to stand for twenty minutes. Check the level again and replenish, as necessary. If filling the battery **PRIOR** to charging, fill to the lower lever only, because the electrolyte level will rise during charging.

During hot weather and periods of heavy use, the electrolyte level should be checked more often than during normal operation. Add distilled water to bring the level of electrolyte in each cell to the proper level. **TAKE CARE** not to overfill, because adding an excessive amount of water will cause loss of electrolyte and any loss will result in poor performance, short battery life, and will contribute quickly to corrosion. **NEVER** add electrolyte from another battery. **NEVER** add sulphuric acid because such acid would make the electrolyte too strong and permanently damage the battery. **NEVER** add ordinary tap water. The minerals in tap water will shorten battery life.

Battery Testing

A hydrometer is a device to measure the percentage of sulphuric acid in the battery electrolyte in terms of specific gravity. When the condition of the battery drops from fully charged to discharged, the acid leaves the solution and enters the plates, causing the specific gravity of the electrolyte to drop.

Use a temperature corrected hydrometer to test the specific gravity of the electrolyte. At 20°C (68°F) the hydrometer reading should be 1.20-1.26 on the scale.

It may not be common knowledge, but hydrometer floats are calibrated for use at 80°F (27°C). If the hydrometer is used at any other temperature, hotter or colder, a correction factor must be applied. Remember, a liquid will expand if it is heated and will contract if cooled. Such expansion and contraction will cause a definite change in the specific gravity of the liquid, in this case the electrolyte.

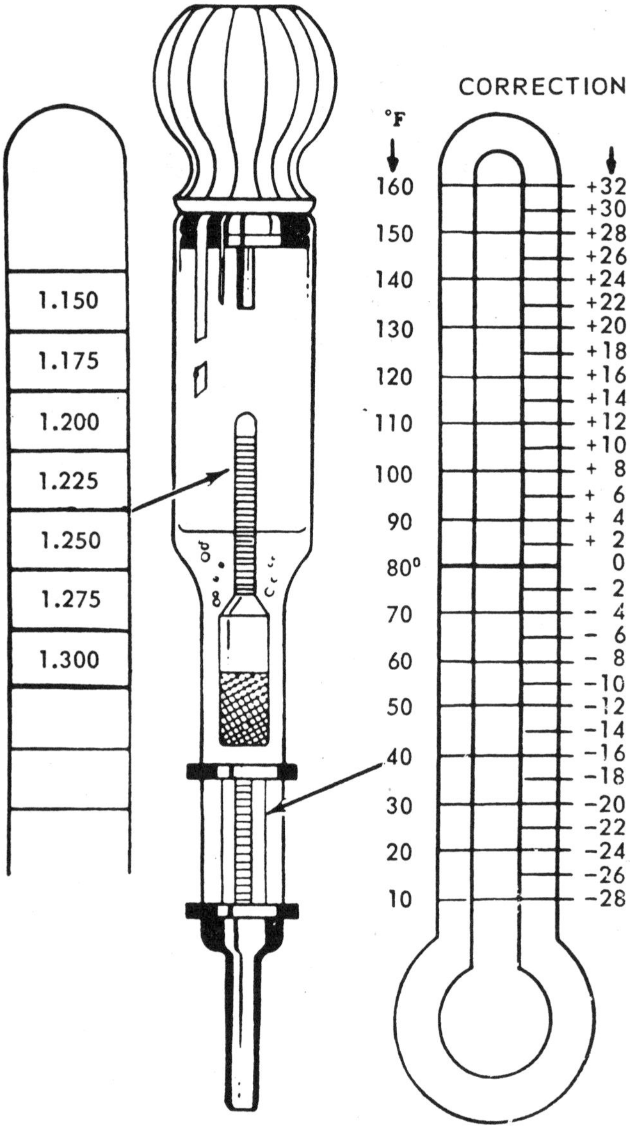

A check of the electrolyte in the battery should be on the maintenance schedule for any boat. A hydrometer reading of 1.300, or in the "Green" band, indicates the battery is in satisfactory condition. If the reading is 1.150 or in the "Red" band, the battery must be charged. Observe the six safety points listed in the text when using a hydrometer.

A quality hydrometer will have a thermometer/temperature correction table in the lower portion, as shown in the accompanying illustration. By knowing the air temperature around the battery and from the table, a correction factor may be applied to the specific gravity reading of the hydrometer float. In this manner, an accurate determination may be made as to the condition of the battery.

The following six points should be observed when using a hydrometer.

1- **NEVER** attempt to take a reading immediately after adding water to the battery. Allow at least 1/4 hour of charging at the recommended rate to thoroughly mix the electrolyte with the new distilled water. This time will also allow for the necessary gases to be created.

2- **ALWAYS** be sure the hydrometer is clean inside and out as a precaution against contaminating the electrolyte.

3- If a thermometer is an integral part of the hydrometer, draw liquid into it several times to ensure the correct temperature before taking a reading.

4- **BE SURE** to hold the hydrometer vertically and suck up liquid only until the float is free and floating.

5- **ALWAYS** hold the hydrometer at eye level and take the reading at the surface of the liquid with the float free and floating.

Disregard the light curvature appearing where the liquid rises against the float stem. This phenomenon is due to surface tension.

6- **DO NOT** drop any of the battery fluid on the boat or on your clothing, because it is extremely caustic. Use water and baking soda to neutralize any battery liquid that does accidentally drop.

After withdrawing electrolyte from the battery cell until the float is barely free, note the level of the liquid inside the hydrometer.

Reading the Hydrometer

Different manufacturers of battery hydrometers use different methods of displaying specific gravity readings. Three methods are used:

Red, white, and green bands
Small floating balls
Graduated scale

Colored Band Hydrometer

When using a battery hydrometer with colored bands of red, white, and green, the electrolyte level is interpreted as follows:

Draw electrolyte from the battery cell until the float is barely free, note the level of the liquid inside the hydrometer.

If the level is within the green band range for all cells, the condition of the battery is satisfactory. If the level is within the white band for all cells, the battery is in fair condition.

If the level is within the green or white band for all cells except one, which registers in the red, the cell is shorted internally. No amount of charging will bring the battery back to satisfactory condition.

If the level in all cells is about the same, even if it falls in the red band, the battery may be recharged and returned to service. If the level fails to rise above the red band after charging, the only solution is to replace the battery.

Small Float Ball Hydrometer

If using a battery hydrometer with small floating balls, the electrolyte level is interpreted as follows:

If four or five balls are floating on top of the electrolyte drawn into the hydrometer, the battery is 100% charged. If three balls are floating, the battery is 75% charged. If two balls are floating, the battery is 50% charged. If only one ball is floating the battery is 25% charged. If no balls float, the battery is 0% charged.

If the same number of balls float for each cell, the condition of the battery is satisfactory.

If all the cells but one float balls, the cell is shorted internally. No amount of charging will bring the battery back to satisfactory condition.

If the number of floated balls for all cells is about the same, even if it is only one or two, the battery may be recharged and returned to service. If the number of balls fails to increase after charging, the only solution is to replace the battery.

Graduated Scale Hydrometer

If using a battery hydrometer with a graduated scale, note the level of the liquid inside the hydrometer. If the level is between the 1.280 and 1.265 mark, the battery is 100% charged. If the level is closer to the 1.210 mark, the battery is 75% charged. If the level is closer to the 1.160 mark, the battery is 50% charged. If it is closer to the 1.120 mark the battery is only 25% charged. If the level is below 1.100 the battery is at 0% charge.

If the level is the same and above 1.160 for all cells, the condition of the battery is satisfactory. If the level is the same and above 1.120 for all cells, the battery is in fair condition.

If the level is the same for all cells except one, which registers low on the scale, the cell is shorted internally. No amount of charging will bring the battery back to satisfactory condition.

If the level in all cells is about the same, even if it registers low on the scale, the battery may be recharged and returned to service. If the level fails to rise above 1.210 after charging, the only solution is to replace the battery.

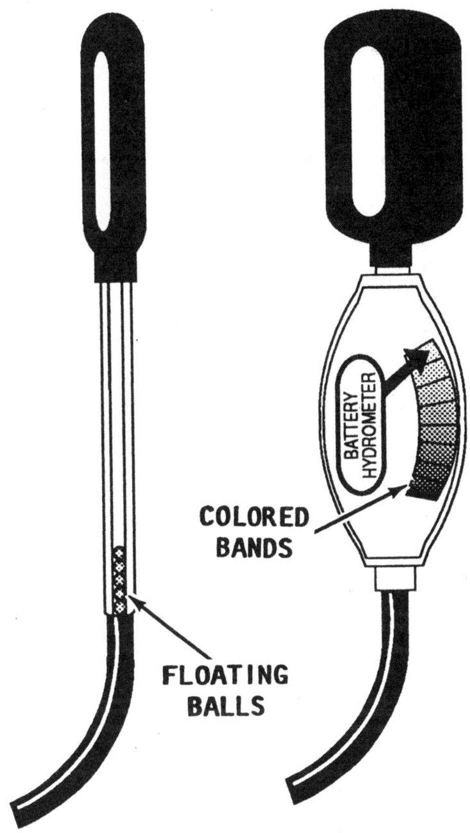

Two types of battery hydrometers, slightly different than the "old style". Their action is explained in the text.

Charging the Battery

If it is necessary to charge the battery, leave the filler caps lightly resting on the cell openings to allow the gases to escape.

The charging current should not exceed 1.9 amps for 10 hours.

NEVER use a fast charger, such as those found at automotive service stations, to charge a personal watercraft battery. These chargers operate at too high an output, ideal for automotive batteries, but very damaging to personal watercraft batteries. If such a battery is fast charged, excessive heat will be generated which will warp the plates and cause internal shorting. The plates will also shed active material which will accumulate at the bottom of the battery and cause internal shorting.

If, under the recommended charging procedures, the temperature of the electrolyte rises above 115°F (45°C) during charging, reduce the charging rate and increase the charging time proportionately. If possible, stop, allow the battery to cool and then resume charging for the recommended length of time.

After charging, push each filler cap into place and wipe the top of the battery clean before installation.

Installing the Battery

Check to be sure the battery is fastened securely in position. The hold-down rubber straps should be tight enough to prevent any movement of the battery in the holder.

Clean the battery posts and battery cable ends with a wire brush to ensure good, clean connections. If the battery posts or cable terminals are corroded, the cables should be cleaned separately with a baking soda solution and a wire brush. Apply a thin coating of Multi-purpose Lubricant to the posts and cable clamps before making the connections. The lubricant will help to prevent corrosion.

Identify the "POS" or "+" and "NEG" or "-" embossed symbols. Correctly connect the battery cables to the battery terminals. If the cables are connected incorrectly, the ignition system **WILL** be destroyed the first time the engine is started.

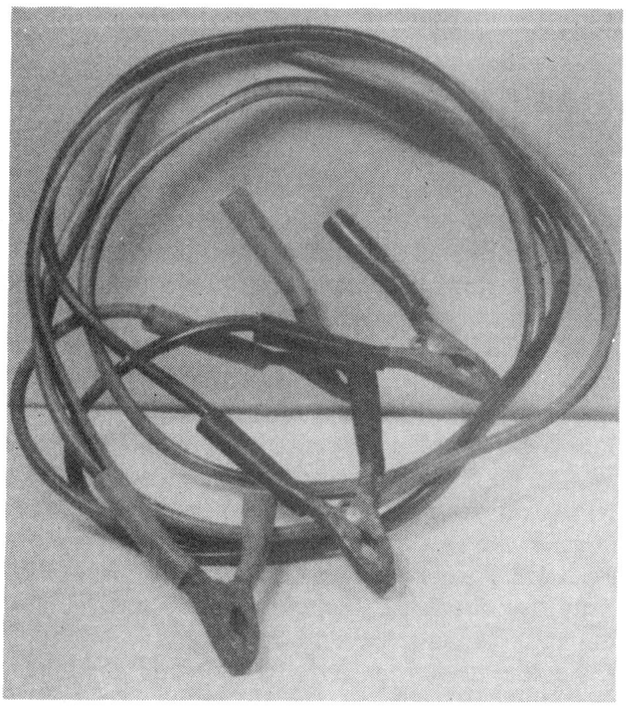

A common set of heavy-duty jumper cables. The booster battery must be connected correctly and in the proper sequence, as outlined in the text. Proper procedure will prevent damage to the battery, the diodes, or the rectifier.

Check to be sure the breather pipe is attached to the battery and not pinched by any part of the engine compartment.

Jumper Cables

If a booster battery is used for starting an engine, the jumper cables must be connected correctly and in the proper sequence to prevent damage to either battery, or to the diodes in the regulator/rectifier.

ALWAYS connect a cable from the positive terminal of the dead battery to the positive terminal of the good battery **FIRST. NEXT,** connect one end of the other cable to the negative terminal of the good battery and the other end to a good ground on the engine. **DO NOT** connect the negative jumper from the good battery to the negative terminal of the low battery. Such action will almost always cause a spark which could ignite gases escaping through the vent holes in the battery filler caps. Igniting the gases may result in an explosion destroying the battery and causing severe personal **INJURY.**

By making the negative (ground) connection on the engine, if an arc is created, it will not be near the battery.

DISCONNECT the battery ground cable before replacing a stator assembly or lighting coil, or before connecting any type of meter to the ignition system.

If it is necessary to use a trickle charger on a dead battery, **ALWAYS** disconnect one of the cables from the battery **FIRST,** to prevent burning out the diodes in the regulator/rectifier.

NEVER use a trickle charger as a booster to start the engine because the diodes will be **DAMAGED.**

Storage

If the craft is to be laid up for the winter or for more than a few weeks, special attention must be given to the battery to prevent complete discharge or possible damage to the terminals and wiring. Before putting the craft in storage, disconnect and remove the battery. Clean the battery thoroughly of any dirt or corrosion, and then charge it to full specific gravity reading. After the battery is fully charged, store the battery in a clean cool dry place where it will not be damaged or knocked over, preferably on a couple blocks of wood. Storing the battery up off the deck, will permit air to circulate freely around and under the battery and will help to prevent condensation.

NEVER store the battery with anything on top of it or cover the battery in such a manner as to prevent air from circulating around the filler caps. All batteries, both new and old, will discharge during periods of storage, more so if they are hot than if they remain cool. Therefore, the electrolyte level and the specific gravity should be checked at regular intervals. A drop in the specific gravity reading is cause to charge the battery back to a full reading.

One of the largest personal watercraft battery manufacturers recommends that a battery in storage should be checked every two weeks and charged if necessary. The electrolyte level can also be replenished at this time to prevent sulfation occurring.

In cold climates, care should be exercised in selecting the battery storage area. A fully charged battery will freeze at about 60° below zero. A discharged battery, almost dead, will have ice forming at about 19° above zero.

9-3 TACHOMETER

An accurate tachometer can be installed on any engine. Such an instrument provides an indication of engine speed in revolutions per minute (rpm). This is accomplished by measuring the number of electrical pulses per minute generated in the primary circuit of the ignition system.

Maximum engine performance can only be obtained through proper tuning using a tachometer.

The meter readings range from 0 to 6,000 rpm, in increments of 100. Tachometers have solid-state electronic circuits which eliminates the need for relays or batteries and contributes to their accuracy. The electronic parts of the tachometer susceptible to moisture are coated to prolong their life.

SPECIAL WORDS ON TACHOMETERS AND CONNECTIONS

A tachometer connected to the engine must be used to accurately determine engine rpm during idle and high-speed adjustments.

Theoretically, it should be possible to connect a tachometer to any engine and receive an accurate count of crankshaft revolutions -- **RIGHT? WRONG!**

Unfortunately, this is not the case. Tachometer manufacturers admit, on certain two-stroke applications where points, and an ignition coil are **NOT** used, an attempt to connect a tachometer to the unit could "go up in smoke".

Therefore, see the "Special Words on Tachometers" in Chapter 3 -- Pages 3-5 and 3-6 explaining tachometers, leads and connections.

9-4 ELECTRICAL SYSTEM GENERAL INFORMATION

The electrical system consists of three circuits:

- Charging circuit
- Cranking motor circuit
- Ignition circuit

Charging Circuit

The charging circuit consists of permanent magnets attached to the inside perimeter of the flywheel; a lighting coil installed on the stator plate; a regulator/rectifier located elsewhere on the engine; an external battery; and the necessary wiring to connect the units.

The negative side of the regulator/rectifier is grounded. The positive side of the regulator/rectifier is connected to the battery. The negative side of the battery is connected to a good ground on the engine.

The alternating current generated in the stator windings passes to the regulator/rectifier. The regulator/rectifier changes the alternating current (AC) to direct current (DC) to charge the 12-volt battery.

Cranking Motor Circuit

The cranking motor circuit consists of a cranking motor and a starter-engaging mechanism. A starter relay is used as a heavy-duty switch to carry the heavy current from the battery to the cranking motor. The starter relay is actuated by either depressing the **START** button, or on craft equipped with an ignition key, the ignition key is turned to the **START** position.

Ignition Circuit

The ignition circuit is covered extensively in Chapter 7.

9-5 CHARGING CIRCUIT SERVICE

The stator is located behind and protected by, the flywheel. Therefore, the stator, including the lighting coil, seldom causes problems in the charging circuit. Most problems in the charging circuit can be traced to the regulator/rectifier or to the battery. If either the stator or the regulator/rectifier fails the troubleshooting tests, the defective unit cannot be repaired, it **MUST** be replaced. Resistance tests on the lighting coil and the regulator/rectifier are presented in Chapter 7.

9-6 CRANKING MOTOR CIRCUIT SERVICE

DESCRIPTION

As the name implies, the sole purpose of the cranking motor circuit is to control operation of the cranking motor to crank the engine until the air/fuel mixture ignites and the flywheel develops enough torque to continue under its own steam. The circuit includes a solenoid or magnetic switch to connect or disconnect the motor from the battery. The operator controls the switch with a push button or key switch.

The rectifier/regulator is secured to the side of the electrical box on all models covered in this manual, as shown here on a Model 1100 Series unit.

The cranking motor is a series wound electric motor which draws a heavy current from the battery. It is designed to be used only for short periods of time to crank the engine for starting. To prevent overheating the motor, cranking should not be continued for more than 30-seconds without allowing the motor to cool for at least three minutes. Actually, this time can be spent in making preliminary checks to determine why the engine fails to start.

Theory of Operation

Power is transmitted from the cranking motor to the engine flywheel through meshed

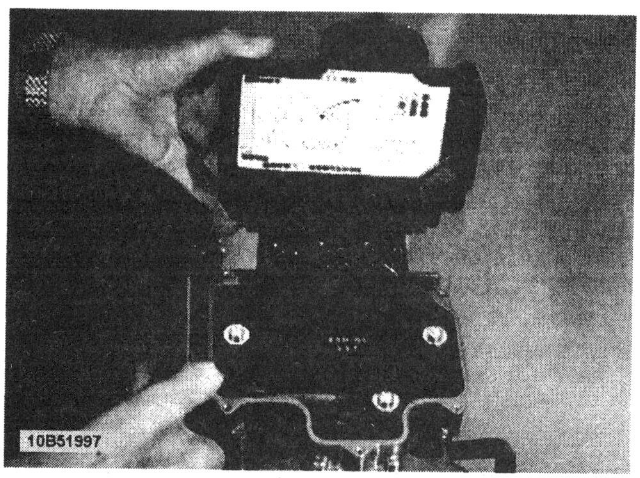

The electrical box cover removed, exposing the CDI unit.

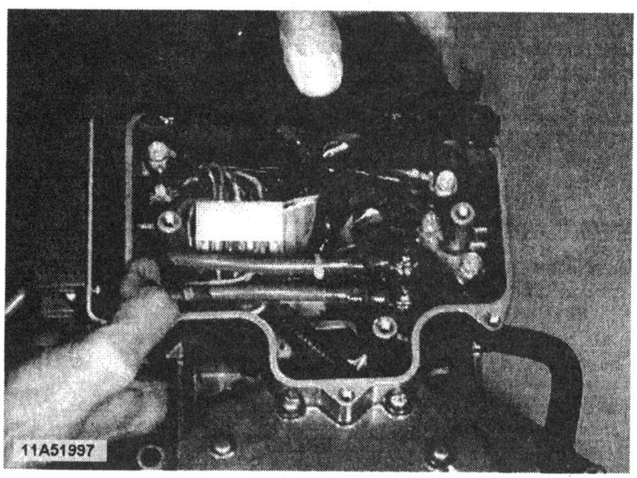

Once the CDI unit is removed and set aside, much of the electrical wiring and the cranking motor relay assembly are easily accessible.

gears. An idler gear, housed in the flywheel cover contains a Bendix drive. The armature shaft has a splined end which meshes inside the idler gear. The flywheel cover must be removed to gain access to the idler gear assembly. The cranking motor is easily removed by disconnecting the electrical lead at the solenoid removing just two mounting mounts and moving the motor aft and clear of the engine.

When the motor is operated, the pinion gear, a part of the idler gear assembly, moves forward and meshes with the teeth on the flywheel ring. Engine cranking takes place.

When the engine starts, the pinion gear is driven faster than the armature shaft, and as a result, it screws out of mesh with the flywheel. A rubber cushion is built into the Bendix drive to absorb the shock when the pinion meshes with the flywheel ring gear. The parts of the drive **MUST** be properly assembled for efficient operation. If the drive is removed for cleaning, **TAKE CARE** to assemble the parts in the correct order. If the screw shaft assembly is reversed, it will strike the splines and the rubber cushion will not absorb the shock.

The sound of the motor during cranking is a good indication of whether the cranking motor is operating properly or not. Naturally, temperature conditions will affect the speed at which the cranking motor is able to crank the engine. The speed of cranking a cold engine will be much slower than when cranking a warm engine. An experienced operator will learn to recognize the favorable sounds of the engine cranking under various conditions.

Faulty Symptoms

If the cranking motor spins, but fails to crank the engine, the cause is usually a

Typical cranking motor installed on the engines covered in this manual. These motors drive the idler gear assembly shown at the top of the next column.

Idler gear assembly used with the cranking motor shown at the bottom of the adjacent column.

corroded or gummy Bendix drive. The drive should be removed, cleaned, and given an inspection.

If the cranking motor cranks the engine too slowly, the following are possible causes and the corrective actions that may be taken:

a- Battery charge is low. Charge the battery to full capacity.

b- High resistance connections at the battery, solenoid, or motor. Clean and tighten all connections.

c- Undersize battery cables. Replace cables with sufficient size.

d- Battery cables too long. Relocate the battery to shorten the run to the solenoid.

Maintenance

The cranking motor does not require periodic maintenance or lubrication, except for lubrication of the pinion gear. If the

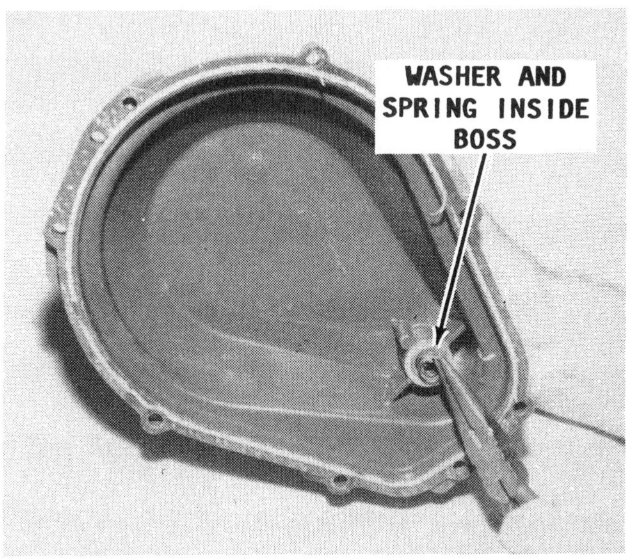

The end of the idler gear shaft fits into and is supported by a "boss" cast into the stator plate cover.

motor fails to perform properly, the checks outlined in the previous paragraph should be performed.

Naturally, the motor will have to be removed if the corrective actions outlined under **Faulty Symptoms** above, does not restore the motor to satisfactory operation.

Otherwise, the cranking motor is not normally removed from the engine until it fails.

CRANKING MOTOR TROUBLESHOOTING

Before wasting too much time troubleshooting the cranking motor circuit, the following checks should be made. Many times, the problem will be corrected.

a- Battery fully charged.
b- Main 10-amp fuse is "good" (not blown).
c- All electrical connections clean and tight.
d- Wiring in good condition, insulation not worn or frayed.

The following troubleshooting procedures are presented in a logical sequence, with the most common and easily corrected areas listed first in each problem area. The connection number refers to the numbered positions in the accompanying illustrations.

Perform the following quick checks and corrective actions for following problems:

1- Cranking Motor Rotates Slowly

a- Battery charge is low. Charge the battery to full capacity.

Make a thorough check of the battery, including terminal fittings -- clean and tight -- along with the electrolyte -- full to the mark -- and ensure the battery has a complete charge before troubleshooting the cranking motor circuit.

b- Electrical connections corroded or loose. Clean and tighten.

c- Defective cranking motor. Perform an amp draw test. Lay an amp draw-gauge on the cable leading to the cranking motor. Turn the key on or depress the **START** button and attempt to crank the engine. If the gauge indicates an excessive amperage draw, the cranking motor **MUST** be replaced or rebuilt.

2- Cranking Motor Fails to Crank Engine

a- Disconnect the cranking motor lead from the solenoid to prevent the engine from starting during the testing process.

NOTE:

The cranking motor lead is to remain disconnected from the solenoid during tests No. 2 thru No. 6.

b- Disconnect the black ground wire from the No. 2.

c- Connect a voltmeter between the No. 2 and a common engine ground.

d- Turn the key switch to the **START** position or depress the **START** button.

e- Observe the voltmeter reading. If there is the slightest amount of reading, check the black ground wire connection or check for an open circuit. Connect the ground wire back to the No. 2 and move to Step 6. If there is no voltmeter reading, proceed with Step 3.

3- Test Cranking Motor Solenoid

a- Connect a voltmeter between the engine common ground and No. 3.

b- Turn the ignition key switch to the **START** position, or depress the **START** button.

c- Observe the voltmeter reading. If there is the slightest indication of a reading, the solenoid is defective and must be replaced. If there is no reading, proceed with Step 4.

4- Test for Open Wire

a- Connect a voltmeter between the common engine ground and No. 5.

b- The voltmeter should indicate 12-volts. If the meter needle flickers (fails to hold steady), check the circuit between No. 5 and common engine ground. If meter fails to indicate voltage, replace the positive battery cable.

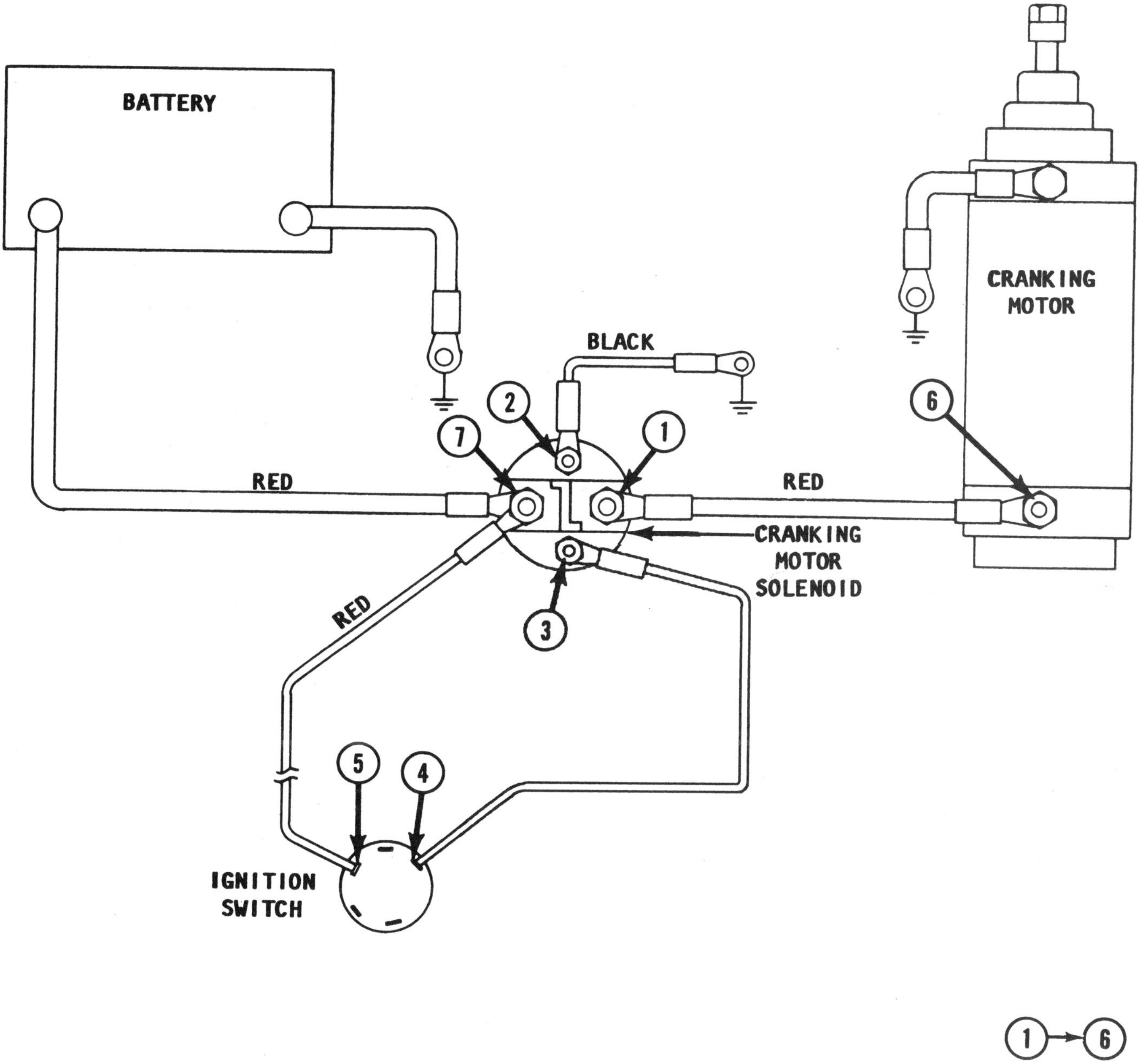

5- Further Tests for Solenoid

a- Connect the voltmeter between the common engine ground and No. 1.

b- Turn the ignition key switch to the **START** position or depress the **START** button.

c- Observe the voltmeter. If there is no reading, the cranking motor solenoid is defective and must be replaced. If a reading is indicated and a click sound is heard, proceed to Step 6.

6- Test Large Red Cable

a- Connect the red cable to the cranking motor solenoid.
b- Connect the voltmeter between the engine common ground and No. 6.
c- Turn the ignition key switch to the **START** position, or depress the **START** button.
d- Observe the voltmeter. If there is no reading, check the red cable for a poor connection or an open circuit. If there is any indication of a reading, and the cranking motor does not rotate, the cranking motor must be replaced.

CRANKING MOTOR RELAY TROUBLESHOOTING

Description

The cranking motor relay is actually a switch between the battery and the engine. The switch cannot be serviced. Therefore, if troubleshooting indicates the switch to be faulty, it **MUST** be replaced.

Relay Testing While Installed

a- Connect one test lead of a voltmeter to the large positive relay terminal. Connect the other meter lead to a good ground on the engine.

b- Check the battery voltage under load by turning the ignition switch to the **START** position or depressing the **START** button and observing the voltmeter reading.

If the reading is 9-1/2 volts or greater, and the cranking motor fails to operate, disconnect all the leads from the relay and perform the following bench test.

Relay Testing Bench Test

a- Connect an ohmmeter across the two large positive and negative relay terminals.

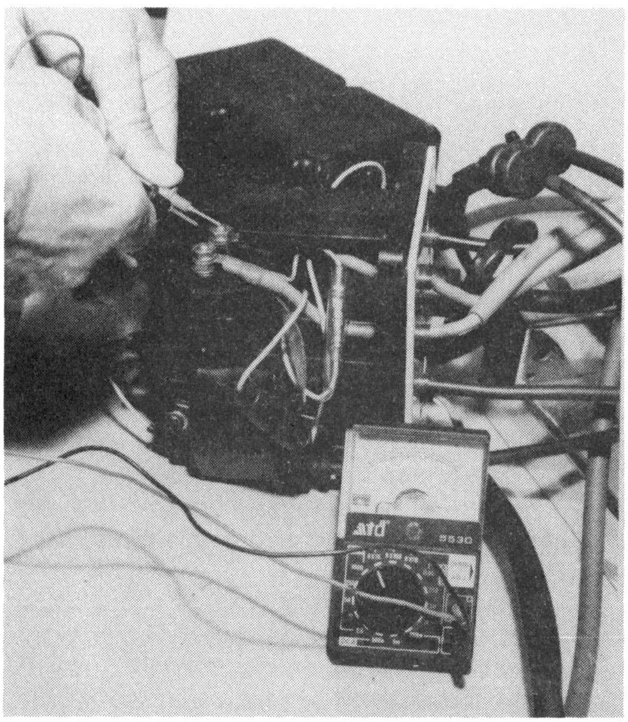

Bench testing the cranking motor relay, as explained in the text.

b- Connect a 12-volt battery to the small terminals; the positive battery terminal to the small Brown relay lead and the negative battery terminal to the small Black relay lead. As soon as the last connection is made listen for a click from the relay and observe the meter needle. The relay is functioning if both a click is heard **AND** the meter needle deflects. If either or both fail to occur the relay is defective and must be replaced.

9-7 CRANKING MOTOR SERVICE

Description

Only one type cranking motor is used on the engines covered in this manual.

Marine cranking motors are very similar in construction and operation to the units used in the automotive industry.

NEVER operate a cranking motor for more than 30-seconds without allowing it to cool for at least three minutes. Continuous operation without the cooling period can cause serious damage to the cranking motor.

REMOVAL

Before beginning any work on the cranking motor, disconnect the positive (+) lead from the battery terminal.

All Models

Simply disconnect the cranking motor lead from the terminal on the motor. Remove the two mounting bolts securing the motor to the block, and then move the cranking motor aft and free of the engine.

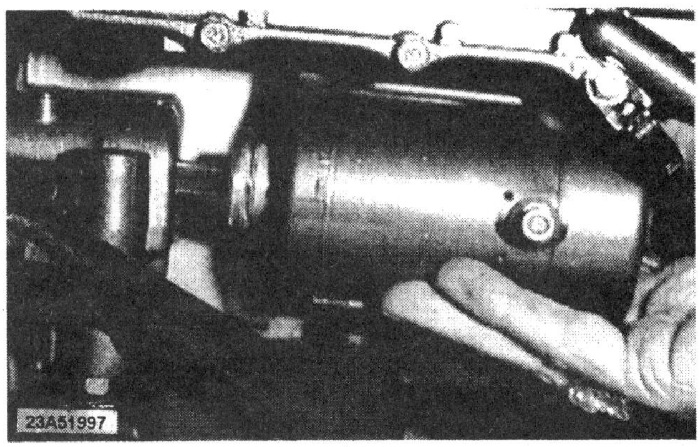

Typical cranking motor installation on a Model 1100 Series engine. The motor on a Model 650 and 700 Series is mounted to a bracket instead of directly to the block.

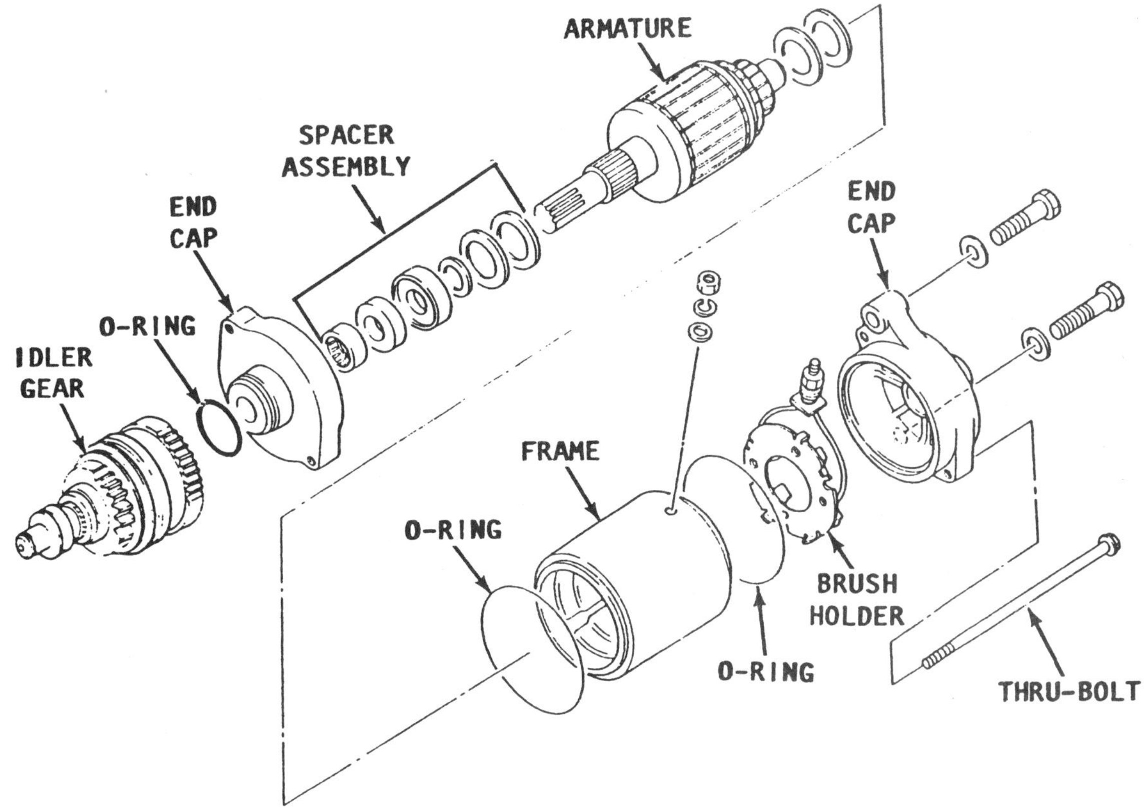

Exploded drawing of a typical cranking motor used on the engines covered in this manual. Principle parts have been identified. The text explains the "tricky" task of passing the thru-bolts from one end cap to the other.

CRANKING MOTOR DISASSEMBLING

FIRST, THESE WORDS

Almost all towns of any size in the United States and Canada have an electrical repair shop, whose only business is the repair and rebuild of electric motors -- cranking motors, alternators, old time generators and the like. If an item is taken to such a shop, usually an exchange is made with a rebuilt unit and the customer is out the door in a matter of minutes, knowing the replacement will give extended satisfactory service.

HOWEVER, if the situation requires the reader to rebuild the cranking motor, detailed procedures are presented in this section to completely rebuild the unit. Separate illustrations in support of the steps are not provided but the exploded diagram on this page should prove most helpful during disassembling and assembling of the motor.

Some illustrations for testing and repair of certain cranking motor components are included.

SPECIAL IDLER GEAR WORDS

The cranking motor has splines at the end of the armature shaft which index with the splines of a short idler gear assembly mounted inside the flywheel cover. If the idler gear needs service, follow the procedures in Chapter 8 -- Engine -- to remove the flywheel cover and gain access to the idler gear assembly.

Disassembling

1- Remove the large **O**-ring around the upper end cap. Discard this **O**-ring, **ONLY** if a replacement is available.

2- Make a mark on both end caps and matching marks on the field frame assembly as an aid to alignment and installation of the thru-bolts.

SPECIAL THRU-BOLT WORDS

Without some type of alignment marks, the task of inserting the thru-bolts and starting the threads into the end cap is almost impossible.

Checking an idler gear used on a Model 650, Model 700, Model 1100, or Model 1200 engine, as described in the text.

Remove the thru bolts, and then the upper end cap, armature assembly and lower end cap. Note the number of washers on each end of the armature. Incorrect placement of these washers will cause the armature to be misaligned with the brushes and the field magnets during assembling.

Remove the O-ring around each end cap, if so equipped. Discard this O-ring **ONLY** if a replacement is available.

The brush assembly is always attached to the large terminal. Remove the locknut/s and lockwasher/s from the terminal on the motor frame or the end cap and slide the brush assembly from the end of the motor frame or the lower end cap with the terminal still attached.

CLEANING AND INSPECTING

Pinion Gear Assembly

Inspect the pinion gear teeth for chips, cracks, or a broken tooth. Check the splines inside the pinion gear for burrs and to be sure the gear moves freely on the armature shaft.

BAD NEWS

This type of cranking motor pinion gear assembly cannot be repaired if the unit is defective. Replacement of the pinion gear assembly as a unit is the only answer.

Check to be sure the return spring (not found on the Yamaha 650 series) is flexible and has not become distorted. Check both ends of the spring for signs of damage.

Clean the armature shaft and check to be sure the shaft is free of any burrs. If burrs are discovered, they may be removed with crocus cloth.

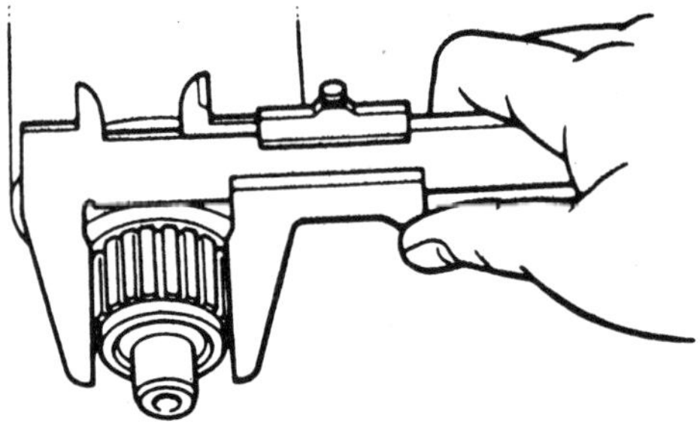

Simple drawing to depict using a micrometer to check the commutator diameter. This measurement should be 1.06" (27mm). Manufacturer does not give a tolerance.

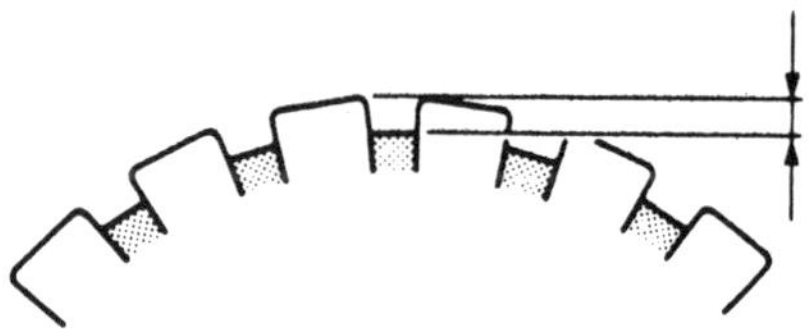

The commutator undercut should not be more than 0.01" (0.2mm).

Frame Assembly

Clean the field coils, armature, commutator, armature shaft, brush assembly, and end caps with a brush or compressed air. Wash all other parts in solvent and blow them dry with compressed air.

Inspect the insulation and the unsoldered connections of the armature windings for breaks or burns.

GOOD WORDS

Most marine shops and all electrical motor rebuild shops will test an armature for a very modest charge. If the armature has a short, it **MUST** be replaced.

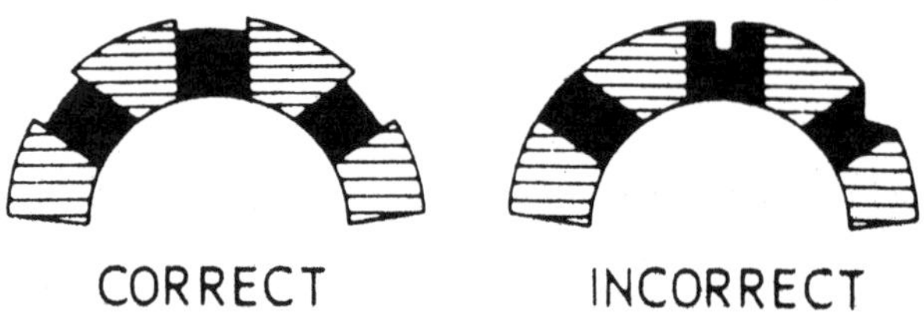

Comparison of armature segments properly cleaned (left), and improperly cleaned (right).

Perform electrical tests on any suspected defective part, according to the procedures outlined in Section 9-10.

Check the commutator for runout. Inspect the armature shaft and both bearings for scoring.

Turn the commutator in a lathe if it is out-of-round by more than 0.005" (0.13mm).

Check the springs in the brush holder to be sure none are broken. Check the insulated brush holders for shorts to ground. If the brushes are worn down to 1/2" (13mm) or less, they must be replaced.

The armature, fields, and brush holders must be checked before assembling the starter motor. See Section 9-10 for detailed procedures to test cranking motor parts.

Both the positive and negative brushes are mounted on the brush assembly plate. The positive brush is attached to the positive terminal. The negative brush is attached to the lower end cap with a screw or grounded to the motor frame.

Remove the screws attaching the brush leads to the brush plate. Some cranking motors have brushes with small loose springs tensioning the brushes against the commutator. Take care not to lose these small springs. Other cranking motors use wound spring steel coils mounted horizontally to provide the tensioning force. These coils are permanently riveted to the brush plate and are not removable. If they are broken or missing, a new plate must be purchased.

If small loose springs are used, installation of a new brush is accomplished by first inserting the small spring into the brush retainer, and then sliding the new brush into the slot of the brush holder. Secure each lead with the attaching screw.

If wound spring coils are used, installation is accomplished by sliding the new brush into the slot of the brush holder until it makes contact with the wound spring. Secure each lead with the attaching screw.

Models With Oil Seal In End Cap

Some cranking motors are equipped with an oil seal in the upper end cap. Inspect the condition of the seal and replace as necessary. If a new seal is installed, or the old seal is still serviceable, pack the seal lip with multi-purpose water resistant lubricant before assembling the cranking motor. Install the new oil seal with the seal lip **TOWARD** the motor frame.

TESTING CRANKING MOTOR PARTS

SPECIAL WORDS

Most marine shops and all electrical motor rebuild shops will test an armature for a modest charge. If the armature has a short, it **MUST** be replaced.

Check the armature for a short circuit by placing it on a growler and holding a hack saw blade over the armature core while the armature is rotated. If the saw blade vibrates, the armature is shorted. Clean between the armature bars, and then check again on the growler. If the saw blade still vibrates, the armature must be replaced. Occasionally carbon dust from the brushes will short the armature. Therefore, blow the slots in the armature clean with compressed air.

1- Make contact with one probe of the test light or ohmmeter on the armature core or shaft. Make contact with the other probe on the commutator. If the light comes on, or the meter indicates continuity, the armature is grounded and must be replaced.

Turning the Commutator

2- True the commutator, if necessary, in a lathe. **NEVER** undercut the mica because the brushes are harder than the insulation. Undercut the insulation between the commutator bars 1/32" (0.80mm) to the full width of the insulation and flat at the bottom. A triangular groove is not satisfactory. After the undercutting work is completed, clean out the slots carefully to remove dirt and copper dust. Sand the com-

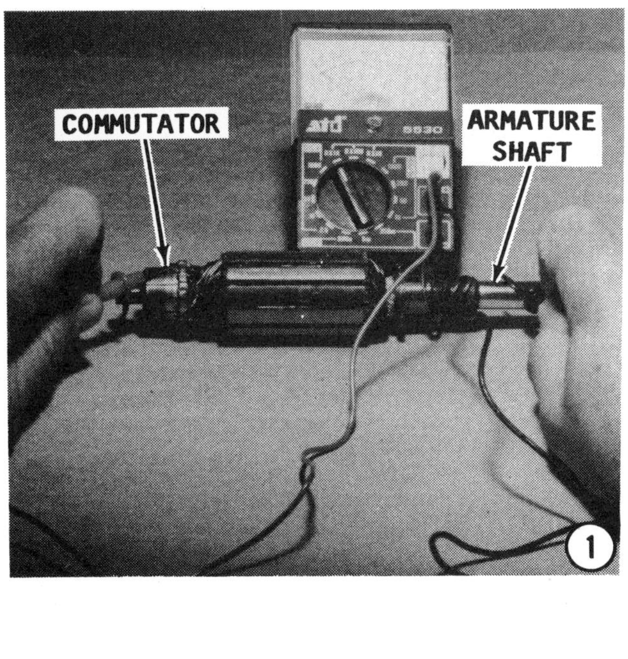

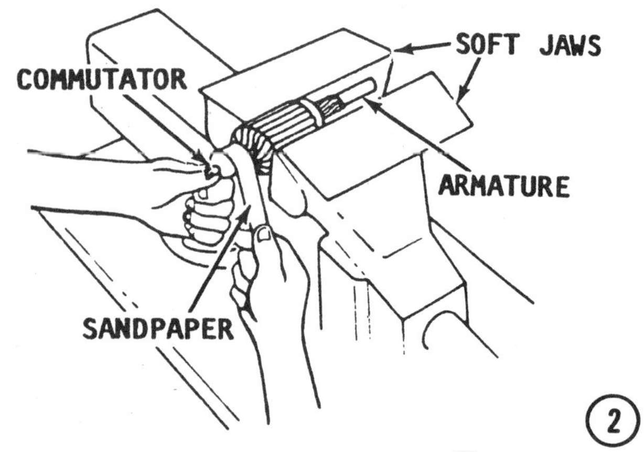

2

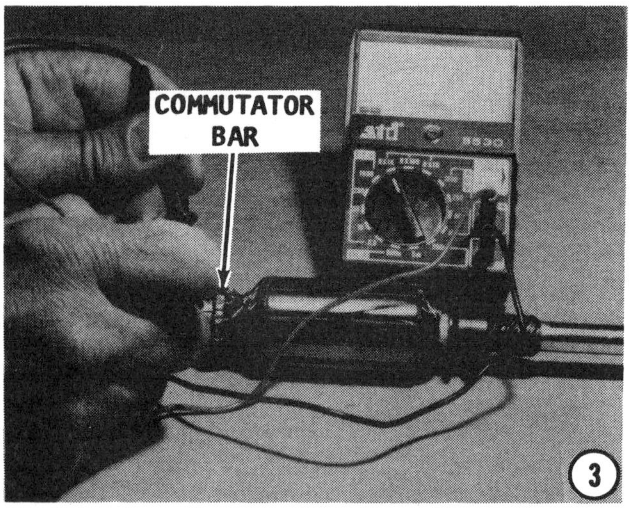

3

mutator lightly with No. 500 or No. 600 sandpaper to remove any burrs left from the undercutting.

3- Test light probes, placed on any two commutator bars, should light and indicate continuity.

4- Check the armature a second time on the growler for possible short circuits.

Positive Brush

5- Obtain an ohmmeter. Make contact with one lead of the ohmmeter to the positive brush. Make contact with the other test lead to the end cap/motor frame. The

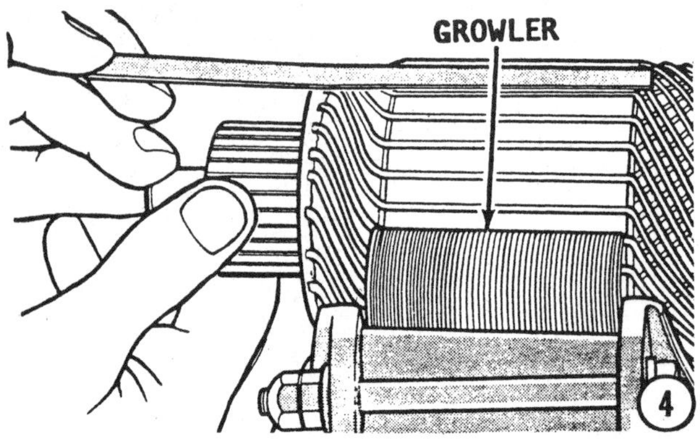

4

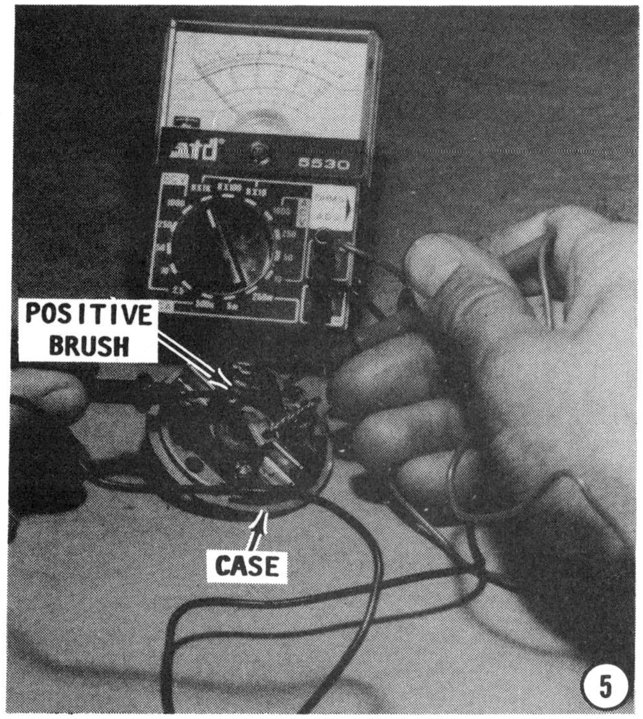

5

ohmmeter should indicate **NO** continuity. If the meter indicates continuity, the positive lead is shorted to the end cap/motor frame and must be replaced.

Negative Brush

6- Make contact with one lead of the ohmmeter to the negative brush. Make contact with the other test lead to the end cap/motor frame. The ohmmeter should indicate continuity. If the meter indicates no continuity, there is an open in the negative lead or the lead is not grounded properly to the end cap/motor frame.

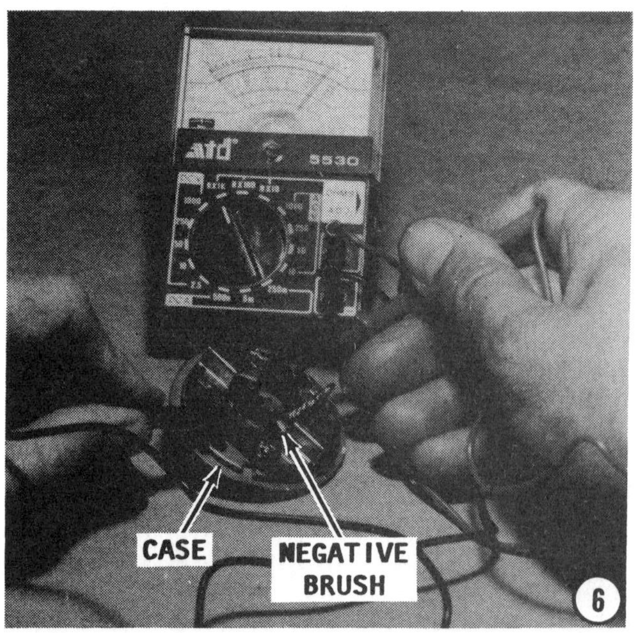

6

SPECIAL WORDS ON CRANKING MOTOR ASSEMBLING

Separate illustrations are not provided for the following steps. The exploded drawing on Page 9-13 will be most helpful while assembling the cranking motor.

1- Stretch a new **O**-ring around the circumference of the lower end cap.

2- Slide the two washers over the commutator end of the armature shaft.

3- Apply a thin coating of Yamaha All Purpose Lubricant, or equivalent waterproof anti-seize lubricant, onto the bushing in the end cap. Hold the brushes back and insert the small end of the armature into the end cap bushing. **TAKE CARE** not to distort the brush springs. Once assembled, rotate the shaft inside the bushing and check to be sure there is no binding and the brushes sweep across the commutator smoothly.

4- Slide the free end of the armature into the field frame end with the magnets recessed. Again, **TAKE CARE** not to lose the brushes from the commutator. Seat the end cap into the field frame with the marks made prior to disassembly aligned.

5- Stretch a new **O**-ring around the circumference of the upper end cap.

6- Install the two washers over the armature shaft. Seat the upper end cap with the marks made during disassembly aligned.

Now, hold it all together and slide the two thru-bolts through the lower end cap, through the motor frame, and then threaded them into the upper end cap.

SPECIAL THRU-BOLT WORDS

Installing the two thru-bolts is not as simple a task as it sounds. The reason: as the bolts pass the magnets inside the motor frame, the magnets will attract the bolts, "pulling" them out of line. With a bit of patience, the bolts can be made to align with the holes in the upper end cap and the threads started.

7- After the bolts are successfully threaded into the end cap, tighten them securely.

Model 650 and 700 Series Only

8- Install a new small **O**-ring around the armature shaft and against the upper end cap.

9- Slide the armature shaft through the opening in the stator plate

INSTALLATION

Model 650 and 700 Series Only

Slide the armature shaft through the opening in the stator plate until the motor is seated against the plate. Check to be sure the splines at the end of the armature have indexed into the internal splines of the idler gear assembly.

Secure the cranking motor to the engine with the two securing bolts and washers. The cranking motor on Model 650 and 700 Series is secured with two bolts passing through a bracket on the block in a fore-and-aft direction. Tighten the bolts to a torque value of 13 ft lbs (18Nm). Connect the Red lead to the cranking motor terminal.

Coat the connection with some type of dialectic grease, and then slide the "boot" over the connection

Model 1100 And 1200 Series

Move the cranking motor into place against the block with the splined armature shaft passing through the small opening and indexing with the splines of the idler gear shaft.

Secure the cranking motor with the two mounting bolts and washers after the bolt threads have been treated with Loctite. Tighten the bolts securely. The accompanying illustration shows the cranking motor being installed on a Model 1100 Series engine.

Connect the electrical lead to the terminal on the cranking motor. Coat the connection with some type of dialectic grease, and then slide the boot over the connection.

Cranking motor installed, ready for the electrical line to be connected to the terminal and covered by the "boot".

Check Completed Work

Secure the craft in a test tank or body of water. If a body of water or tank is not possible, connect a flush attachment and hose to the jet pump.

CAUTION

Water must circulate through the jet pump -- to and from the engine, anytime the engine is operating. Circulating water will prevent overheating -- which could cause damage to moving engine parts and possible engine seizure.

NEVER, AGAIN, NEVER operate the engine at high speed with a flush device attached. The engine, operating at high speed with such a device attached, would **RUNAWAY** from lack of a load on the impeller, causing extensive damage.

Crank the engine with the cranking motor and start the unit. Shut the engine down and start it several times to check operation of the cranking motor.

9-8 TESTING OTHER ELECTRICAL COMPONENTS

This short section provides testing procedures for other electrical parts installed on the engine. If a unit fails the testing, the faulty part must be replaced. In most cases, removal and installation is through attaching hardware.

Thermo- switch

Trace the thermo-switch harness containing two wires from the switch, located in the cylinder head, to their quick disconnect fitting inside the electrical box. The harness contains a Pink and a Black wire.

Disconnect the two leads and connect an ohmmeter across the disconnected leads. The meter should register no continuity.

The thermo-switch is a one piece sealed unit and cannot be serviced.

Start Button Test

Trace the start button harness containing two wires from the switch to their nearest quick disconnect fitting. The colors may vary for different models. Refer to the wiring diagram in the Appendix for proper color identification.

Disconnect the two leads and connect an ohmmeter across the disconnected leads. Depress the start button. The meter should register continuity. Release the button and the meter should now register no continuity. Both tests **MUST** be successful. If the tests are not successful, the start button **MUST** be replaced. The start button is a one piece sealed unit and cannot be serviced.

"Kill" Switch Test

Trace the "Kill" switch button harness containing two wires from the switch to their nearest quick disconnect fitting. The colors may vary for different models. Refer to the wiring diagram in the Appendix for proper color identification.

Disconnect the two leads and connect an ohmmeter across the disconnected leads. Verify the emergency tether is in place behind the "Kill" switch button. Select the Rx1000 scale on the meter. Depress the "kill" button. The meter should register continuity. Release the button. The meter should now register no continuity. Both tests must be successful. If the switch fails either test, the switch is defective and **MUST** be replaced. The switch is a one piece sealed unit and cannot be serviced.

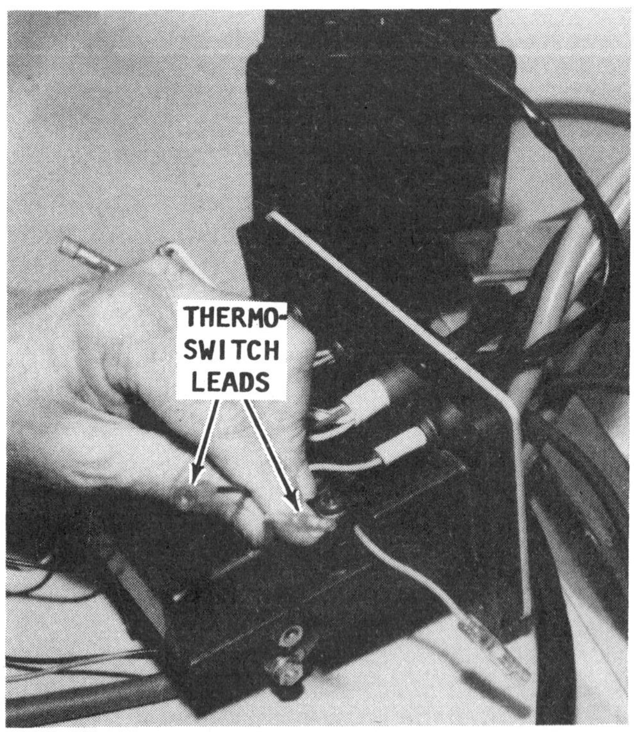

Testing the Thermoswitch on a Yamaha personal watercraft, as outlined in the test procedures on this page.

10
JET PUMP

10-1 INTRODUCTION

This manual covers the Yamaha production models from 1992 through 1997, including the 650, 700, 1100 and 1200 series. From Information received from Yamaha, the mixed flow pump was only installed on the Model WR650Q during a portion of 1992. All others were equipped with an axial flow jet pump.

SPECIAL WORDS ON JET PUMPS

The axial flow pump is installed with larger horsepower engines. These engines are capable of delivering higher engine/-pump shaft rpms, thus moving the craft at greater speeds.

Both the mixed flow and axial flow pumps have the same basic components.

Pump parts are **NOT** interchangable, because many of the castings are of unique design even though they share the same function and are similar in appearance. The main difference between the two pumps, regarding maintenance concerns locating the impeller on the impeller shaft.

The mixed flow pump is equipped with shim material to position the impeller at a specific distance from the impeller housing.

The axial flow pump does not have shim material to position the impeller.

The following paragraphs clarify the engine models and the pumps used.

Pump Identification
Mixed Flow

At press time, very few of the Yamaha Personal Watercraft produced during the years of coverage for this manual were equipped with a mixed flow pump. These units were released on the market during the early part of manual coverage, namely in 1992. By mid 1993 all watercraft used the axial flow pump. According to records available, the WaveRunner WR650Q was the only craft with a mixed flow pump in the production year of 1992. Procedures to service a mixed flow pump are included in this chapter. This particular watercraft was designed to carry either one or two people.

Shimming procedures for a mixed flow pump are covered in Section 10-2. Servicing the pump is included in Section 10-3.

GOOD WORDS

When removing a mixed flow jet pump, it is not necessary to remove the engine. As explained later in the text, the pump may be removed through the bottom of the craft.

Principles of Mixed Flow Operation

Many experts consider the mixed flow system to be the most efficient for personal watercraft application. The water flow is

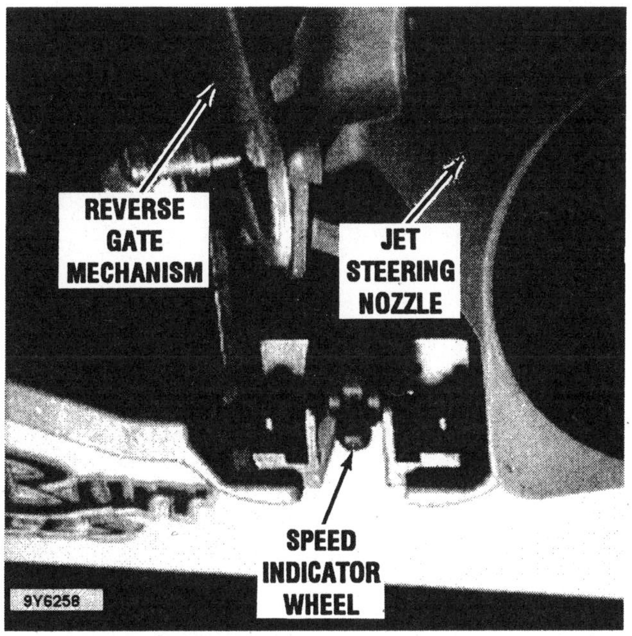

Close view of the jet steering nozzle and the reverse gate mechanism on the port side. A reflection of the mechanism is also installed on the starboard side. The speed wheel (installed on some units), is visible.

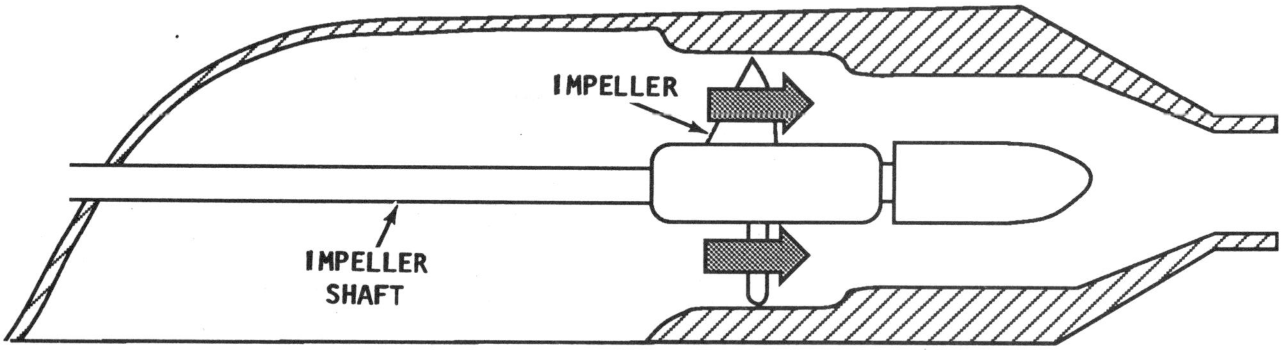

Water flow through an axial jet pump is parallel to the axis of impeller rotation.

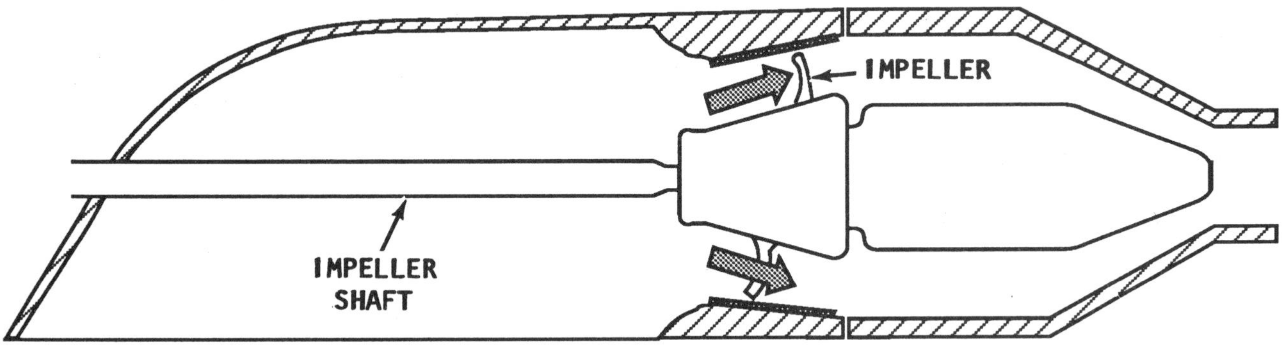

Water flow through a mixed flow jet pump is inclined to the axis of impeller rotation.

discharged at an inclined angle to the axis of impeller rotation, as indicated by the arrows in the accompanying illustration. The impeller blades are inclined in such a manner to cause the water to be thrown off at a 45 degree angle to the impeller shaft within the impeller duct. From the duct, the water is then forced out through the nozzle housing and nozzle. The vanes in the impeller duct help straighten the water flow through the nozzle.

The inside of the impeller housing is inclined at an angle to the water flow. Therefore, this design pump incorporates a liner against the impeller housing and shim material to space the impeller blades at a specified distance from the liner. Mixed flow pump efficiency decreases by 30% as blade-to-liner clearance increases by 0.04" (1mm).

Pump Identification

Axial Flow

With the exception of some WaveRunner WR650Q craft for 1992, the remainder of the personal watercraft covered in this manual have been equipped with an axial flow single stage jet pump. These units include the 650 Series (except the 1992 WR650Q), the 700, 900, 1100, and 1200 Series. These craft are designed to carry one, two, or three adults.

No shimming is necessary for an axial flow pump. Detailed illustrated service procedures for the axial flow pump and the mixed flow pump are presented in Section 10-3 of this chapter.

GOOD WORDS

To remove and service the axial flow pump, it is not necessary to remove the engine. The removal and installation task is accomplished through the bottom of the craft, as outlined later in the text.

Principles of Axial Flow Operation

Water in an axial pump moves on a single axis, as depicted in the adjacent illustration, thus the word "axial". In simple terms, water is ingested and discharged parallel to the axis of impeller rotation.

The inside of the impeller housing is parallel to the water flow. Therefore, this design pump needs no liner against the impeller housing, as in the case of a mixed flow pump.

Axial or Mixed?

Axial and mixed flow pumps are intended for different applications. One is not necessarily better than the other. The axial pump can be operated at higher engine rpm and is more suitable for racing. A mixed flow pump adds thrust at low engine rpm due to the pump design. Therefore, the mixed flow pump performs more efficiently at low engine rpm. This type pump is more suitable for a craft equipped to carry extra weight.

A jet pump seldom requires service except for the following:

Impeller-to-liner clearance becomes excessive -- mixed flow only.
Impeller is damaged.
The oil seal around the impeller shaft fails -- allowing water to enter hull.

Intermediate Housing

All models covered in this manual have an intermediate housing as a "link" between the engine crankshaft and the impeller shaft. Service procedures -- which should be quite rare -- for this housing are presented in Section 10-4.

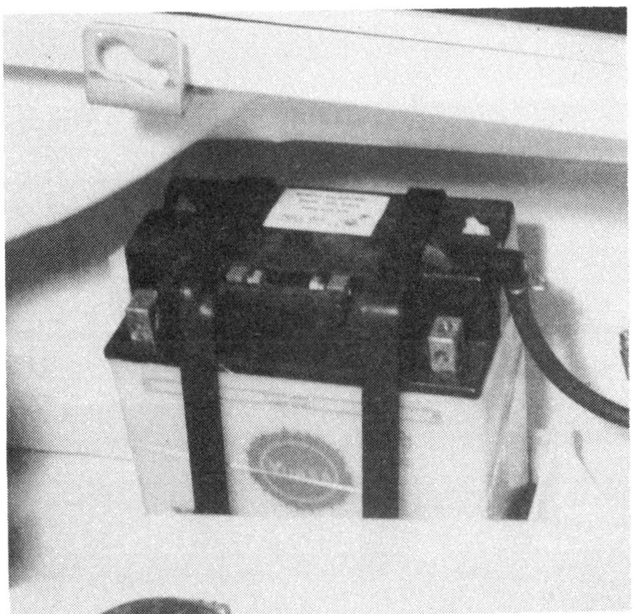

In order to measure the impeller-to-housing clearance, the rock grate must be removed. This task requires the battery to be removed and the craft tilted on its side.

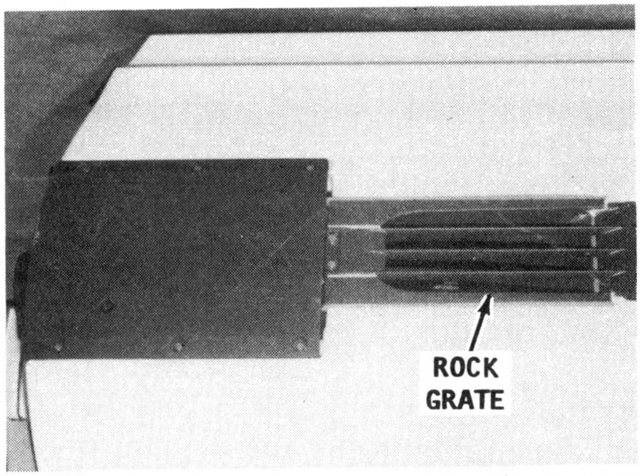

The rock grate must be removed to gain access to the impeller.

10-2 JET PUMP SHIMMING PROCEDURES FOR A MIXED FLOW PUMP -- EARLY MODELS

SPECIAL WORDS

The following procedure may be performed with the watercraft elevated on saw horses enabling a person to work underneath, or with the watercraft on its side allowing access to the rock grate and impeller.

If shimming is to be performed with the watercraft raised on saw horses, the battery may be left secured in the craft.

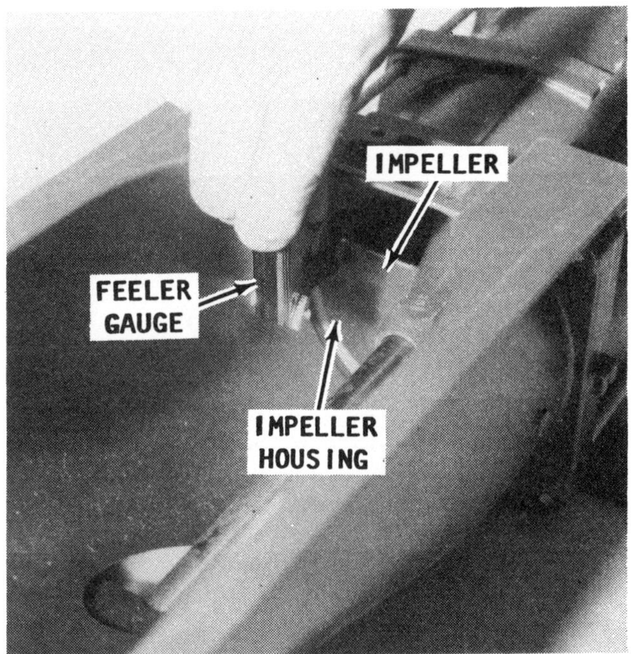

Measuring the impeller-to-housing clearance on a mixed flow pump installation, as explained in the text.

If the watercraft is to be positioned on its side, first disconnect the electrical leads at both battery terminals, and then remove the battery from the watercraft.

Remove the six bolts and washers securing the cover/rock grate to the jet pump. Insert a feeler gauge between each impeller blade and the impeller housing and determine the clearance. Make a note of all three clearances, one for each blade. Calculate the average of the three clearances. The recommended clearance is 0.012" (0.3mm). If the clearance is not to specifications, shim material must be added or removed between the impeller housing and the impeller according to the following table.

Mixed flow pump efficiency decreases by 30% as blade to liner clearance increases by 0.04" (1mm).

Measurement	Change
0.000" (0.0mm)	Remove 0.086" (2.2mm)
0.004" (0.1mm)	Remove 0.059" (1.5mm)
0.008" (0.2mm)	Remove 0.027" (0.7mm)
0.012" (0.3mm)	No change
0.016" (0.4mm)	Add 0.027" (0.7mm)
0.020" (0.5mm)	Add 0.059" (1.5mm)
0.024" (0.6mm)	Add 0.086" (2.2mm)
0.027" (0.7mm)	Add 0.113" (2.9mm)
0.031" (0.8mm)	Add 0.144" (3.7mm)
0.035" (0.9mm)	Add 0.172" (4.4mm)
0.039" (1.0mm)	Add 0.199" (5.1mm)

10-3 JET PUMP SERVICE ALL MODELS -- THIS MANUAL

SPECIAL WORDS

The following series of illustrations were taken of a mixed flow pump. The axial flow pump differs slightly in appearance, but has the same basic components. Where differences occur, they will be clearly identified.

REMOVAL

Disconnect both battery cables from the battery and remove the battery from the craft.

CAUTION

The battery **MUST** be removed to avoid spilling electrolyte into the bilge through the battery vent holes when the craft is tilted to one side.

Rotate the fuel control valve to the **"OFF"** position. Drain or remove the fuel tank. If working on a WaveRunner III or WaveRunner VXR, drain the oil from the oil injection tank. Place an old blanket or equivalent on the workshop floor to cushion the edges of the craft and prevent the craft from sliding around while the work progresses. Rotate the craft on the blanket to expose the rock grate, and then block the hull to hold the desired position.

GOOD WORDS

Before starting service work on a mixed flow jet pump, the impeller blade clearance should be checked, as described in the previous section -- 10-2.

If the clearance is checked, the rock grate/solid cover will have been removed. Therefore, the following paragraphs would not apply.

If working on an axial flow pump, the clearance need not be checked, as outlined in Section 10-2. Therefore, proceed as follows.

Remove the six bolts and washers securing the jet pump ride plate to the hull. Remove the jet pump supply hose and the bilge pump siphon hose from the two fittings on the cover. Remove the cooling system supply hose from the fitting on the jet pump. Pry the steering cable from the ball joint on the output nozzle. If working on a WaveRunner III, pry the reverse shift cable from the ball joint on the reverse gate assembly.

Remove the four bolts and washers securing the solid cover end of the rock grate to the hull. The solid cover over the pump shaft and the rock grate are one piece. Remove the two bolts and washers securing the rock grate to the jet pump. Remove the solid cover/rock grate.

Observe the location and thickness of any shim material placed between the pump mounting brackets and the craft hull. Be sure to identify each of the four stacks to ensure each stack will be installed back in its original location.

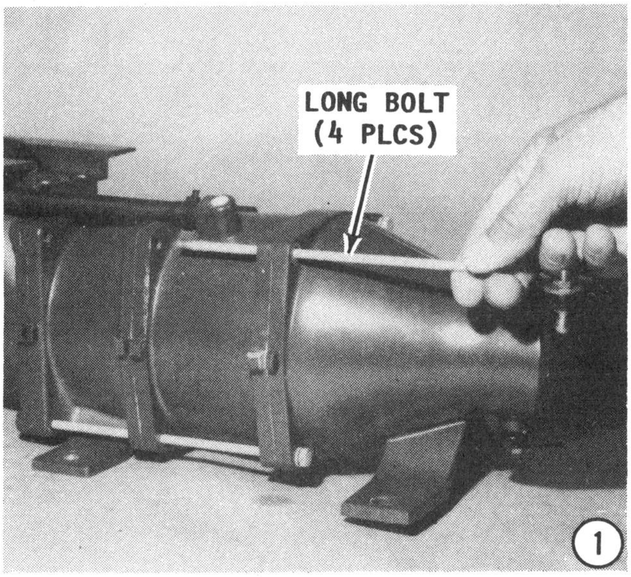

Remove the two forward and two rear jet pump mounting bolts and ease the pump shaft free of the coupler, out and clear of the craft.

The work continues with the jet pump on a suitable work surface.

DISASSEMBLING

1- Remove the four long bolts securing the nozzle and deflector assembly to the jet pump.

2- Obtain two flat blade screwdrivers. Insert the screwdriver blades between the two tabs on the impeller duct and the nozzle deflector, one screwdriver on each side. Tap the top of the screwdrivers alternately and evenly to "break" the seal between the two pieces.

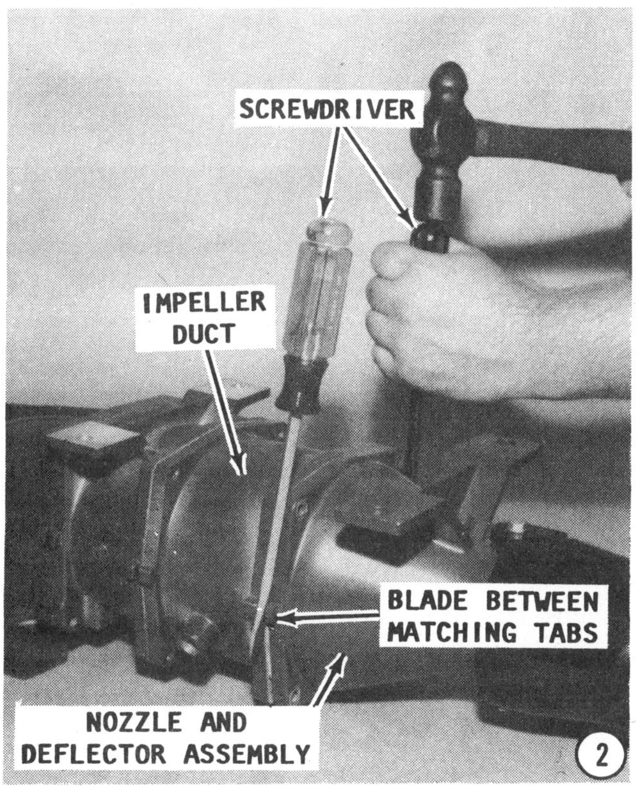

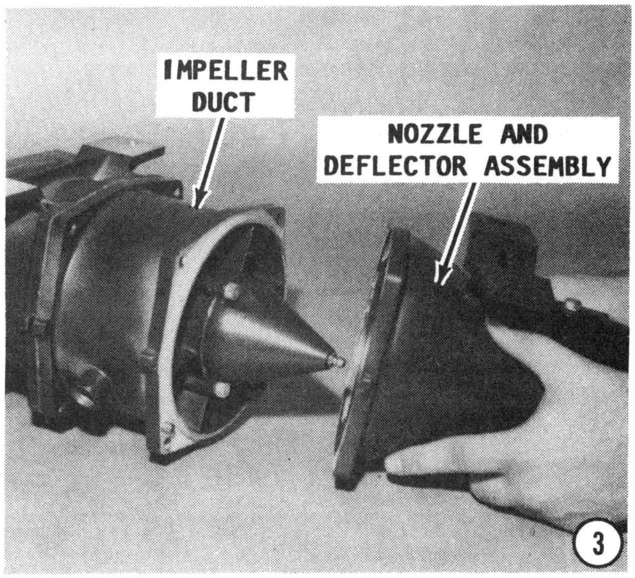

3- Remove the nozzle with deflector assembly attached, from the impeller duct. Clean away all traces of sealant from both contact surfaces.

4- Insert the screwdrivers between the tabs on the impeller housing and the impeller duct, one on each side, and as before, "break" the seal between the two pieces.

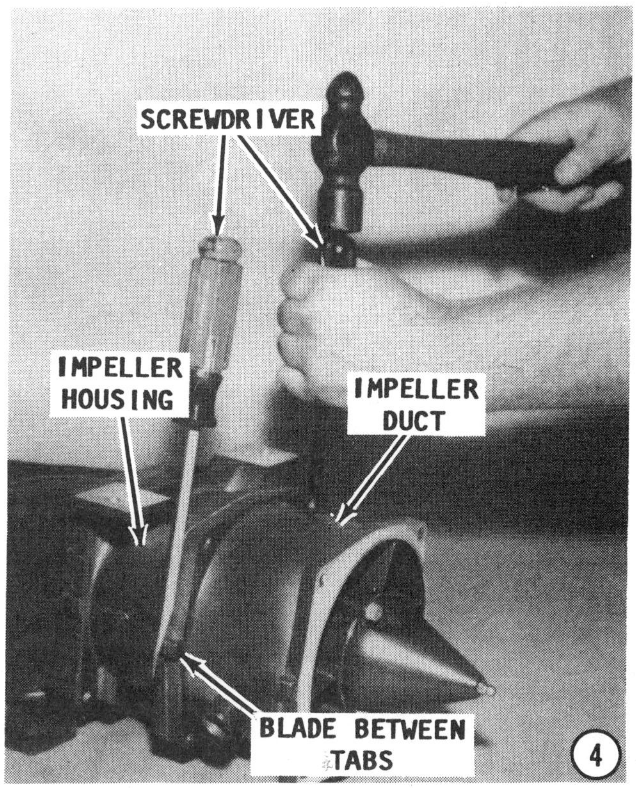

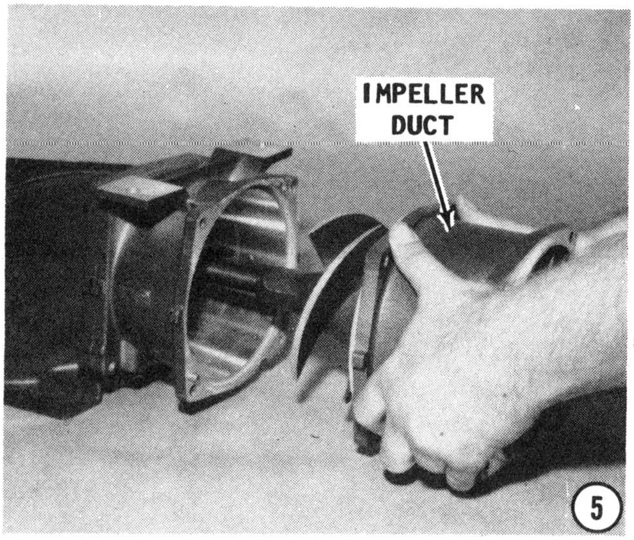

5- Remove the impeller duct from the impeller housing. Clean away all traces of sealant material from both contact surfaces.

Impeller Removal

If servicing a mixed flow pump on a WR650Q -- obtain splined tool Yamaha P/N YB-6079-A. If servicing an axial flow pump -- obtain special Yamaha tool P/N YB-6049. Both style pumps -- slide the tool onto the splined end of the impeller shaft. Clamp the tool in a vise with the impeller housing resting on the workbench, as indicated in the accompanying illustration. If the special splined tool is not available, it might be possible to **CAREFULLY** clamp the driveshaft directly in a vise equipped with soft jaws.

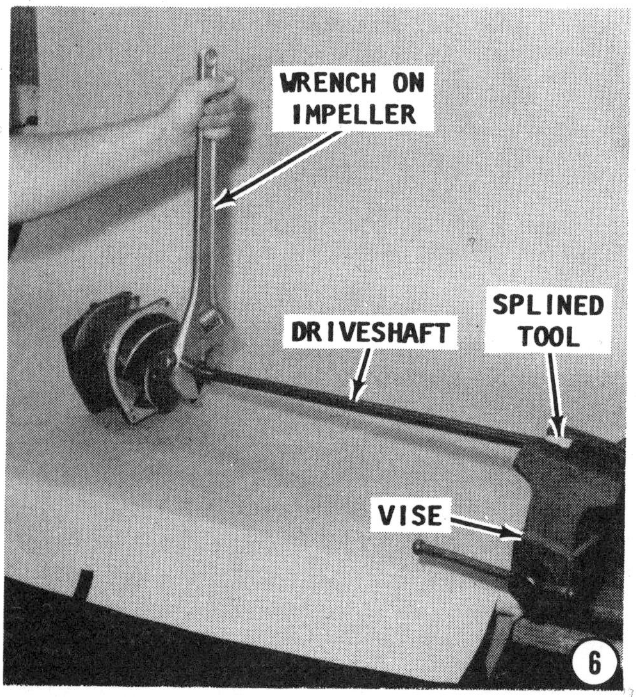

CRITICAL WORDS

The impeller has **LEFT-HAND** threads.

6- Using a large adjustable wrench on the "nut" end of the impeller, rotate the impeller **CLOCKWISE** to "break" it free of the shaft.

7- Remove the impeller from the impeller shaft.

SPECIAL WORDS FOR MIXED FLOW PUMPS EARLY MODELS

These mixed flow models have pieces of shim material between the impeller and the impeller duct. **SAVE** the shim material for later installation. The thickness of shim material is critical to properly position the impeller at a specific clearance from the impeller housing.

SPECIAL WORDS FOR AXIAL FLOW PUMPS MOST MODELS -- THIS MANUAL

Axial flow pumps do not use shim material next to the impeller. The impeller and impeller duct is manufactured to very close tolerances and adjustments with shim material is not necessary.

Remove the cupped washer from the impeller shaft.

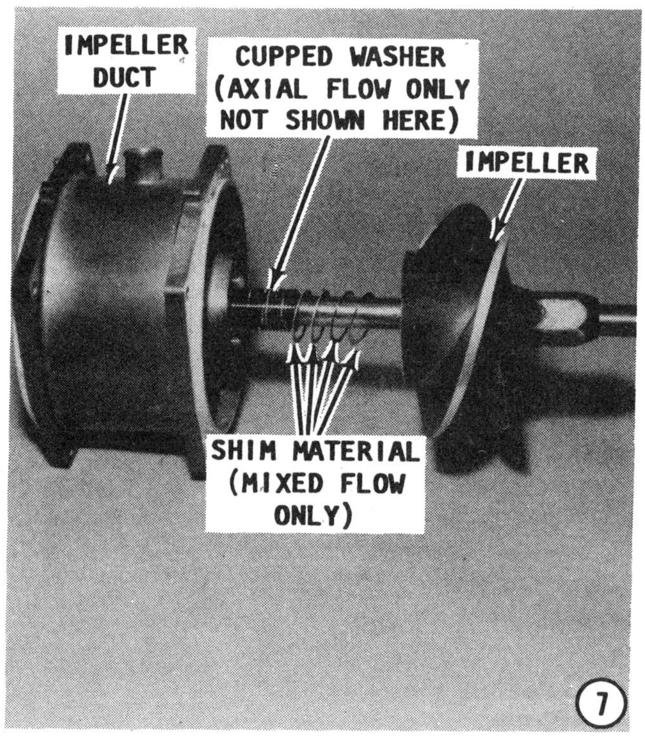

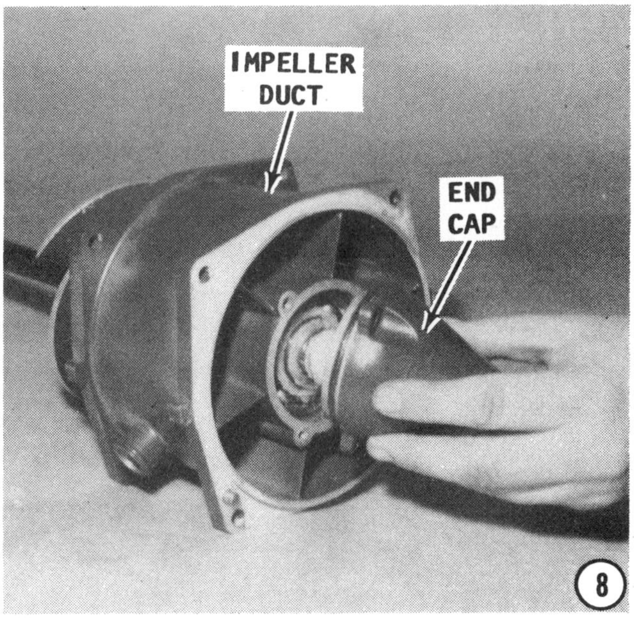

8- Remove the three bolts securing the end cap to the impeller duct.

9- Remove the **O**-ring from the end cap. Discard the **O**-ring if a replacement is available. Scoop out the old lubricant and wipe the cap clean.

Impeller Shaft Removal

10- If the impeller shaft bearings and/or oil seal are no longer fit for further service, the impeller shaft must be pressed free of the impeller duct.

Make a set up at the arbor press, as shown in the accompanying illustration, with the impeller duct resting on two pieces of wood. Due to the shaft length, it **MUST** be pressed from the duct and **NOT** hammered out. Attempting to hammer the shaft free will surely damage the shaft and make it unfit for further service.

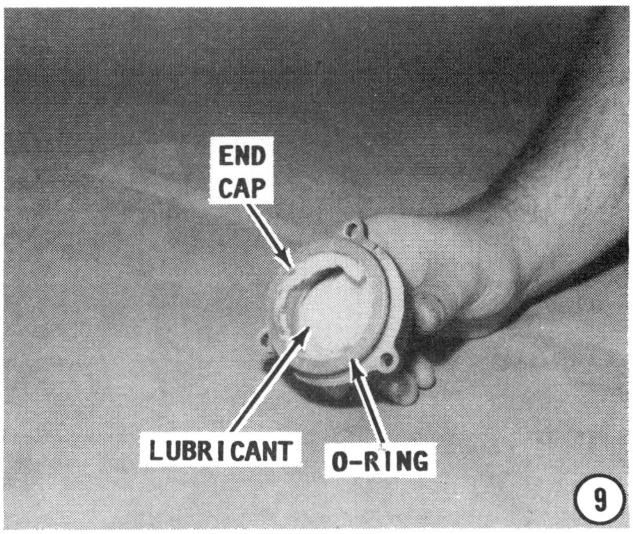

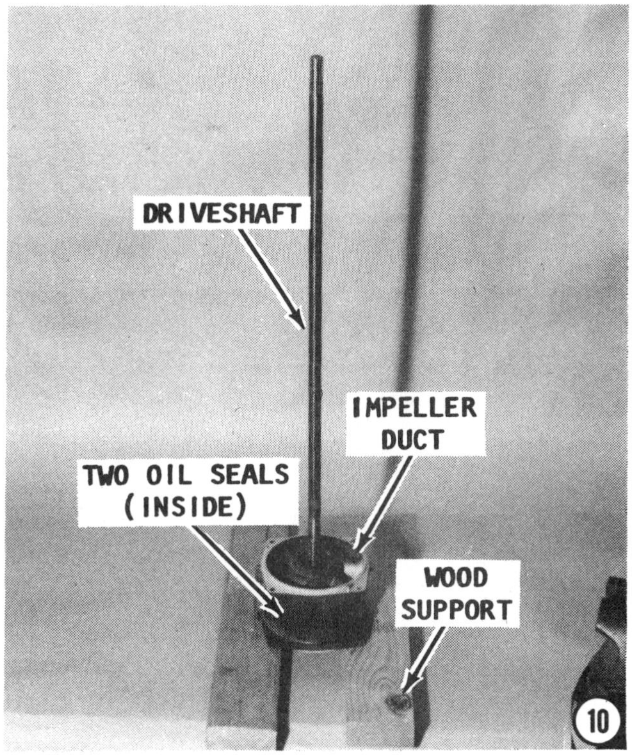

Carefully press the impeller shaft free and take care not to allow the shaft to drop to the floor. One or both of the roller bearings may come out with the shaft. If so, press the shaft free of the bearing/s.

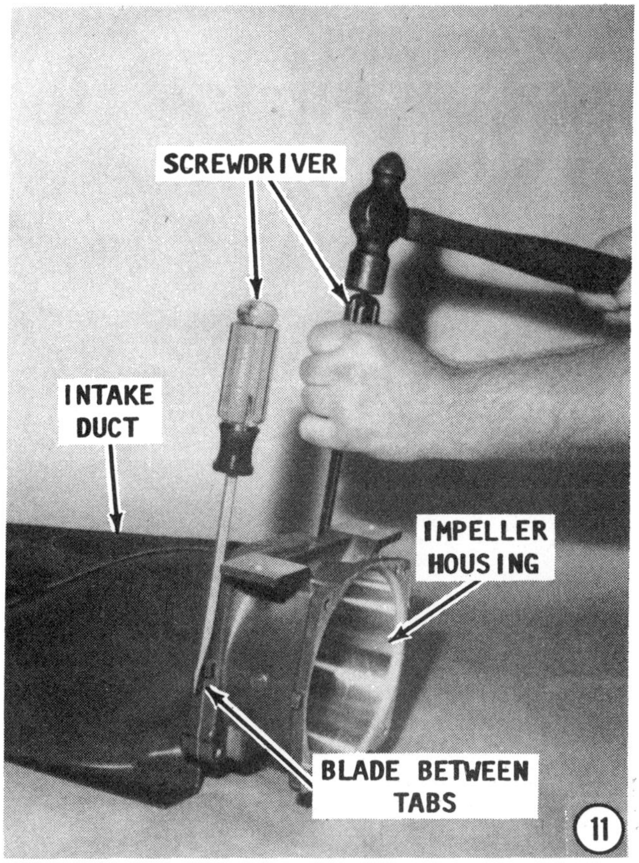

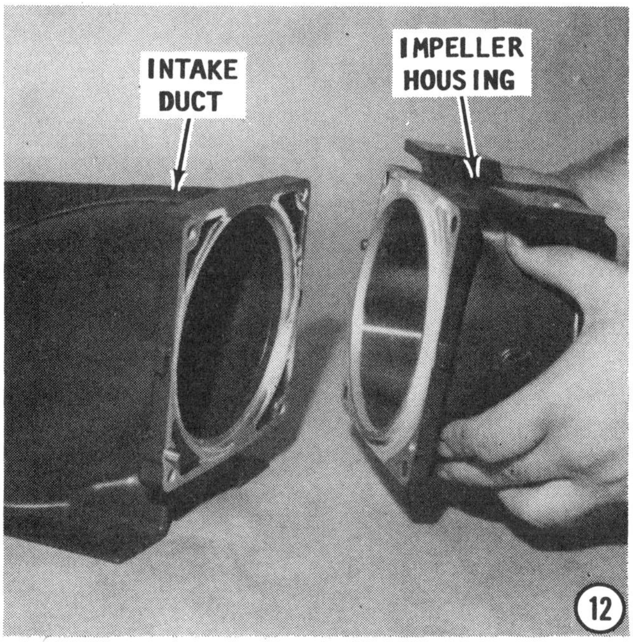

Pry the two forward oil seals out with a screwdriver.

Obtain a slide hammer P/N YB-6096 with a jaw puller attachment and pull the remaining bearing/s out from the forward end of the duct.

11- Insert screwdrivers between the tabs on the impeller housing and the intake duct, one on each side. Using a hammer alternately on the screwdrivers, "break" the seal between the two pieces.

12- Separate the impeller housing from the intake duct. Clean away all traces of sealant from the two contact surfaces.

13- Remove the spacer retaining bolt from the side of the jet pump. This bolt secures the spacer inside the jet pump housing.

GOOD WORDS

The two oil seals and bushing need not be removed in the next two steps unless it is definitely decided they are unfit for further service.

14- If servicing a mixed flow pump, obtain bearing driver P/N YW-6364 and a suitable hammer.

15- Assemble the two special tools, and then insert the driver into the forward end of the jet pump housing. Tap the handle with a hammer to remove the spacer and washer, two oil seals, and the bushing from the housing.

16- Remove the two bolts, one on each side, securing the deflector to the nozzle.

17- Remove the two bushings, one on each side, from the deflector and pull the deflector free from the nozzle.

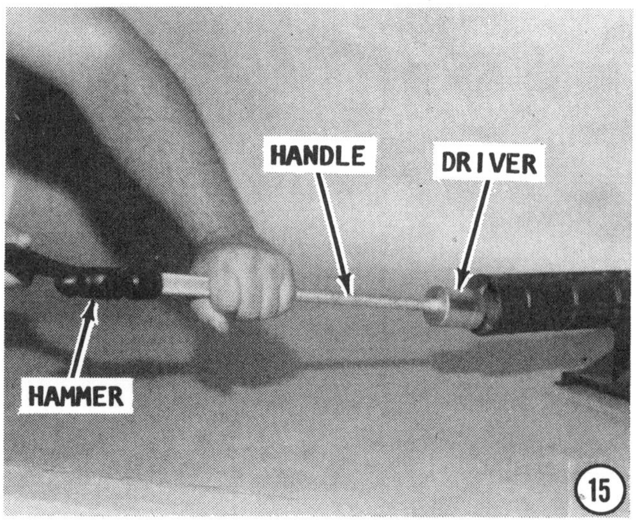

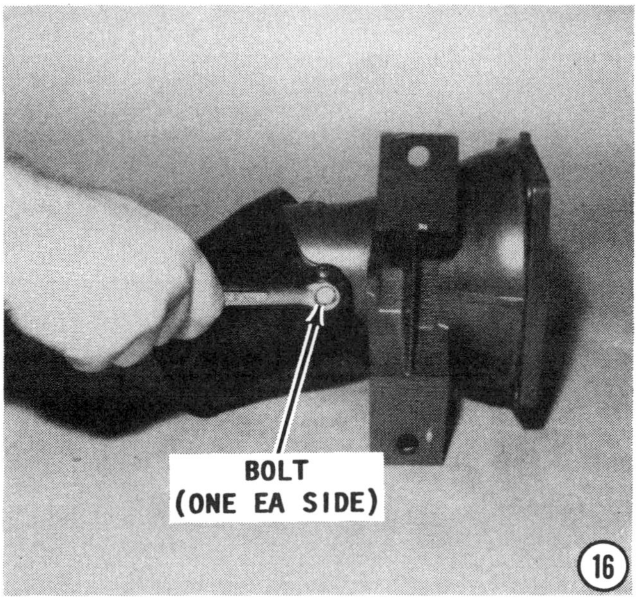

If the impeller is chipped more than 1/4", the impeller should be replaced. Any chip smaller than 1/4" can be evenly filed away along the length of the blade.

CLEANING AND INSPECTING

Inspect the leading edge of each impeller blade. Ideally, the edge should be rounded to a 1/32" radius, **NOT** a knife-edge! The cross-section shape of an impeller blade is similar to that of an airplane wing.

If the craft is consistently operated in shallow water with a sandy or "pebbly" bottom, the leading edge of the impeller blades will become rounded or will become chipped with missing pieces.

Very little material may be removed from the impeller blades during reconditioning work. Therefore, if the edge is rounded off or corroded, a file can be carefully used to "dress" the edge.

If an impeller blade is chipped more than 1/4", the impeller should be replaced. Any chip smaller than 1/4" can be evenly filed away along the length of the blade. Whatever work is done to one blade must be done to all blades in order to maintain impeller balance. If the impeller becomes excessively out of balance, a definite vibration condition will be quite noticeable as the craft moves through the water. Such vibration will also cause premature bearing and shaft wear.

Set the impeller shaft on two V-blocks, one at each end. Position a dial indicator gauge over the center portion of the shaft and measure the runout. The maximum allowable runout is 0.020" (0.5mm).

Check to be sure the rock grate blades are not bent or missing. Such a condition might allow a large rock to pass through and cause damage to the impeller.

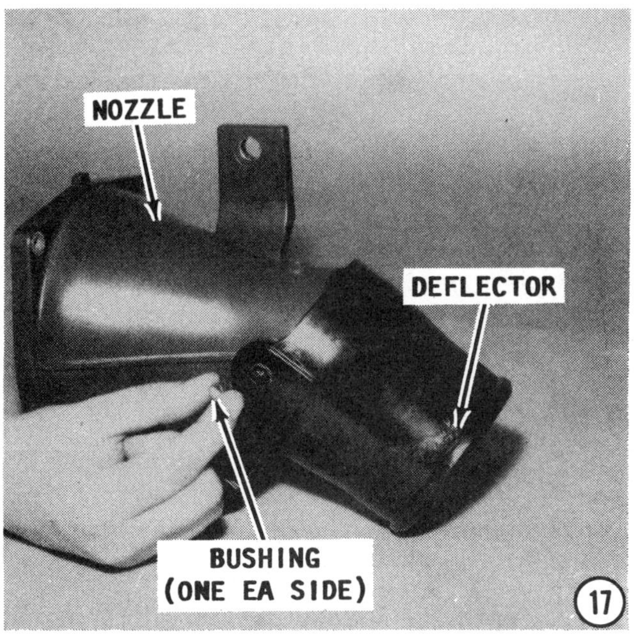

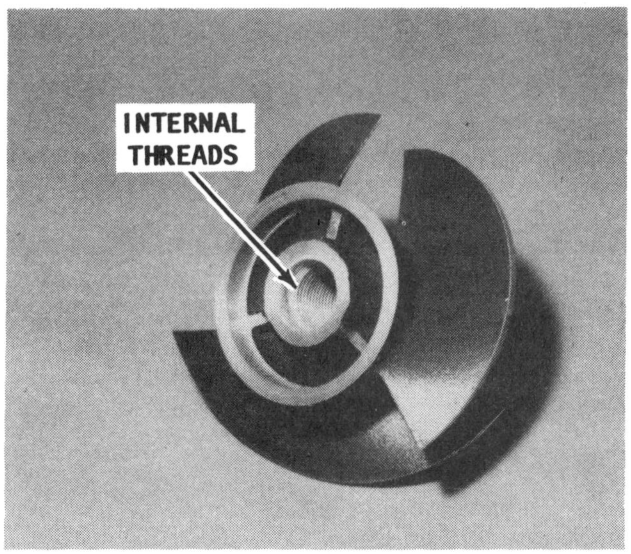

Check the condition of the impeller internal threads. If any stripped threads are discovered, replace the impeller.

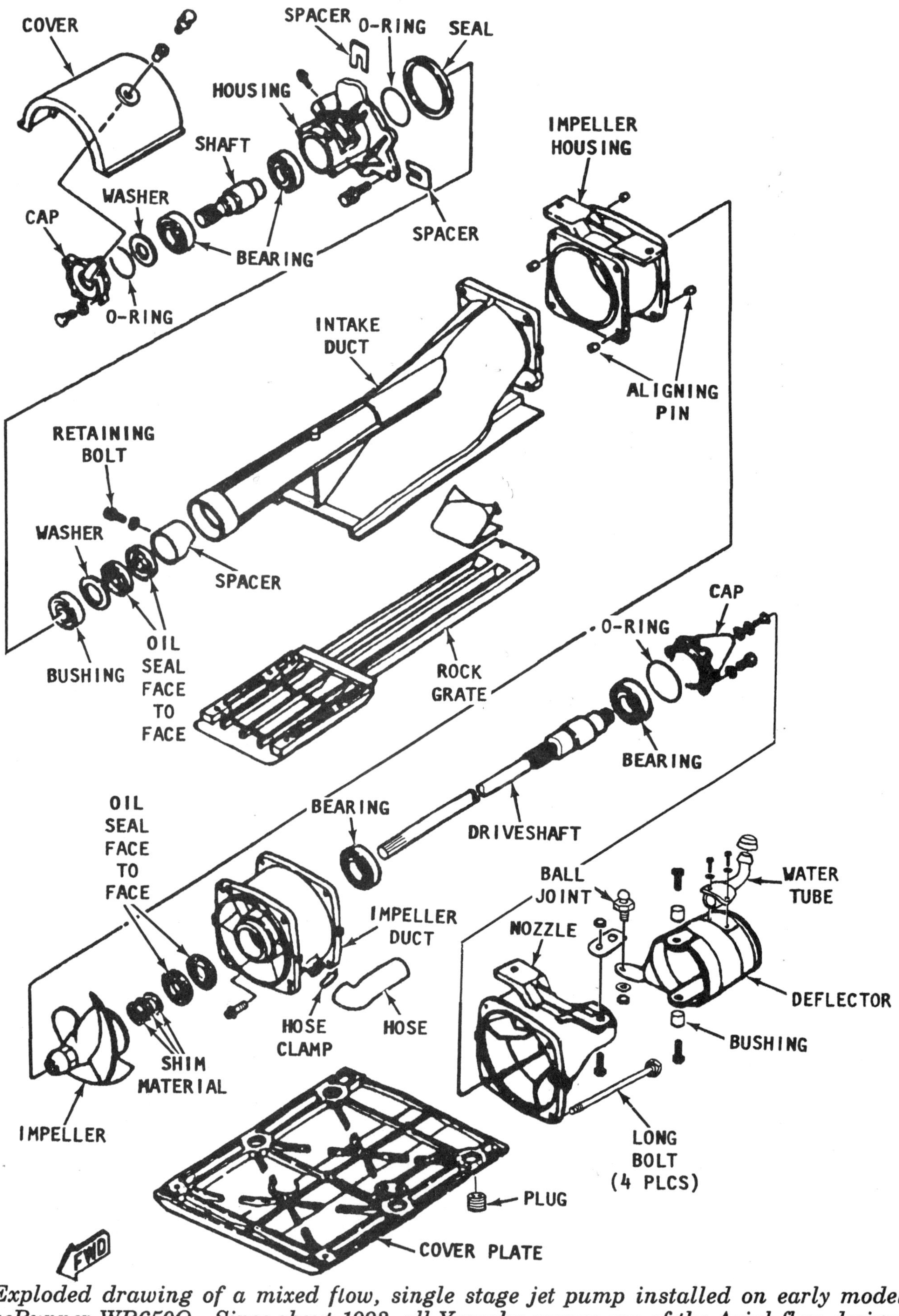

Exploded drawing of a mixed flow, single stage jet pump installed on early model WaveRunner WR650Q. Since about 1993, all Yamaha pumps are of the Axial flow design. Major parts have been identified.

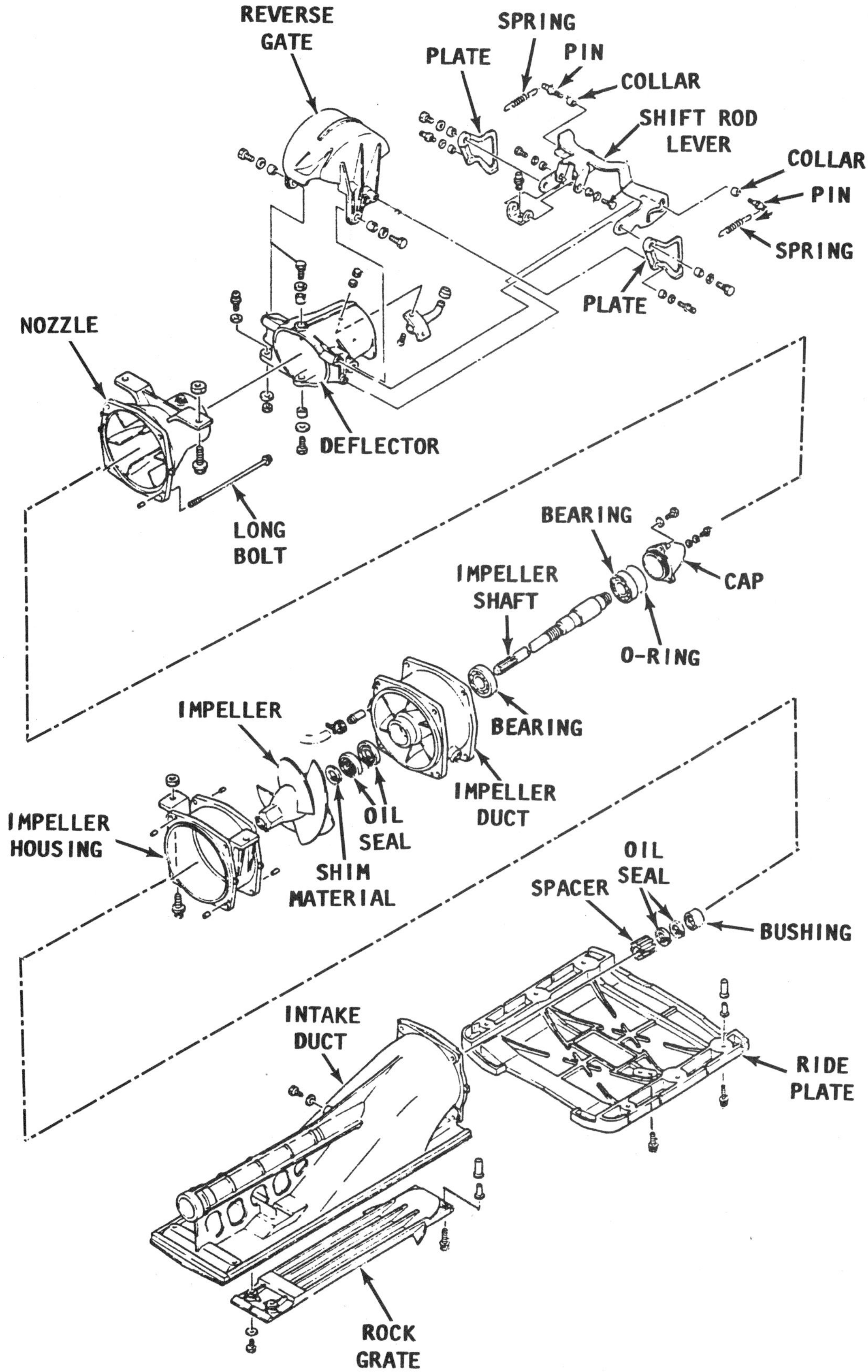

Exploded drawing of an axial flow, single stage jet pump installed on the WaveVenture 700 and 1100; the GP 1200; the WaveRunner 650 and 700; and the WaveRunner III. Major parts have been identified.

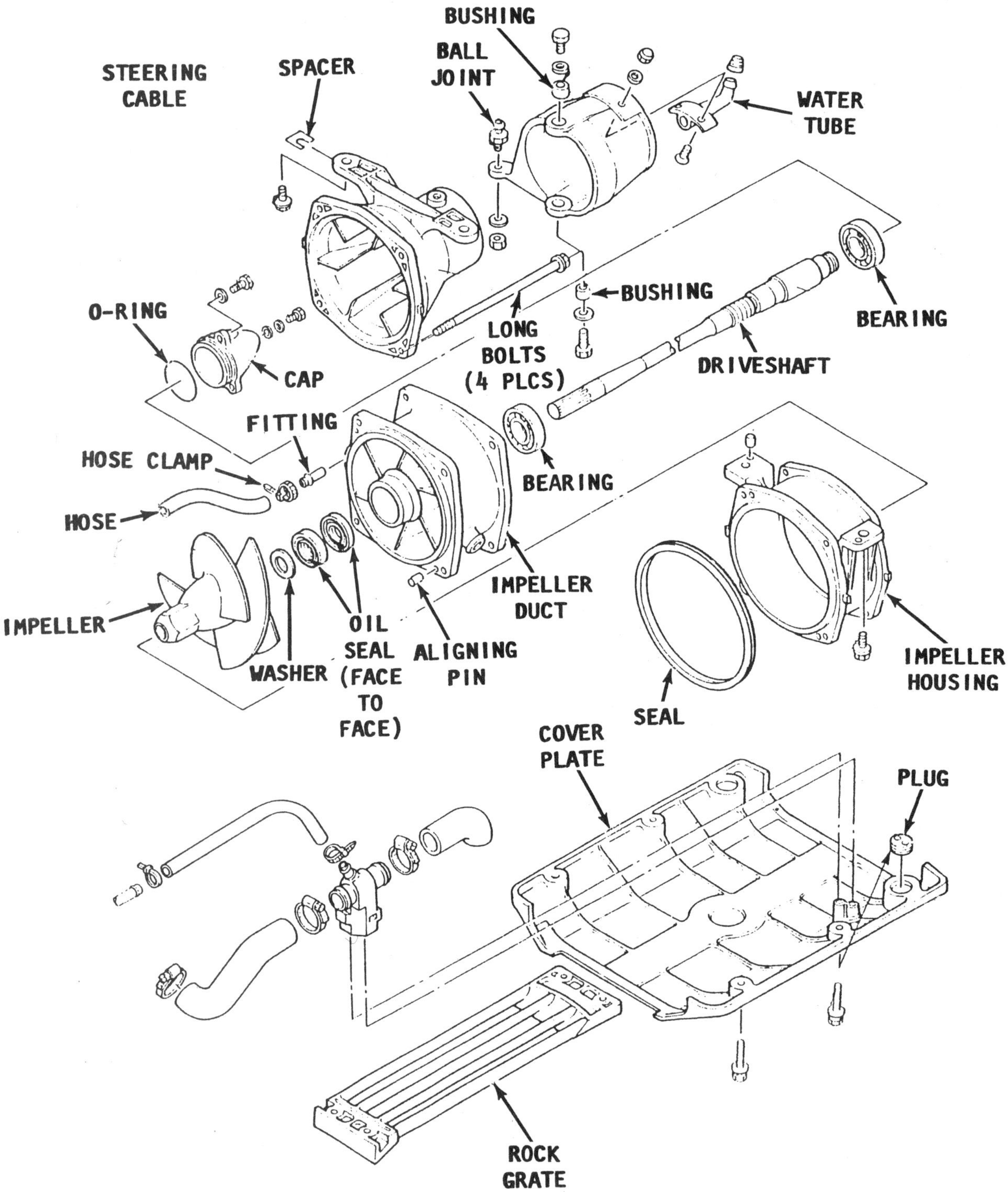

Exploded drawing of an axial flow, single stage jet pump installed on the WaveBlaster and the SuperJet. Major parts have been identified.

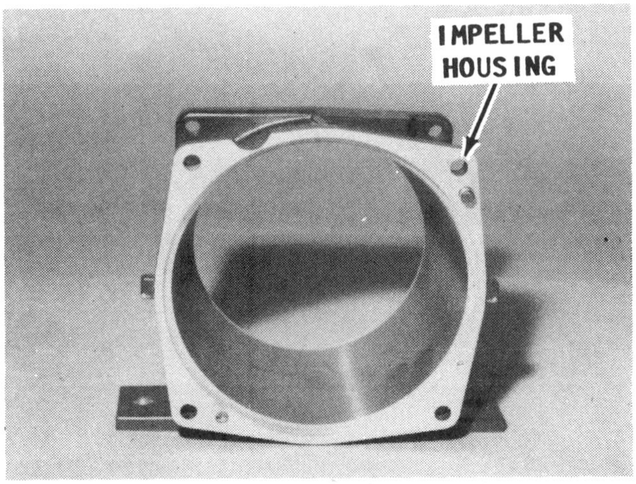

A new impeller housing ready for installation. If the impeller housing is damaged with deep grooves, it should be replaced.

Inspect the vanes in the pump bowl. File the vanes to a sharp edge on the forward end. Be sure to keep all the edges the same distance from the front of the bowl.

ASSEMBLING

The following procedures cover assembly of the complete jet pump. Simply skip any tasks not required because particular items were not removed.

1- Slide the deflector over the nozzle. Align the pivot holes on both sides and insert a bushing into each hole.

2- Install the pivot bolts, one on each side, into the bushings and thread them into the nozzle. Tighten both bolts securely.

3- If servicing a mixed flow pump on a WR650Q, obtain special Yamaha tool P/N YW-6356. For all others with an axial jet pump, obtain special tool P/N YB6021. Obtain special handle Yamaha P/N YB-6229 for all models.

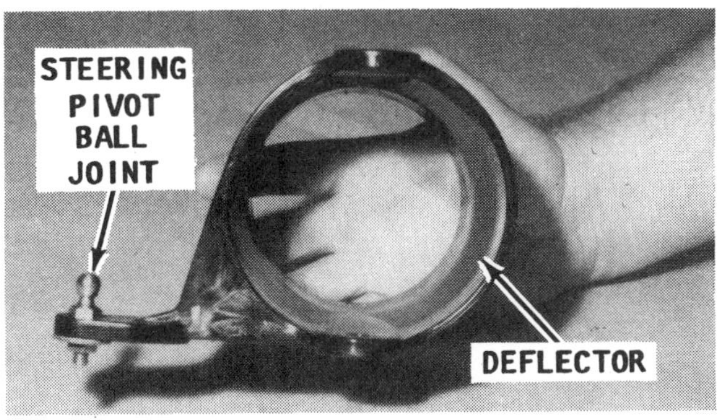

The steering pivot ball joint must be tightly secured to the deflector arm. Apply lubricant to the top of the ball of the joint.

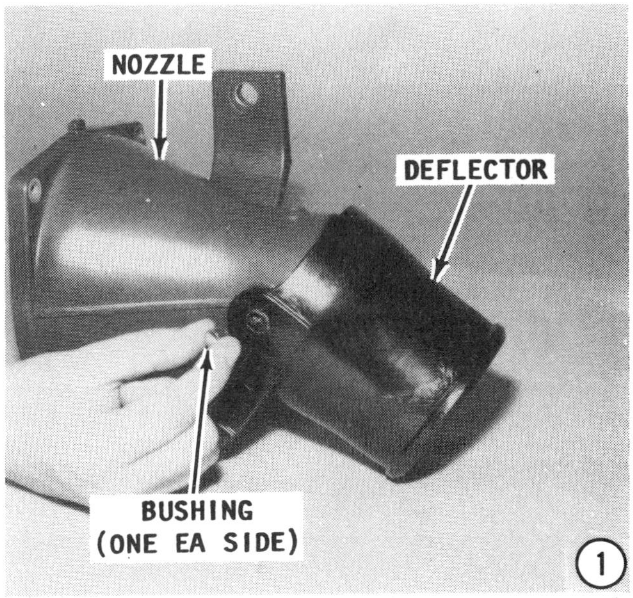

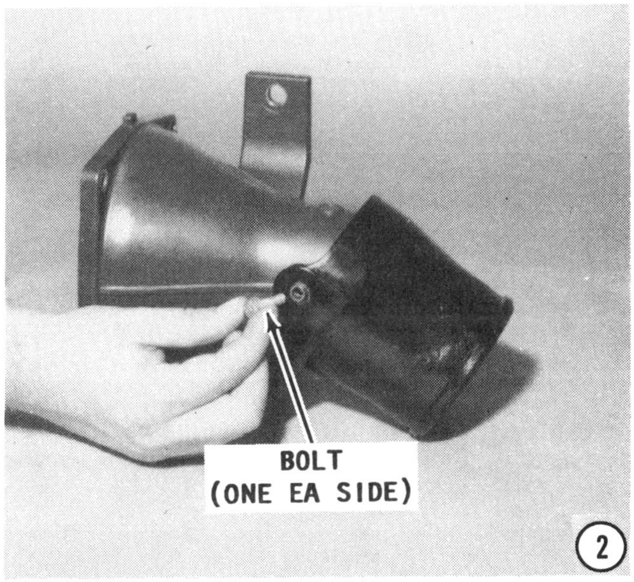

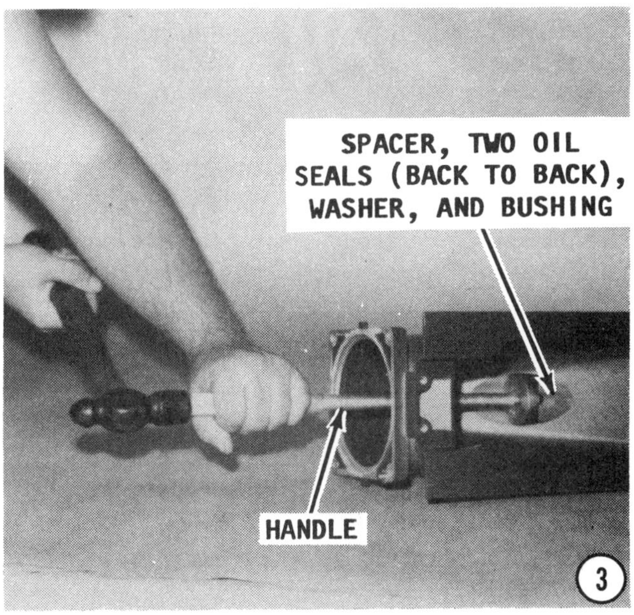

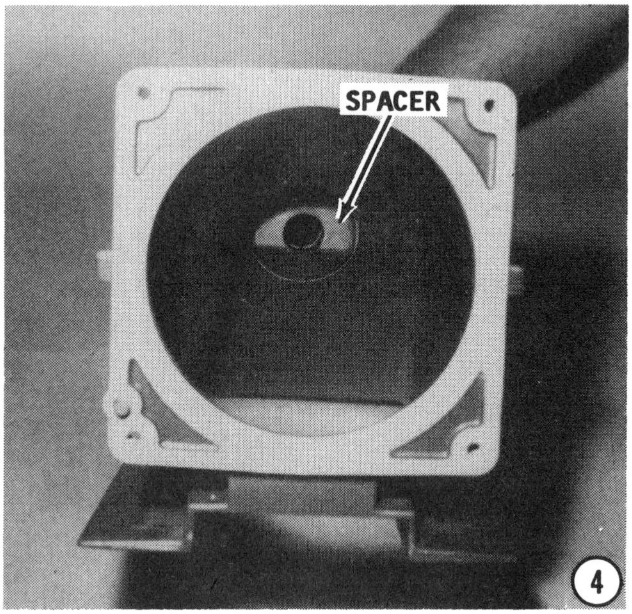

Coat the bushing with Yamalube or equivalent lubricant, and then install the bushing, as shown in the accompanying illustration. Continue to drive the bushing until it contacts an inner shoulder inside the pump casting. Slide the washer into position on top of the bushing.

Pack the lips of the two oil seals with the same lubricant and install them one after the other, back-to-back in the same manner against the washer. One seal prevents lubricant from escaping and the other seal prevents water from entering.

4- Install the tapered spacer using the same special tool. Rotate the spacer until the tapered surface of the spacer seats smoothly with the tapered surface of the casting and with the hole in the spacer aligned with the hole in the pump casting.

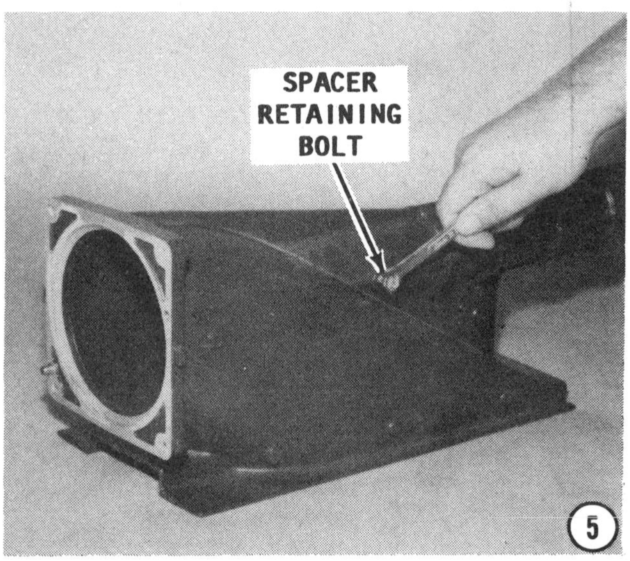

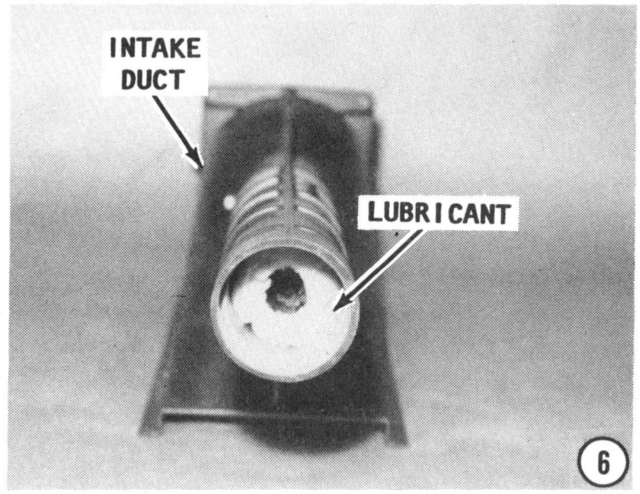

5- Install the spacer retaining bolt through the pump casting. This bolt secures the spacer within the casting. Tighten the bolt securely.

6- Pack the intake duct with Yamalube or equivalent lubricant to a depth of 3 to 4 inches.

7- If the impeller shaft was removed from the impeller duct and the seal and bearings removed, during disassembling, proceed as follows: If servicing a mixed flow pump -- WR650Q, obtain Yamaha special tool YW-6356. If servicing an axial flow pump -- all others except WR650Q, obtain special tool P/N YB-6016. Obtain special handle P/N YB-6229 for all models.

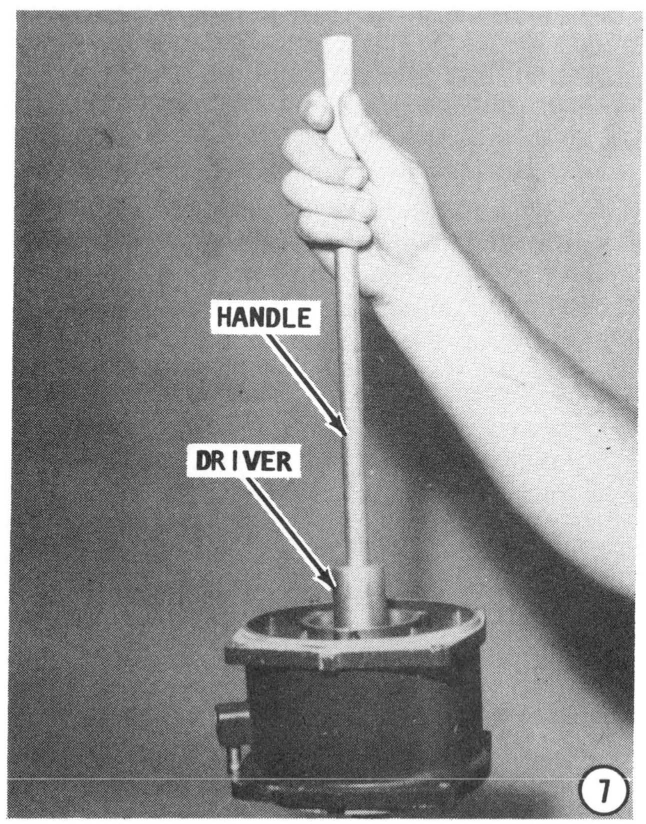

Pack both oil seal lips with Yamalube or equivalent lubricant and install the seals into the forward end of the impeller duct with both seal lips facing **FORWARD.** Engineers have concluded a better seal arrangement is obtained if the lip of both seals face the same direction, instead of having the seals installed "back-to-back".

Place the forward bearing on an arbor press surface with the embossed letters/-numbers facing up. Pass the splined end of the impeller shaft down through the bearing and **CAREFULLY** press on the threaded end of the shaft until the shoulder on the shaft rests against the bearing.

Place the impeller duct on the arbor press with the two installed seals against the press. Pass the splined end of the shaft down into the impeller duct and press on the threaded end of the shaft until the forward bearing on the shaft, rests against a shoulder in the impeller duct. Fill the cavity inside the duct, around the installed shaft, with Yamalube or equivalent lubricant.

If servicing a jet pump on the Model WR650Q with a mixed flow pump, obtain a suitable driver. For all axial flow pumps installed on all other Yamaha watercraft for the production years covered in this manual, obtain special Yamaha tool P/N YB-34473. Also obtain handle Yamaha P/N YB-6229. Install the rear bearing into the impeller duct with the embossed numbers/letters facing **FORWARD.**

8- Fill the end cap with Yamalube or equivalent lubricant. Install a new O-ring into the groove around the cap.

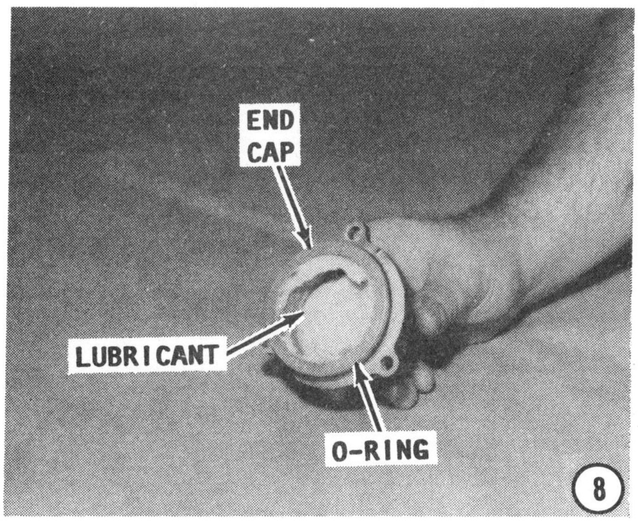

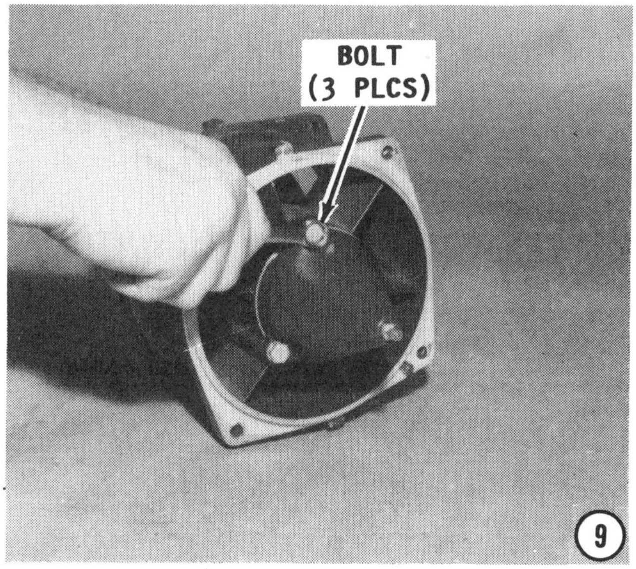

9- Coat the cap bolt threads with Loctite No. 572. Install the end cap onto the impeller duct and tighten the three bolts to a torque value of 5.8 ft lb (8Nm). The WaveRunner III and the SuperJet have a single bolt at the tip of the end cap. This bolt should be tightened to a torque value of 3 ft lb (4Nm). All other models have a grease fitting at this location.

10- If servicing a mixed flow pump on a WR650Q craft, place the correct amount of shim material over the splined end of the impeller shaft, as determined in Section 10-2, Jet Pump Shimming

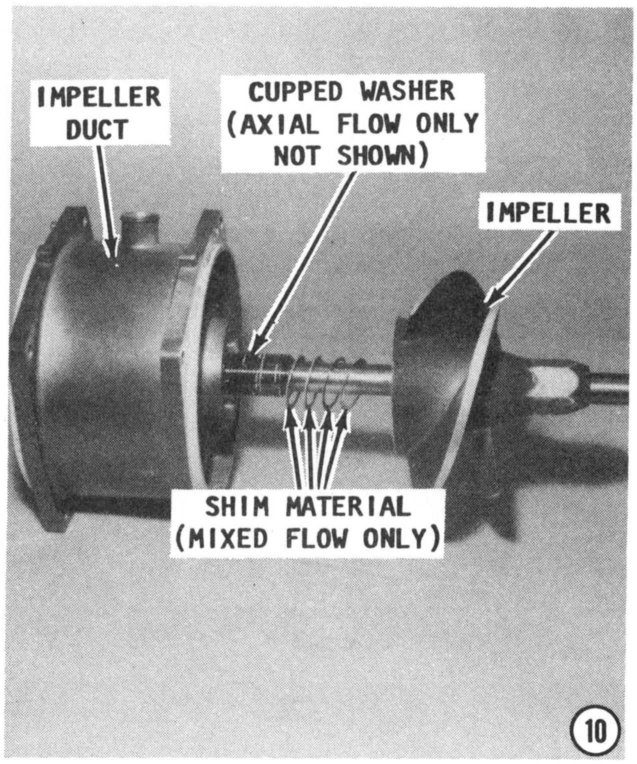

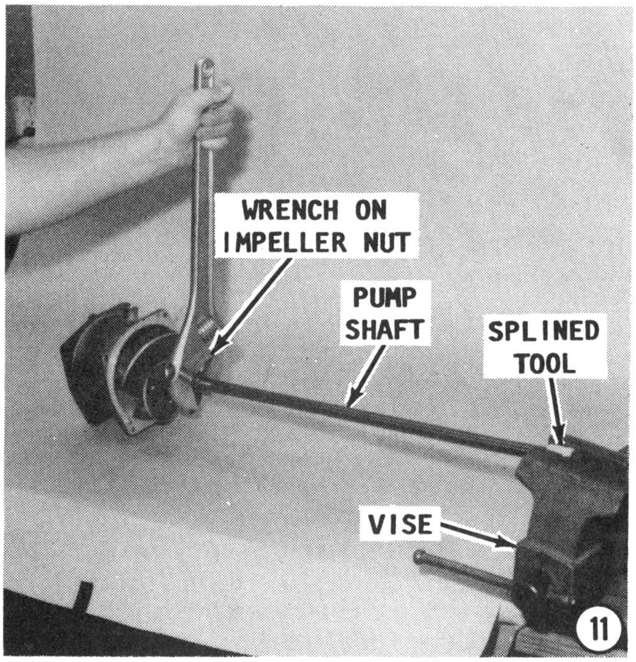

splined end of the shaft with the "cast" nut facing the shaft splines.

11- Obtain splined tool P/N YB-6079. Place the tool over the shaft splines and clamp the tool in a vise with the impeller duct resting on the workbench, as shown.

CRITICAL WORDS

The impeller has **LEFT-HAND** threads. Therefore, the impeller must be rotated **COUNTERCLOCKWISE** to tighten the impeller. A "crowsfoot" wrench the same size as the "cast" nut may be used to tighten the nut to the specified torque value. The crowsfoot wrench has a square hole to accommodate a torque wrench.

The accompanying illustration shows an adjustable wrench being used to tighten the nut before the crowsfoot and torque wrench is used to reach the final torque value.

Procedure, on Page 10-3. Coat the internal threads on the impeller with Loctite No. 572.

If servicing axial flow pumps on all craft except the WR650Q, shim material is not used at this location due to the design of the unit. These units use a cupped washer in place of shim material. Install the washer with the cupped side **TOWARD** the impeller.

All Models

Coat the internal impeller threads with Loctite 572. Slide the impeller down the

Tighten the impeller **COUNTERCLOCKWISE** to a torque value of 13 ft lb (18Nm), as described in the previous "Critical Words".

SPECIAL SEALANT WORDS

The manufacturer recommends the use of Yamabond #4 at each of the four jet pump case joints.

Yamabond #4 is a non-hardening material and is recommended for all metal-to-metal joints. This compound is highly resistant to oil and gasoline. Therefore, make every effort to obtain the closest equivalent, if Yamabond #4 is not available.

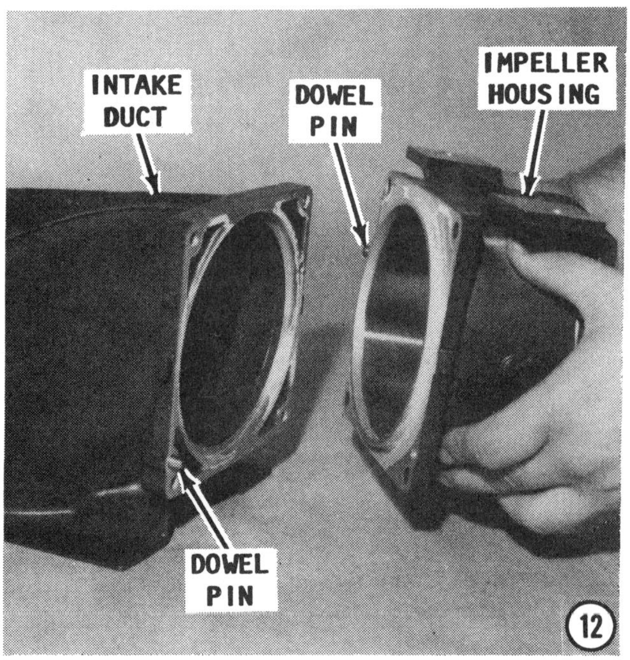

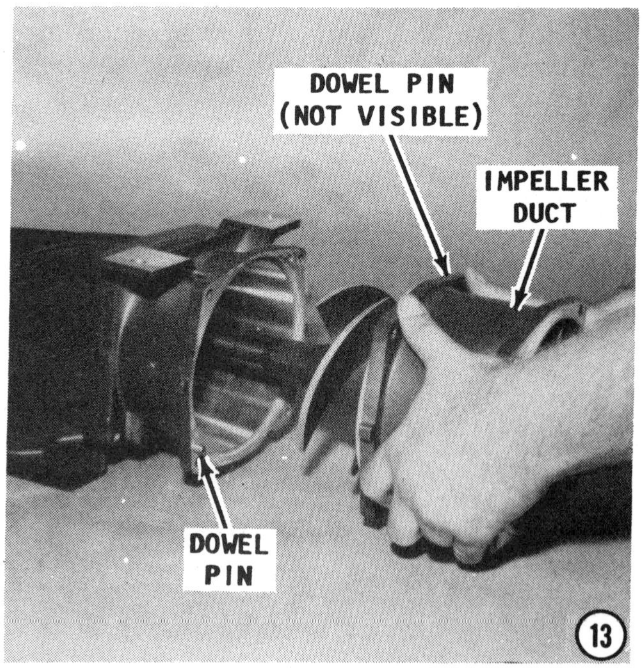

12- Apply a narrow bead of Yamabond #4, or equivalent, to the contact surfaces of the intake duct and the impeller housing. Loop the bead around the two dowel pins and all eight bolts holes, four in each casting. Position the housing against the intake duct, indexing the two dowel pins into the matching holes. Clean away any excess Yamabond.

13- Apply a narrow bead of Yamabond #4, or equivalent, to the contact surfaces of the impeller housing and the impeller duct. Loop the bead around the two dowel pins and all eight bolt holes, four in each casting. Insert the splined end of the impeller shaft into the jet pump. Position the duct against the housing, indexing the two dowel pins into the matching holes. Clean away any excess Yamabond.

14- Apply a narrow bead of Yamabond #4, or equivalent, to the contact surfaces of the impeller duct and the nozzle housing. Loop the bead around the two dowel pins and all eight bolt holes, four in each casting. Position the nozzle housing with the deflector assembly attached, against the impeller duct, indexing the two dowel pins into the matching holes. Clean away any excess Yamabond.

15- Insert the four long bolts through the casting flanges of the jet pump assemblies to secure them together. Tighten the four bolts alternately and evenly to a torque value of 13 ft lb (18Nm).

16- On some models covered in this manual, but not all, a lubrication fitting is accessible through the output nozzle, as shown. Use the fitting and lubricate the rear end of the impeller shaft.

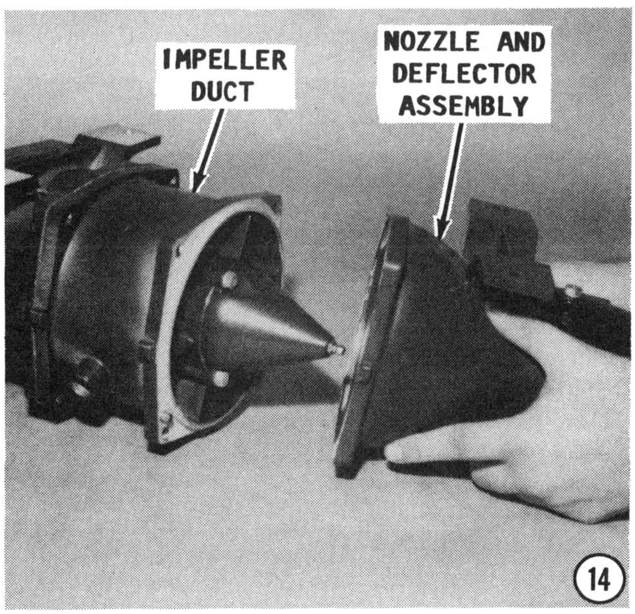

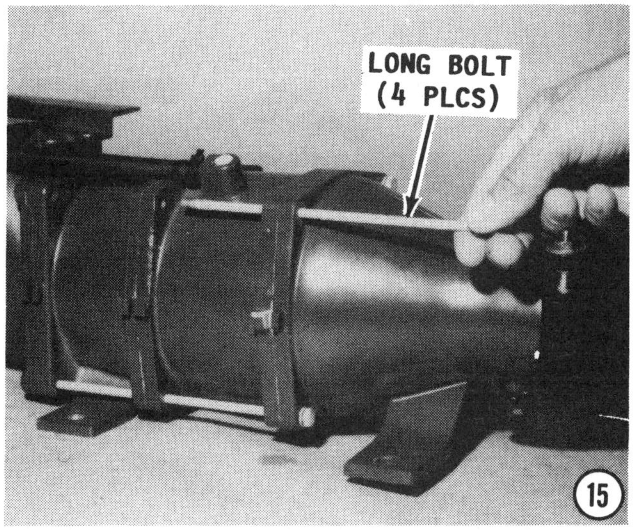

Jet Pump Installation

Attach the larger cooling system supply hose to the fitting on the impeller duct and secure it with a hose clamp. Slide the jet pump into place inside the hull cavity, with the impeller shaft splines indexed with the splines of the coupler, inside the intermediate housing. It may be necessary to rotate the shaft slightly in order for the external and internal splines to index.

Place any shim material, removed during disassembling, back in its original location. Install the four washers and bolts securing the two mounting brackets to the hull. Tighten the four bolts to a torque value of 24 ft lb (34Nm).

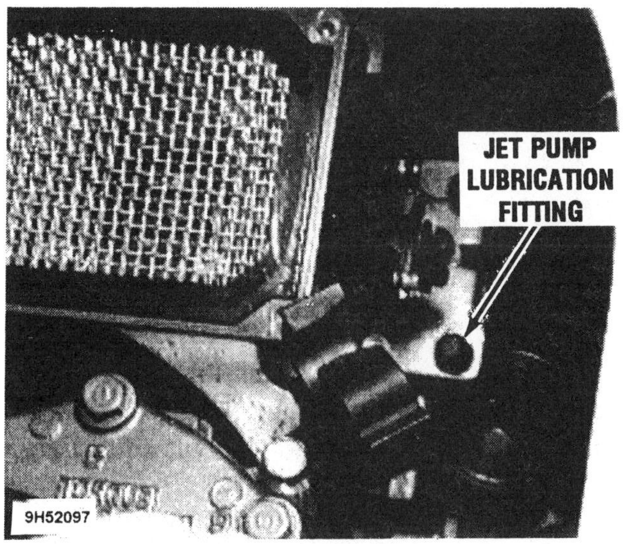

Lubrication fitting for the jet pump is located in the engine compartment just forward of the No.1 carburetor.

Rock Grate Installation

Install the cover/rock grate with the attaching hardware -- four bolts and washers at the cover end -- two bolts and washers at the grate end.

Snap the steering cable end onto the ball joint on the output nozzle. If servicing a unit with a reverse gate, install the reverse shift cable onto the ball joint on the reverse gate assembly.

Lay a bead of silicone sealant around the perimeter of the hull opening. Install the other end of the supply hose to the fitting on the ride plate. Connect the bilge pump siphon hose to the other fitting on the cover plate. Secure both hoses with hose clamps. Install the ride plate over the jet pump and secure it in place with bolts and washers. Tighten these bolts to a torque value of 5 ft lb (7Nm).

Move the craft upright and install the battery, observing the correct cable connections. Install or fill the fuel tank. If the unit being serviced has the oil injection system, fill the oil injection tank. The oil injection system **MUST** be "bled" while operating the engine on a premix as directed in Section 6-8, Page 6-28 and 6-29. Rotate the fuel control valve to the **"ON"** position.

Check Completed Work

Secure the unit in a test tank or in a body of water. If unable to use a tank or body of water, connect a flush attachment and hose to the jet pump.

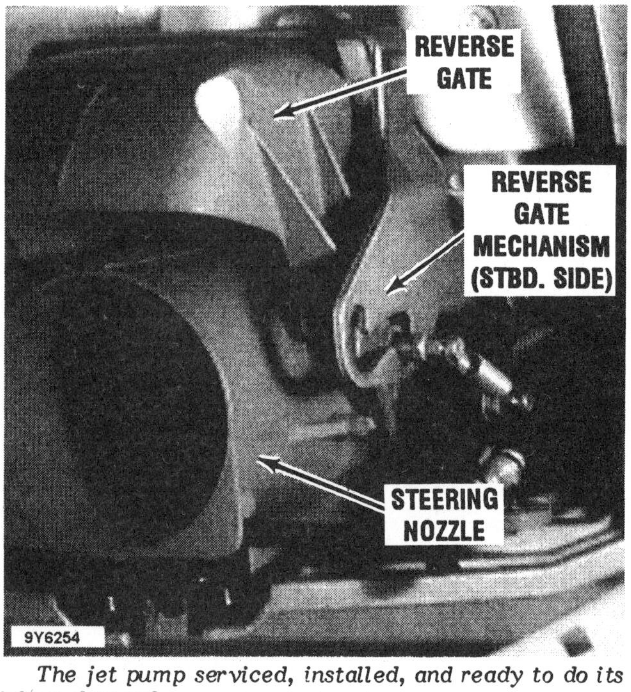

The jet pump serviced, installed, and ready to do its job on demand.

CAUTION

Water must circulate through the jet pump; to and from the engine, anytime the engine is operating. Circulating water will prevent damage by overheating to the engine block; pistons; and rings by overheating moving engine parts and possible engine seizure.

NEVER, AGAIN, NEVER operate the engine at high speed with a flush device attached. The engine, operating at high speed with such a device attached, would **RUNAWAY** from lack of a load on the impeller, causing extensive damage.

10-4 INTERMEDIATE HOUSING

The intermediate housing serves as a "link" between the engine crankshaft and the impeller shaft. Required service on this housing should be quite rare during the life of the craft. However, if the determination is made that the intermediate housing requires attention and service work, this section outlines the necessary tasks to return the housing to a "satisfactory" condition.

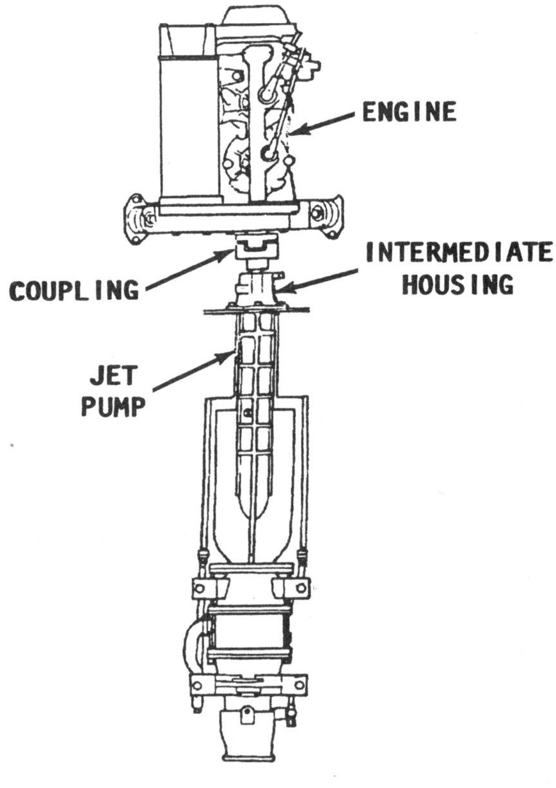

Simple line drawing to show how the intermediate housing serves as a "link" between the engine crankshaft and the impeller shaft.

The housing is mounted inside the engine compartment. Access to the housing can only be gained after the engine has been removed from the craft. See Chapter 8 for instructions on engine removal.

Removal

The following procedures pick up the work after the engine has been removed from the craft, per Chapter 8.

Remove the three bolts securing the housing to the engine compartment wall. Slide the rubber coupler from the coupling. Pull the housing free from the splines of the impeller shaft.

Move the housing to a suitable work surface.

Disassembling

1- Obtain special tool P/N YW-6355. Clamp the tool in a vise with the splined end facing up, as shown. If this tool is not available, locate an old short impeller shaft and clamp it securely in the vise. Without either the tool or a section of impeller

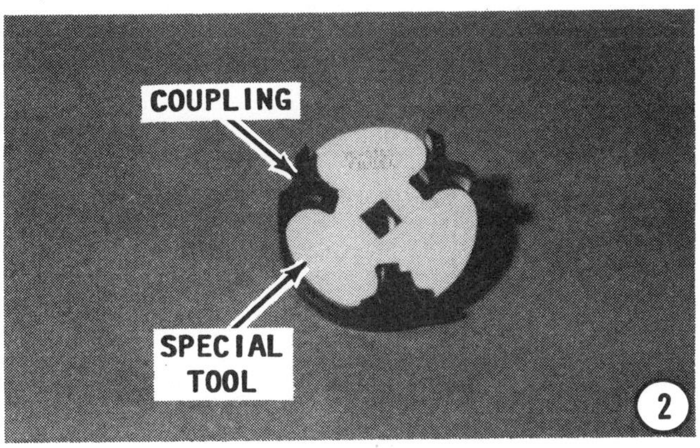

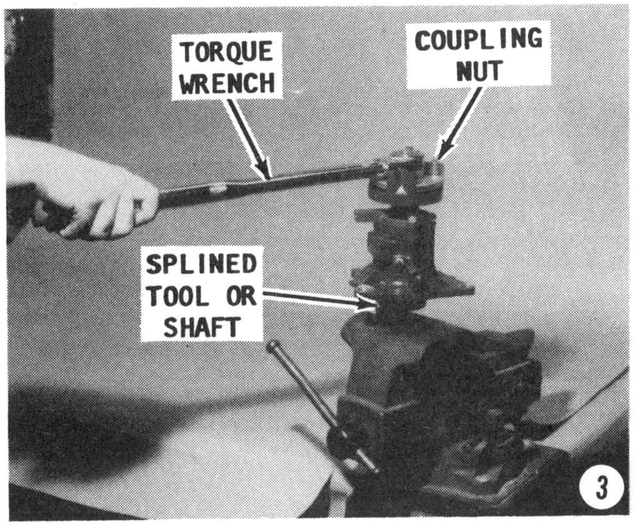

shaft, it is impossible to remove the coupling from the housing.

2- Obtain special tool P/N YW6365. Insert the tool into the fingers of the coupling. If this tool is not available proceed to the following step. A method of removing the coupling without the use of this special tool follows.

3- Position the intermediate housing over the splined tool or shaft clamped in the vise. The purpose of this setup is to "break loose" the coupling from the housing. The coupling is tightened to a high torque value, and may be loosened by two different methods. The first method is the most desirable. Use a long breaker bar or torque wrench indexed into the special tool and rotate the coupling **COUNTERCLOCKWISE** to "break" it free.

4- The second method is less desirable, as it may damage the coupling. Obtain a

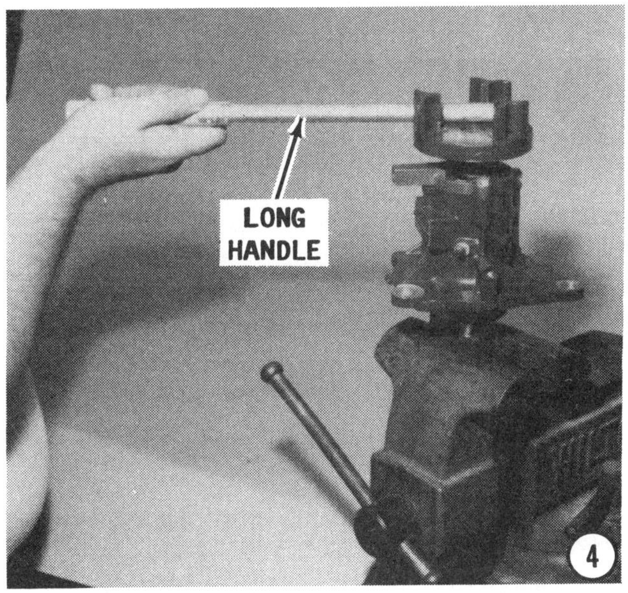

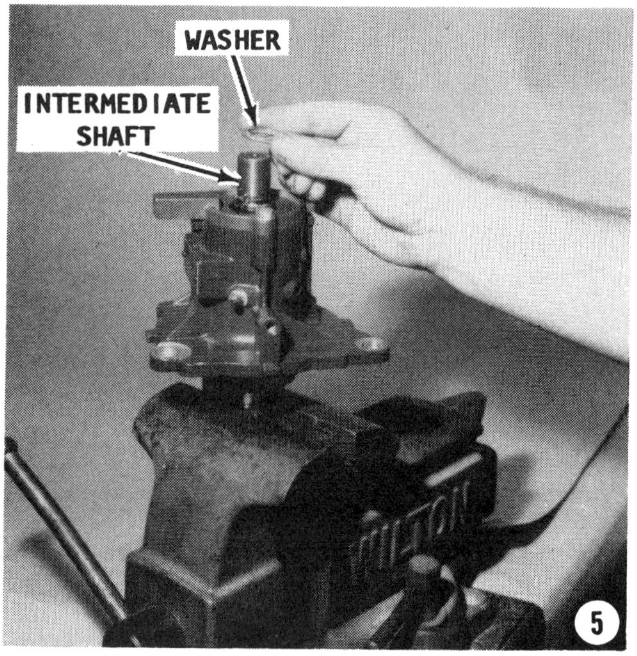

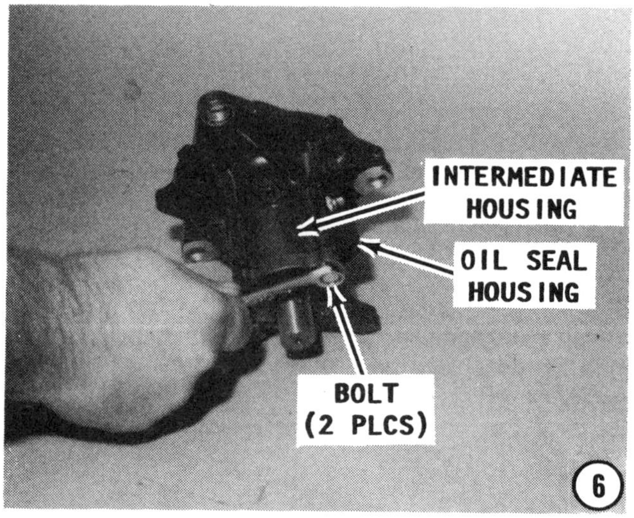

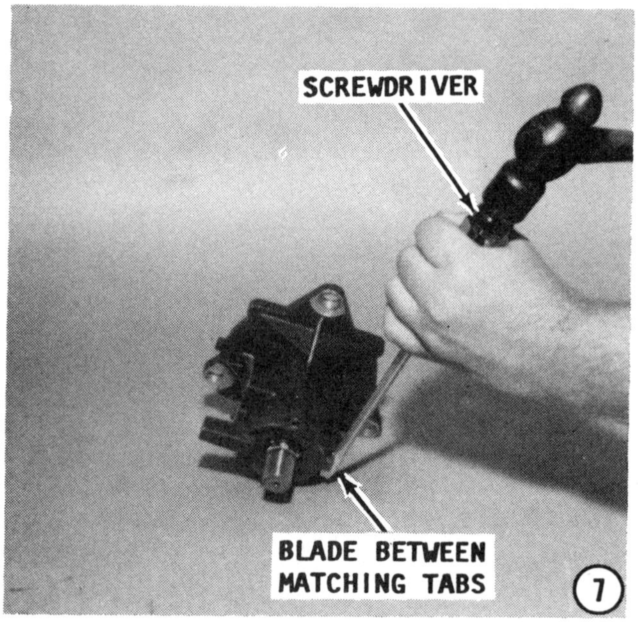

long bar. Insert the bar through the coupling fingers as shown and rotate the coupling **COUNTERCLOCKWISE** to "break" it free.

5- Remove the coupling from the intermediate shaft, and then remove the washer.

6- Remove the two small bolts securing the oil seal housing to the intermediate housing.

7- Insert a screwdriver blade between the two tabs on the housings to be separated and pry them apart.

8- Lift out the oil seal housing.

9- Remove and discard the O-ring from the groove around the housing. Pry out the oil seal if the seal is no longer fit for further service.

10- Obtain two blocks of wood to support the housing on an arbor press. Position the housing on the press with the aft face facing **UP**. Press out the shaft free of the housing. Take care to prevent the shaft

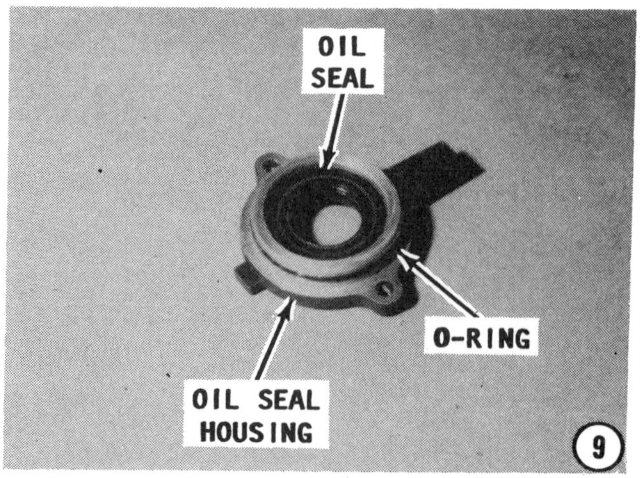

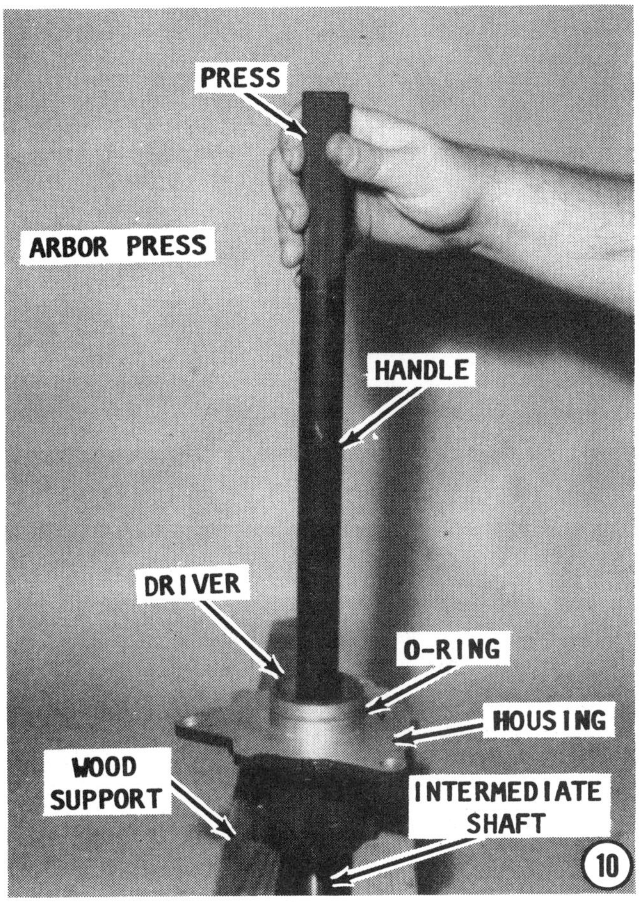

from falling to the floor, once it is free of the housing.

Obtain driver P/N YW-6356 and handle P/N YB-6229. With the housing in the same position as before, drive both bearings free of the housing.

Remove and discard the O-ring around the housing. Pry out the oil seal if the seal is no longer fit for further service.

The rubber coupler absorbs shocks applied to the driveshaft and impeller shaft. The most likely areas to show wear are indicated.

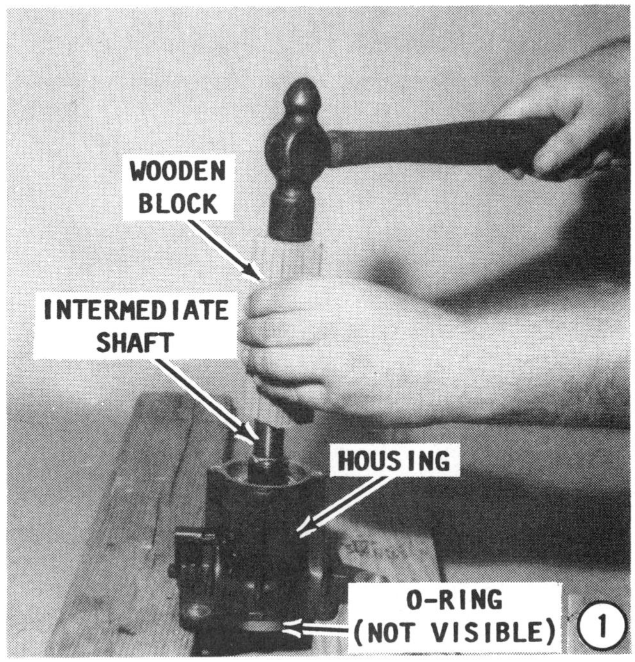

CLEANING AND INSPECTING

Inspect the condition of the rubber coupler. If the coupler shows signs of wear or damage, replace the coupler. Inspect the shaft. The internal threads must be in good condition to engage the external threads on the impeller shaft or slippage will occur. Inspect the shaft surface for pitting. Pitting takes place when water is allowed to enter the housing due to the failure of one or both oil seals. If the shaft shows signs of pitting, the bearings will also have water damage.

ASSEMBLING

1- First, using an arbor press, install both bearings into the shaft. Install the bearings -- one at each end of the shaft. Press the bearings into position until they contact the shoulder on the shaft.

Install the assembled shaft and bearings into the housing from the forward end.

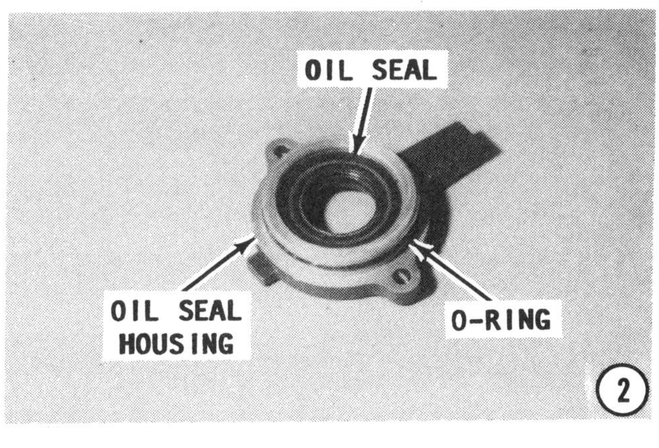

Using a wooden block for cushioning -- tap the shaft in until the lower bearing seats against the housing. Install a **NEW** O-ring into the groove on the aft housing face.

2- Pack the lip of a **NEW** oil seal with water resistant multi-purpose lubricant. Install the oil seal into the oil seal housing with the lip facing **UP**. Install a **NEW** O-ring into the groove around the housing.

3- Position the oil seal housing over the shaft, with the projection (arm), on the same side as the decal on the housing, as shown.

4- Coat the threads of the two bolts securing the oil seal housing to the intermediate housing with Loctite 242. Install

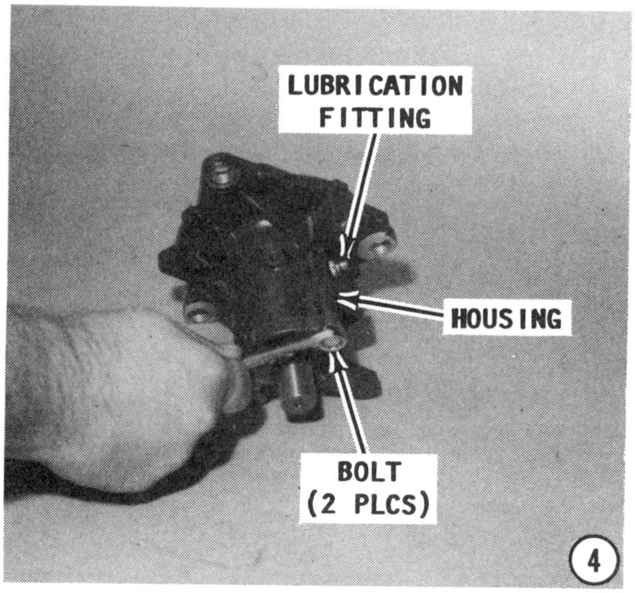

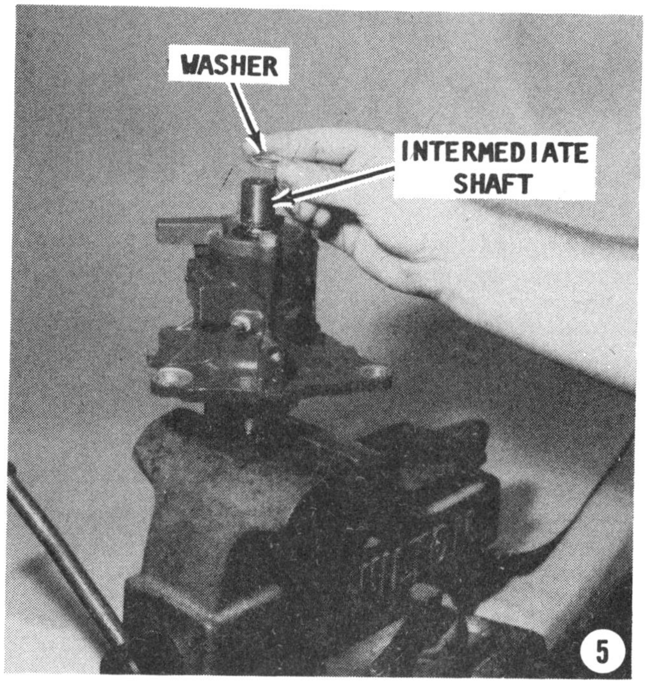

and tighten both bolts securely. Obtain a grease gun with the cartridge filled with water resistant multi-purpose lubricant. Pump lubricant into the lubrication fitting on the side of the housing.

5- Place the washer over the shaft.

SPECIAL WORDS

The coupling is tightened to the shaft to a torque value of 27 ft lb. (37Nm). The preferred method of achieving this torque value is to tighten the coupler with a torque wrench. Special tools P/N YW-6355 and YW-6365 are required, as described in Step 6.

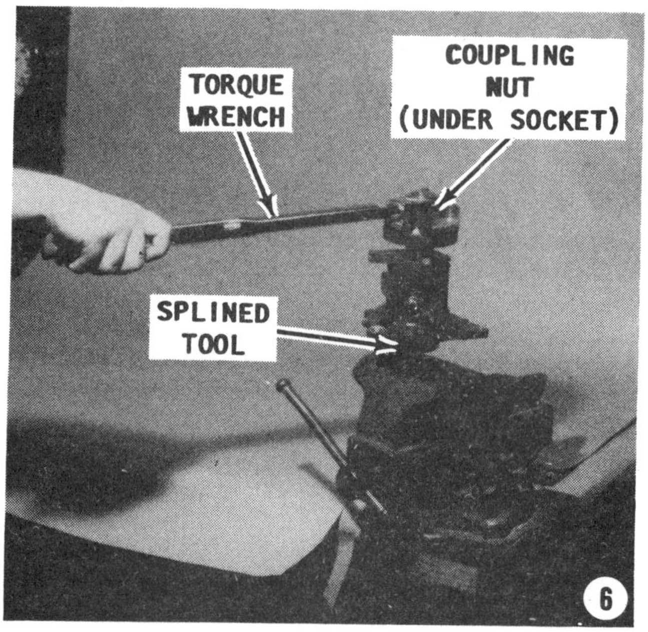

An alternate method may be used, as outlined in Step 7.

Therefore, if the tools are available, proceed with Step 6. If the tools are not available, proceed directly to Step 7.

6- Clamp special tool P/N YW-6355 in a vise. Slide the intermediate housing over the tool engaging the splines of the tool with the internal splines of the shaft. Thread the coupler onto the shaft by hand. Place special tool P/N YW-6365 between the fingers of the coupler. Using the torque wrench tighten the coupler to a torque value of 27 ft lb (37Nm).

7- Clamp a section of an old impeller shaft in the vise. Slide the intermediate housing over the shaft. Thread the coupler onto the shaft by hand. Using a long bar inserted between the fingers of the coupler, tighten the coupler to the shaft **VERY SECURELY.**

Installation

8- Coat the three securing bolts with Loctite 242. Install the intermediate housing over the impeller shaft and up against the engine compartment wall. Secure the housing to the wall. Place the rubber coupler into the pump coupler. Install the engine -- see Chapter 8.

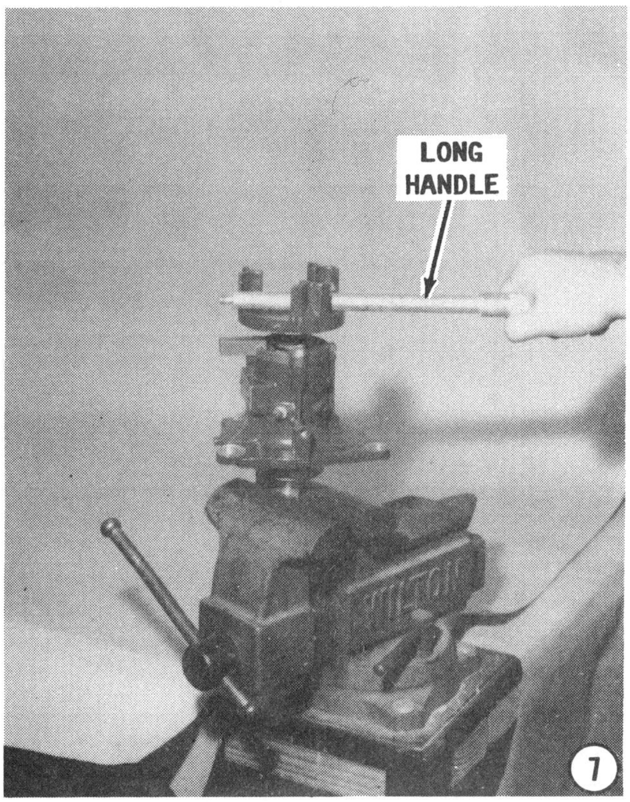

7

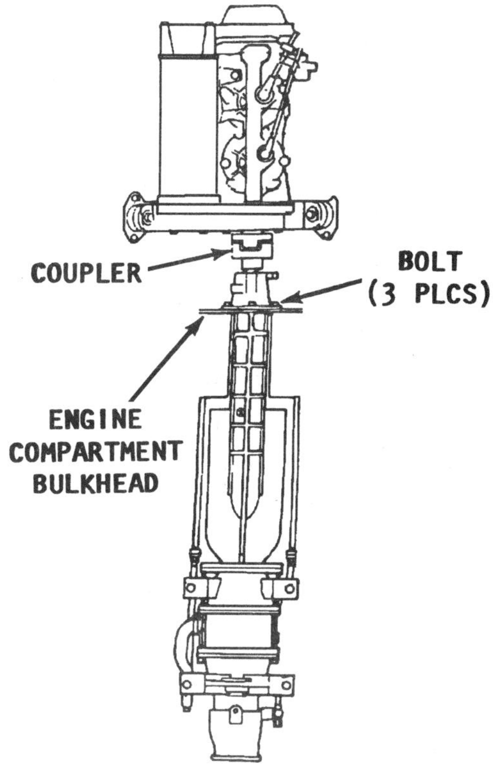

8

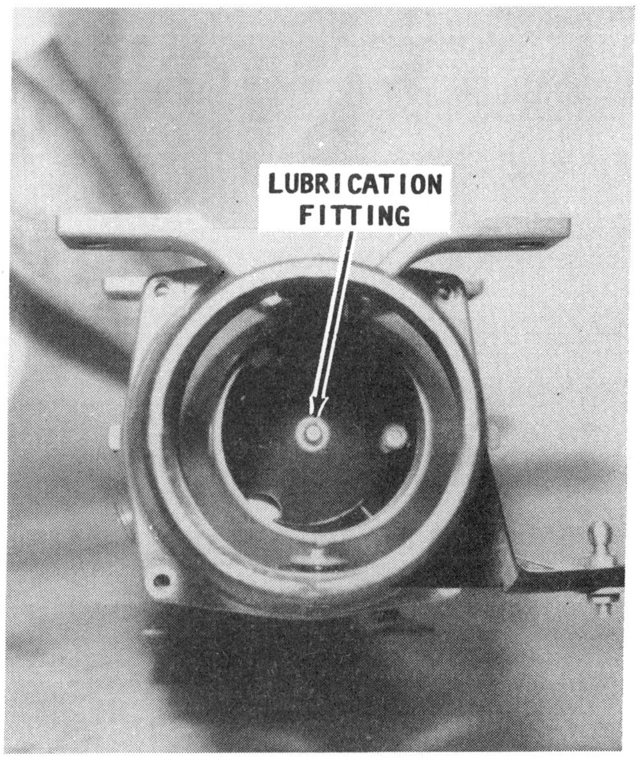

Some early model pumps are equipped with a lubrication fitting on the end cap to permit servicing the aft end of the impeller shaft. New models all have a lubrication fitting readily accessible in the engine compartment, as shown on Page 10-17 -- bottom of right column.

11
CONTROL ADJUSTMENTS

11-1 INTRODUCTION

The procedures outlined in this chapter are general in nature and serve only as a guide to the necessary work. The instructions are valid for all models of Yamaha Personal Watercraft covered in this manual. The principles are all pretty much the same -- but almost all models have some variance in the details.

11-2 ADJUSTMENTS

Throttle Lever Adjustment

Before the throttle lever free play can be adjusted, the engine idle speed must be checked and corrected, if necessary. See Chapter 3 Tuning, Section 3-6.

Measure the clearance between the throttle lever and the throttle stop with a feeler gauge. This clearance is the throttle lever free play and must be between 0.28 - 0.39" (7 - 10 mm). If the clearance is not within this range, loosen the locknut on the throttle cable. Rotate the adjuster to bring the clearance within specifications. Tighten the locknut against the throttle stop to hold the new adjustment.

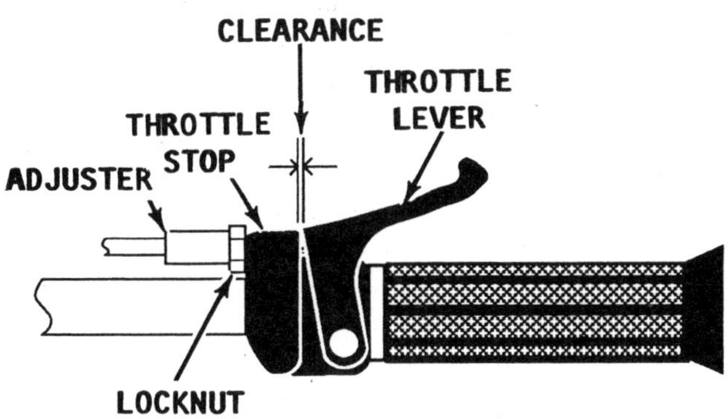

Line drawing to depict the throttle lever adjustment on the handle bar.

Choke Cable Adjustment

Pull the choke knob out as far as possible. Measure the distance between the inside edge of the plastic knob and the outside edge of the knurled nut, as shown in the accompanying illustration. This distance should be between 0.98 - 1.18" (25 - 30mm). If the distance is not within specification the choke knob clearance must be adjusted as follows.

Loosen the screw on the choke lever. Pull the choke knob out the specified distance. Manually close the choke valve, and take-up all but a just a small amount of slack in the choke cable. Tighten the screw on the choke lever to maintain the adjustment.

Reverse Cable Adjustment

The position of the reverse gate determines the direction of thrust of the expelled water.

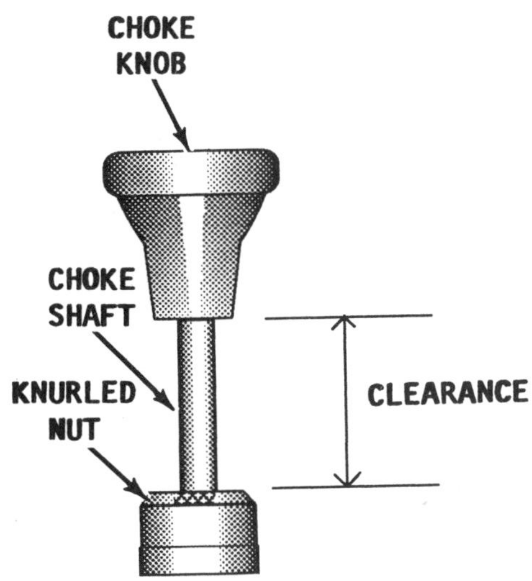

The choke cable adjustment is critical for easier engine startup and efficient operation.

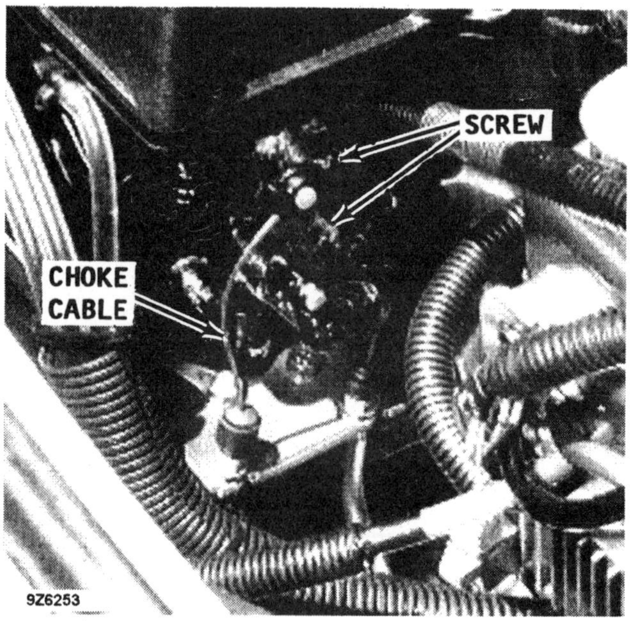

The screw at the engine end of the choke cable must be securely tightened to hold just a small amount of slack in the choke cable, as explained on the previous page.

Improper adjustment of the gate can cause the gate to be unintentionally thrown into reverse, tilting the craft up out of the water.

With the reverse gate in the full down (reverse) position, measure the distance, on the reverse cable between the edge of the pivot barrel on the reverse lever arm and the edge of the clamp bracket, as shown in the accompanying illustration. This distance should be 4.5" (114mm). If the distance is incorrect, the reverse cable needs adjustment.

Remove the cotter pin, washer, and locknut from the pivot barrel on the reverse lever arm. Set the reverse gate to the full reverse position. Move the pivot barrel along the threaded length of the reverse cable until the specified distance is obtained between the barrel and the clamp bracket. Place the shift lever in the reverse position and temporarily attach the pivot barrel to the shift lever arm. Set the handlebar to the full port or starboard position. Using a pair of calipers, measure the clearance between the collar on the pivot pin on the reverse gate and the groove in the shift rod lever. This measurement should be between 0.0394-0.1181" (1-3mm). If the clearance is not within specifications, adjust the position of the pivot barrel along the shift cable to obtain the correct clearance.

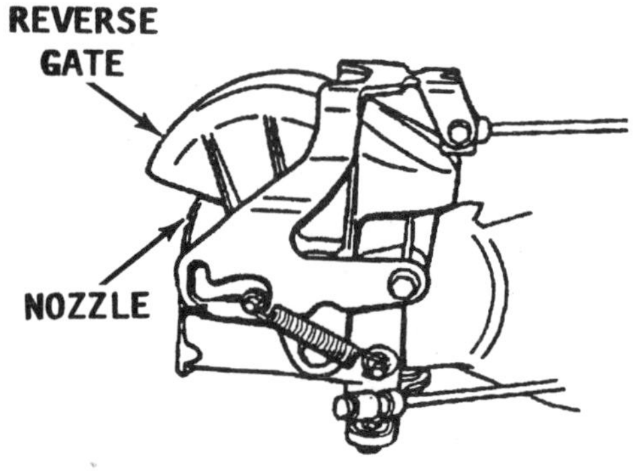

*The reverse gate must be completely clear of the nozzle when the shift lever is in the **FORWARD** position.*

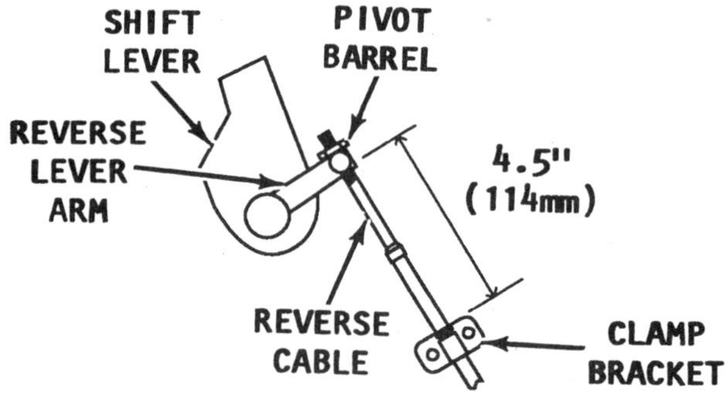

*Line drawing to depict the proper adjustment for the shift lever with the reverse bucket in the full **REVERSE** position.*

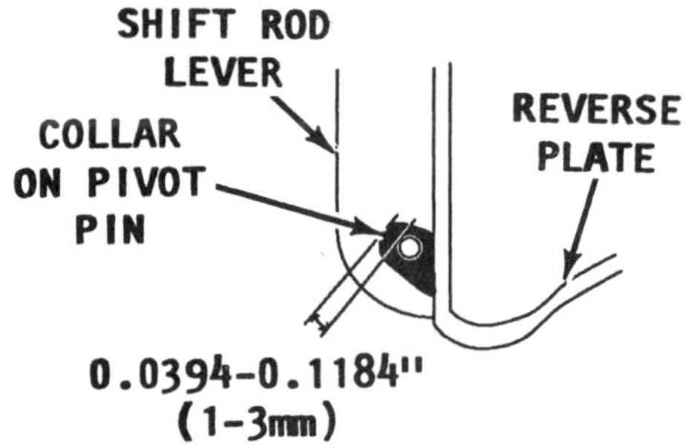

*Simple line drawing to indicate where the measurement is to be taken between the collar on the pivot pin and groove in the shift rod lever when adjusting the shift cable, with the bucket in **REVERSE**.*

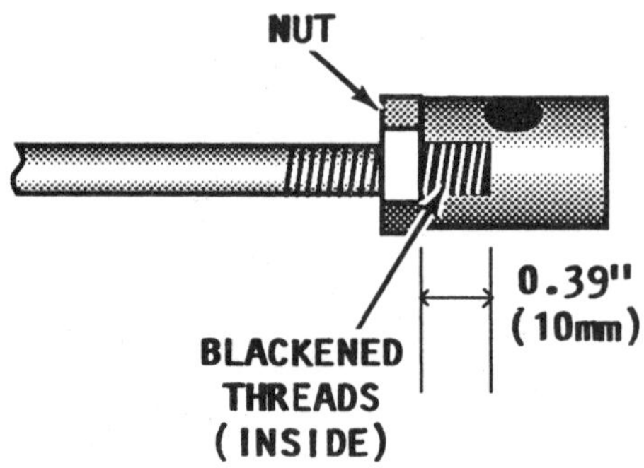

*The entire blackened portion of the reverse cable threaded end **MUST** be engaged with the barrel, before the nut is tightened, as explained in the text.*

CAUTION

The entire blackened portion of the reverse cable threaded end, 0.591" (15mm) must be engaged with the barrel, before the locknut is tightened.

If blackened threads are not visible on the reverse cable, then tighten the locknut against the barrel to hold the adjustment.

If any blackened threads are visible after adjustment, the barrel must be rotated further down to cover the blackened threads. The adjustment is then made at the barrel located on the shift lever at the other end of the reverse cable. The manufacturer considers engagement of the blackened threads a **MINIMUM** safety requirement.

CRITICAL WORDS

If the reverse cable should accidentally disengage from the ball joint -- the reverse gate would quickly be lowered -- throwing the craft into reverse -- perhaps at full throttle. Such action would most certainly cause injury to person/s riding the craft.

Secure the pivot barrel to the shift lever arm with the washer, cotter pin, and locknut to maintain the adjustment.

Steering Cable Adjustment

Measure the clearance between the outside of the nozzle and the transom opening when the handlebars are turned fully to port. Next, turn the handlebars fully to starboard. Again, measure the distance on the other side of the nozzle between the outside of the nozzle and the transom opening. If these clearances are not the same, pry the steering cable free of the ball joint on the steering post arm. Loosen the locknut and rotate the barrel along the threaded portion of the cable. Snap the barrel back into place on the ball joint and measure the clearances again. Adjust the position of the barrel along the cable until the clearances are identical. The manufacturer gives no specific value for this clearance.

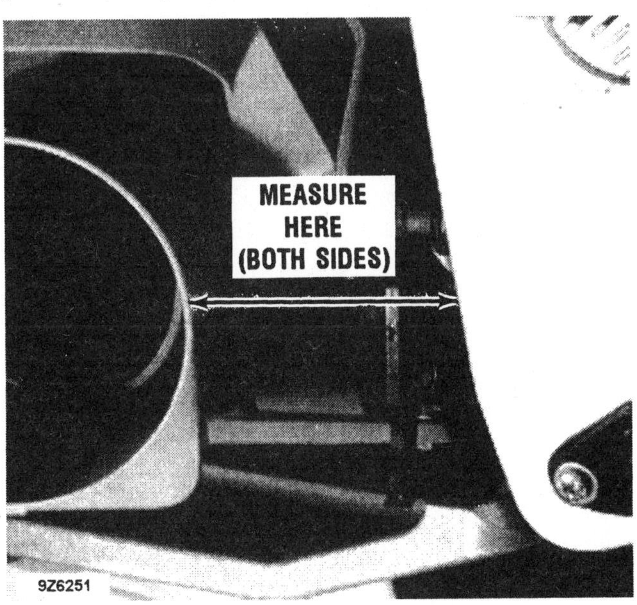

Close view of the steering nozzle. When making "dead ahead" adjustment -- distance from the nozzle to the side of the opening must be equal -- port and starboard.

CAUTION

The entire blackened portion of the steering cable threaded end, 0.39" (10mm) must be engaged with the barrel, before the locknut is tightened.

If blackened threads are not visible on the steering cable, then tighten the locknut against the barrel to hold the adjustment.

If any of the blackened threads become visible after adjustment, the barrel must be rotated further down to cover the blackened threads. The adjustment is then made at the barrel located on the steering nozzle at the other end of the steering cable. The manufacturer considers engagement of the blackened threads a **MINIMUM** safety requirement. Should the steering cable accidentally disengage from the steering post -- all steering control of the craft would be lost.

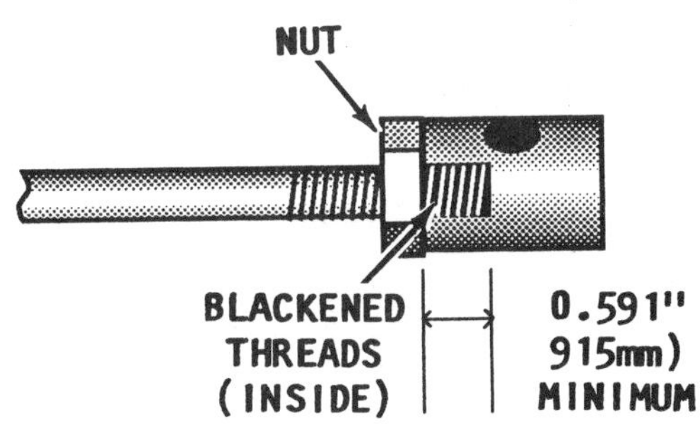

The entire blackened portion of the shift cable threaded end MUST be engaged with the barrel before the nut is tightened, as explained in the text.

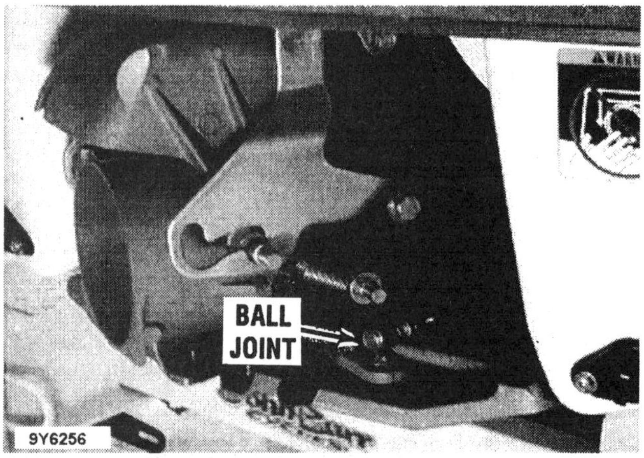

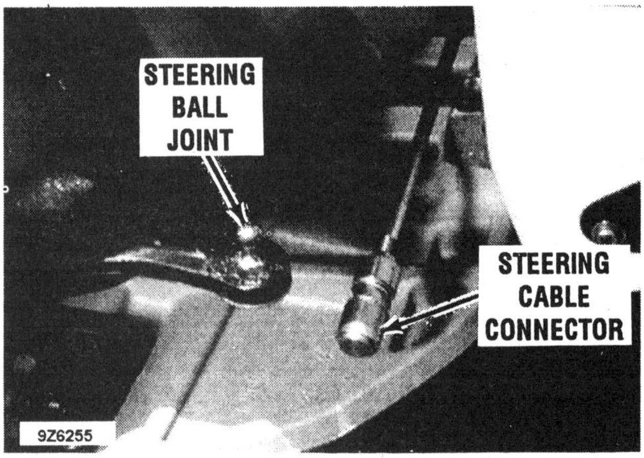

Aft steering ball joint with the cable connected (upper picture), and disconnected for lubrication (bottom). The disconnect is accomplished by simply sliding the outer sleeve forward and lifting the cable joint up and free.

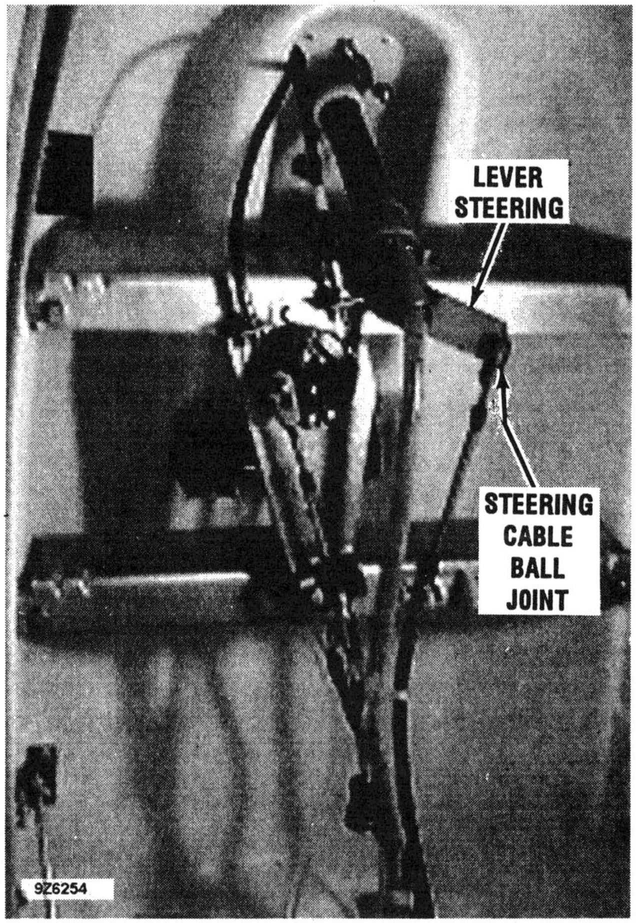

Close view of the forward steering cable ball joint with the cable connected. The other control cables shown do not require service or maintenance at this location.

APPENDIX

METRIC CONVERSION CHART

LINEAR

inches	X 25.4	= millimetres (mm)
feet	X 0.3048	= metres (m)
yards	X 0.9144	= metres (m)
miles	X 1.6093	= kilometres (km)
inches	X 2.54	= centimetres (cm)

AREA

inches^2	X 645.16	= millimetres^2 (mm^2)
inches^2	X 6.452	= centimetres^2 (cm^2)
feet^2	X 0.0929	= metres^2 (m^2)
yards^2	X 0.8361	= metres^2 (m^2)
acres	X 0.4047	= hectares (10^4 m^2) (ha)
miles^2	X 2.590	= kilometres^2 (km^2)

VOLUME

inches^3	X 16387	= millimetres^3 (mm^3)
inches^3	X 16.387	= centimetres^3 (cm^3)
inches^3	X 0.01639	= litres (l)
quarts	X 0.94635	= litres (l)
gallons	X 3.7854	= litres (l)
feet^3	X 28.317	= litres (l)
feet^3	X 0.02832	= metres^3 (m^3)
fluid oz	X 23.57	= millilitres (ml)
yards^3	X 0.7646	= metres^3 (m^3)

MASS

ounces (av)	X 28.35	= grams (g)
pounds (av)	X 0.4536	= kilograms (kg)
tons (2000 lb)	X 907.18	= kilograms (kg)
tons (2000 lb)	X 0.90718	= metric tons (t)

FORCE

ounces - f (av)	X 0.278	= newtons (N)
pounds - f (av)	X 4.448	= newtons (N)
kilograms - f	X 9.807	= newtons (N)

ACCELERATION

feet/sec^2	X 0.3048	= metres/sec^2 (m/S^2)
inches/sec^2	X 0.0254	= metres/sec^2 (m/s^2)

ENERGY OR WORK (watt-second - joule - newton-metre)

foot-pounds	X 1.3558	= joules (j)
calories	X 4.187	= joules (j)
Btu	X 1055	= joules (j)
watt-hours	X 3500	= joules (j)
kilowatt - hrs	X 3.600	= megajoules (MJ)

FUEL ECONOMY AND FUEL CONSUMPTION

miles/gal	X 0.42514	= kilometres/litre (km/l)

Note:
235.2/(mi/gal) = litres/100km
235.2/(litres/100 km) = mi/gal

LIGHT

footcandles	X 10.76	= lumens/metre^2 (lm/m^2)

PRESSURE OR STRESS (newton/sq metre - pascal)

inches HG (60° F)	X 3.377	= kilopascals (kPa)
pounds/sq in	X 6.895	= kilopascals (kPa)
inches H_2O (60° F)	X 0.2488	= kilopascals (kPa)
bars	X 100	= kilopascals (kPa)
pounds/sq ft	X 47.88	= pascals (Pa)

POWER

horsepower	X 0.746	= kilowatts (kW)
ft-lbf/min	X 0.0226	= watts (W)

TORQUE

pound-inches	X 0.11299	= newton-metres (N·m)
pound-feet	X 1.3558	= newton-metres (N·m)

VELOCITY

miles/hour	X 1.6093	= kilometres/hour (km/h)
feet/sec	X 0.3048	= metres/sec (m/s)
kilometres/hr	X 0.27778	= metres/sec (m/s)
miles/hour	X 0.4470	= metres/sec (m/s)

TEMPERATURE

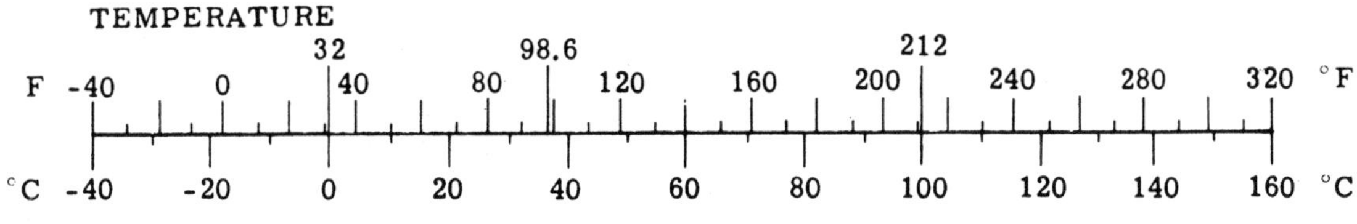

Celsius = 0.556 (°F -32) °F = (1.8°C) +32

SPECIFICATIONS AND TUNE-UP ADJUSTMENTS

MODEL YEAR	RATED OUTPUT (hp)	BORE/ STROKE INCHES (mm)	DIS-PLACE-MENT	CARBUR-ETION	IGN.	SPARK PLUG NGK	PLUG GAP INCH	TIMING IDLE WOT	RPM IDLE WOT	CARB. LOW SPEED (TURNS OUT)	CARB. HIGH SPEED (TURNS OUT)
SUPER JET 1992-'95	63hp @ 6300	3.19/2.68 (81/68)	42.8 cu in (701 cc)	SINGLE MIKUNI BN44	CDI	B8HS or BR8HS	0.024	15 BTDC 21 BTDC	1200 5500	1-7/8 ± 1/4	1-5/8 ± 1/4
SUPER JET 1996-'97	135 hp @ 6750	3.19/2.68 (81/68)	42.8 cu in (701 cc)	DUAL MIKUNI BN38	CDI	B7HS	0.024	15 BTDC 21 BTDC	1200 5500	1-7/8 ± 1/4	BOTH 1-5/8 ± 1/4
WAVERUNNER WRB 650 1992-	50 hp @ 6000	3.03/2.68 (77/68)	38.62 cu in (633 cc)	SINGLE MIKUNI BN 44	CDI	B8HS or BR8HS	0.024	15 BTDC 21 BTDC	1200 5500	FN8 1-1/16±1/4 GDO 1-5/8±1/4	FN8 1-1/16±1/4 GDO 1-7/8±1/4
WAVERUNNER WRB 700 1992-	47 hp @ 6250	3.19/2.68 (81/68)	42.8 cu in (701 cc)	SINGLE MIKUNI	CDI	BR8HS	0.024	15 BTDC 21 BTDC	1200 5500	FN8 1-1/16±1/4 GDO 1-5/8±1/4	FN8 1-1/16±1/4 GDO 1-7/8±1/4
WAVE-RUNNER III 1992-'97	65 hp @ 6300	3.19/2.68 (81/68	42.8 cu in (701 cc)	SINGLE MIKUNI BN44	CDI	B7HS	0.024	15 BTDC 21 BTDC	1200 5500	1-1/8 ± 1/4	1-1/8 ± 1/4
VXR 650 1993	50 HP @6000	3.03/2.68 (77/68)	38.62 cu in (633 cc)	SINGLE MIKUNI BN44	CDI	B8HS	0.024	15 BTDC 21 BTDC	1200 5500	1-1/16 ± 1/4	1-1/4 ± 1/4
PROVXR 700 1993	64 @6250	3.19/2.68 (81/68)	42.78 (701 CC)	SINGLE MIKUNI BN44	CDI	BR8HS	0.024	15 BTDC 21 BTDC	1200 5500	1-7/8 ± 1/4	1-5/8 ± 1/4
WAVE-RAIDER 700 1994-'97	70 hp @6300	3.19/2.68 (81/68)	42.8 cu in (701 cc)	DUAL MIKUNI BN44	CDI	B7HS	0.024	15 BTDC 21 BTDC	1200 5500	5/8 ± 1/4	F 5/8 ± 1/4 R 1-1/8 ± 1/4
WAVE-RAIDER 1100 1994-'96	110 @ 6500	3.19/2.68 (81/68)	64.14cu in (1051 cc)	TRIPLE BN44	CDI	BR8HS	0.024	15 BTDC 19 BTDC	1200 6500	1-1/8 ± 1/4	ALL THREE 7/8 ± 1/4
WAVE-BLASTER 1993-'97	73 hp @ 6300	3.19/2.68 (81/68)	42.8 cu in (701 cc)	DUAL MIKUNI BN38	CDI	BR7HS	0.024	15 BTDC 19 BTDC	1200 5500	7/8 ± 1/4	F 1-1/8 ± 1/4 R 1-1/2 ± 1/4

SPECIFICATIONS AND TUNE-UP ADJUSTMENTS

MODEL YEAR	RATED OUTPUT (hp)	BORE/ STROKE INCHES (mm)	DIS-PLACE-MENT	CARBUR-ETION	IGN.	SPARK PLUG NGK	PLUG GAP INCH	TIMING IDLE WOT	RPM IDLE WOT	CARB. LOW SPEED (TURNS OUT)	CARB. HIGH SPEED (TURNS OUT)
WAVE-BLASTER II 1996-'97	90 hp @ 6350	3.31/2.68 (84/68)	46 cu in (754 cc)	DUAL MIKUNI BN44	DIGITAL CDI	BR8HS	0.024	15 BTDC 20 BTDC	1200 5500	1-3/4 ± 1/4	BOTH 1/2 ± 1/4
WAVE-VENTURE 760 1995-'97	90 HP @ 6350	3.19/2.68 (81/68)	46 cu in (754 cc)	DUAL MIKUNI BN44	DIGITAL CDI	BR8HS	0.024	15 BTDC 21 BTDC	1200 5500	5/8 ± 1/4	F 5/8 ± 1/4 R 1-1/8 ± 1/4
WAVE-VENTURE 1100 1995-'97	110 hp @ 6500	3.19/2.68 (81/68)	64.1cu in (1051 cc)	TRIPLE MIKUNI BN38	CDI	BR8HS	0.024	15 BTDC 19 BTDC	1200 5500	1-1/8 ± 1/4	ALL THREE 7/8 ± 1/4
GP 760 1997	90 hp @6350	3.31/2.68 (84/68)	46 cu in (754 cc)	DUAL MIKUNI BN44	DIGITAL CDI	BR8HS	0.024	15 BTDC 22 BTDC	1200 5500	1-5/8 ± 1/4	BOTH 3/8 ± 1/4
GP 1200 1997	135 hp @6750	3.31/2.68 (84/68)	69 cu in (1131 cc)	TRIPLE MIKUNI BN44	DIGITAL CDI	BR8HS	0.024	15 BTDC 22 BTDC	1200 5500	F 1-1/4 ± 1/4 C 1-1/4 ± 1/4 R 1-1/8 ± 1/4	F 1/2 ± 1/4 C 7/8 ± 1/4 R 1/2 ± 1/4

RECOMMENDED TORQUE VALUES

	Engine Mount. Bolt	Cy. Head Bolt	Flywheel Bolt	Crankcase Bolt	Cyl. Body Bolt	Muffler 1 & 2 Bolt	Eng. Coupling Nut	Spark Plug	Jet Mount. M10 Bolt	Jet Mount. M6 Bolt	Jet Coupling	Impeller L.H. Threads
Super Jet	11 ft lbs 16Nm	22 ft lbs 30Nm	47 ft lbs 65Nm	20 ft lbs 28Nm	29 ft lbs 40Nm	22 ft lbs 30 ft lbs		14 ft lbs 20 Nm	24 ft lbs 33Nm	*11 ft lbs 16Nm	25 ft lbs 36Nm	11 ft lbs 16Nm
WaveRunner WR 500Q & 650Q	12 ft lbs 17Nm	20 ft lbs 28Nm	**100 ft lbs 140Nm	Note 4		Note 3	27 ft lbs 37Nm	14 ft lbs 20Nm	24 ft lbs 33Nm			13 ft lbs 18Nm
WaveRunner III WRA 650R, T, U	12 ft lbs 17Nm	22 ft lbs 30Nm	50 ft lbs 70Nm	20 ft lbs 28Nm	22 ft lbs 30Nm	Note 3		14 ft lbs 20Nm	24 ft lbs 33Nm		27 ft lbs 37Nm	13 ft lbs 18Nm
VXR & PROVXR	12 ft lbs 17Nm	Note 1	50 ft lbs 70Nm	20 ft lbs 28Nm	Note 2	Note 3	27 ft lbs 37Nm	14 ft lbs 20Nm	12 ft lbs 17Nm		27 ft lbs 37Nm	13 ft lbs 18Nm
WaveRunner 650 & 700	11 ft lbs 16Nm	22 ft lbs 30Nm	50 ft lbs 70Nm	20 ft lbs 28Nm	29 ft lbs 40Nm	Note 3		14 ft lbs 20Nm	24 ft lbs 33Nm			13 ft lbs 18Nm
WaveRaider 700 & 1100	12 ft lbs 17Nm	25 ft lbs 34Nm	50 ft lbs 70Nm	20 ft lbs 28Nm	29 ft lbs 40Nm	22 ft lbs 30Nm	27 ft lbs 37Nm	14 ft lbs 20Nm	24 ft lbs 34Nm	5.1 ft lbs 7Nm	27 ft lbs 37Nm	13 ft lbs 18Nm
WaveBlaster WB 700 R-U	12 ft lbs 17Nm	26 ft lbs 35Nm	50 ft lbs 70Nm	20 ft lbs 28Nm	29 ft lbs 40Nm	22 ft lbs 30Nm	27 ft lbs 37Nm	14 ft lbs 20Nm	12 ft lbs 17Nm		26 ft lbs 35Nm	13 ft lbs 18Nm
WaveBlaster II WB 760U	12 ft lbs 17Nm	26 ft lbs 35Nm	50 ft lbs 70Nm	20 ft lbs 28Nm	29 ft lbs 40Nm	29 ft lbs 40Nm	27 ft lbs 37Nm	14 ft lbs 20Nm	24 ft lbs 33Nm		27 ft lbs 37Nm	13 ft lbs 18Nm
WaveVenture 760 & 1100	12 ft lbs 17Nm	25 ft lbs 34Nm	50 ft lbs 70Nm	11 ft lbs 16Nm	29 ft lbs 40Nm	29 ft lbs 40Nm	27 ft lbs 37Nm	14 ft lbs 20Nm	24 ft lbs 33Nm	5.1 ft lbs 7Nm	27 ft lbs 37Nm	13 ft lbs 18Nm
GP 760	12 ft lbs 17Nm	23 ft lbs 32Nm	50 ft lbs 70Nm	20 ft lbs 28Nm	29 ft lbs 40 Nm	Note 5	27 ft lbs 37Nm	18 ft lbs 25Nm	24 ft lbs 34Nm	8.7 ft lbs 12Nm	27 ft lbs 37Nm	13 ft lbs 18Nm
GP1200	12 ft lbs 17Nm	23 ft kbs 32Nm	50 ft lbs 70Nm	20 ft lbs 28Nm	29 ft lbs 40Nm	Note 6	27 ft lbs 37Nm	18 ft lbs 25Nm	24 ft lbs 34Nm	8.7 ft lbs 12Nm	27 ft lbs 37Nm	13 ft lbs 18Nm

Note 1 Cylinder Head -- 61L -- 22 ft lbs, 30Nm; 61X -- 29 ft lbs, 40Nm.
Note 2 Cylinder Body -- 61L -- 22 ft lbs, 30Nm; 61X -- 29 ft lbs, 40Nm.
Note 3 Muffler 1 -- 22 ft lbs, 30Nm; Muffler 2 -- 38 ft lbs, 53Nm.
Note 4 Flywheel Bolt -- WR500 -- 100 ft lbs, 140Nm; WR650 -- 50 ft lbs, 70Nm.
Note 5 Muffler 1 -- 29 ft lbs, 40Nm; Muffler 2 -- 29 ft lbs, 40Nm.
Note 6 Muffler 1 -- 22 ft lbs, 30Nm; Muffler 2 -- 29 ft lbs, 40Nm.

CARBURETOR INSTALLATIONS

MODEL	Years Of Production	Mikuni Carburetor
Super Jet 650	1992-1993	Single BN 44
Super Jet 700	1994-1997	Dual BN 38
WaveRunner	1991-1992	Single BN 44
WaveRunner III 700	1992-1997	Single BN 44
VXR 650 & PROVXR 700	1993	Single BN 44
WaveRunner 700	1993-1995	Single BN 44
WaveRaider 700	1996	Dual BN 44
WaveRaider Deluxe	1994-1995	Dual BN 38
WaveRaider 1100	1995-1996	Triple BN 38
WaveBlaster 700	1994-1995	Single BN 44
WaveBlaster 700	1996-1997	Dual BN 38
WaveBlaster II	1996-1997	Dual BN 44
WaveVenture 760	1995-1997	Dual BN 38
WaveVenture 1100	1995-1997	Triple BN 38
GP 760	1997	Dual BN 44
GP 1200	1997	Triple BN 44

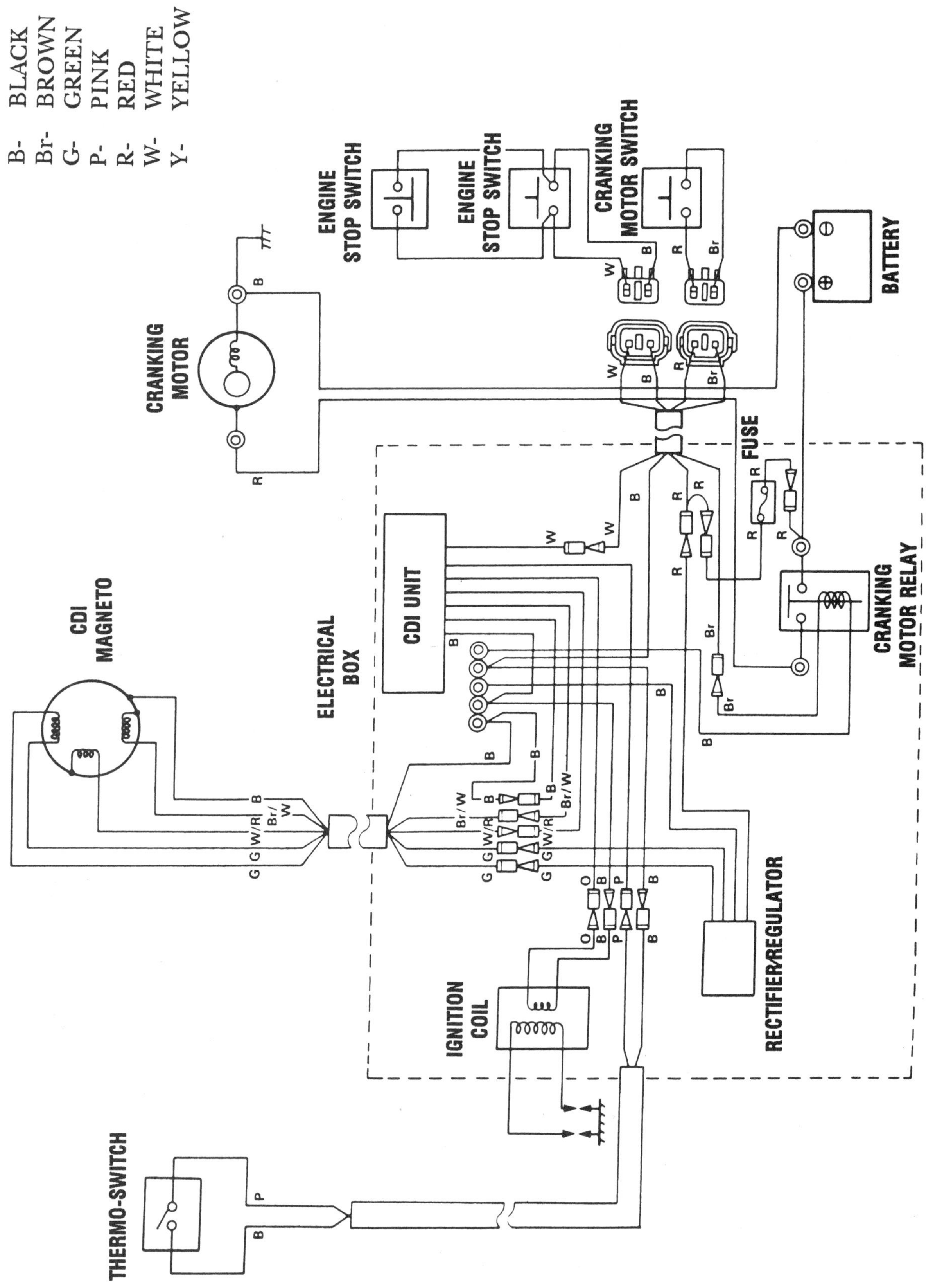

Electrical wiring diagram and wire color code for the ***Super Jet 650, WaveRunner WR650****. Major components of the system are identified.*

B-	BLACK	W-	WHITE
Br-	BROWN	Y-	YELLOW
G-	GREEN	O-	ORANGE
P-	PINK	W/R-	WHITE/RED
R-	RED	Br/W-	BROWN/WHITE
		W/L	WHITE/BLUE

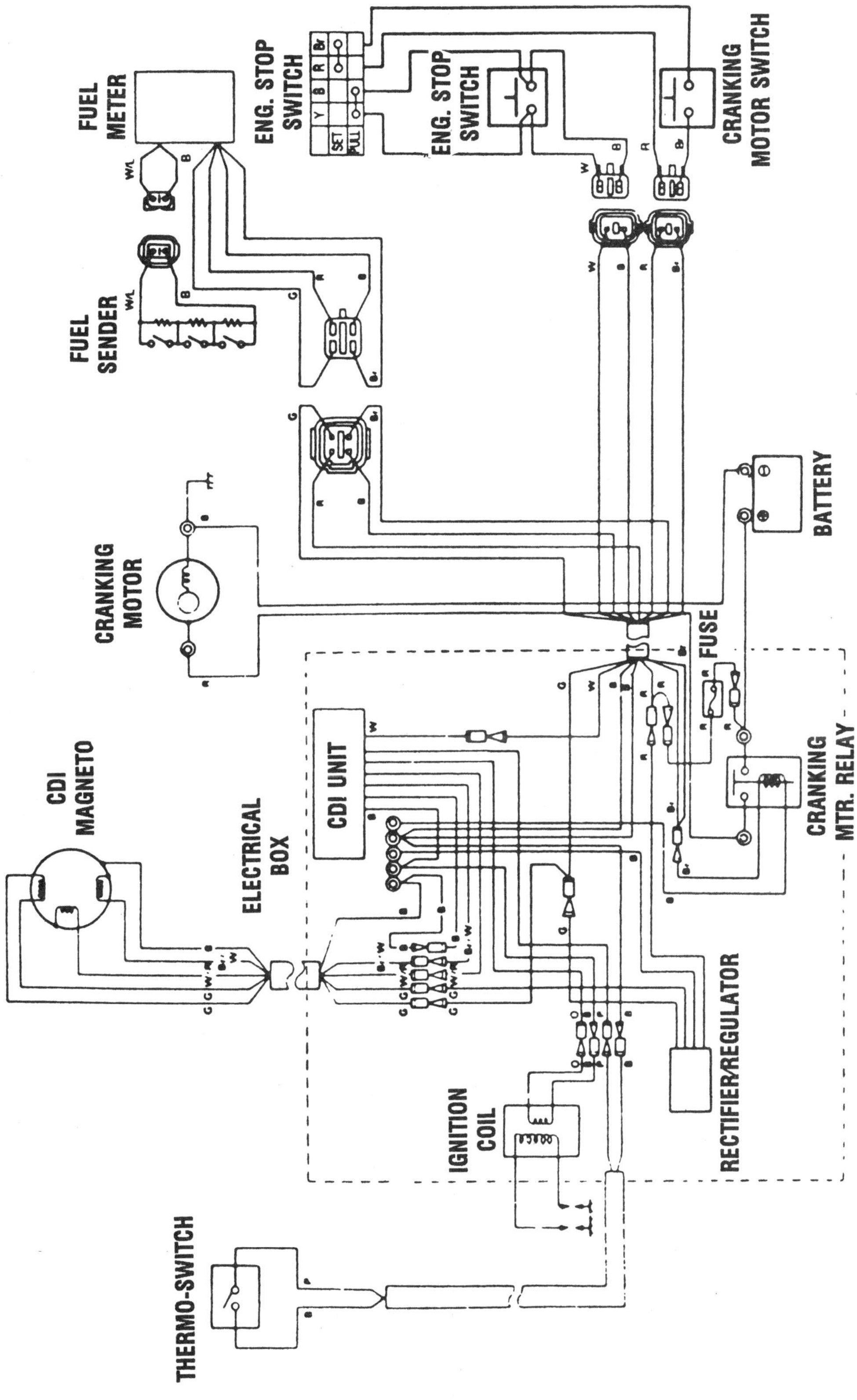

Electrical wiring diagram and wire color code for the ***WaveRunner 650R, T, U,*** *the* ***700 S & T.*** *Major components of the system are identified.*

B-	BLACK
Br-	BROWN
G-	GREEN
P-	PINK
R-	RED
W-	WHITE
Y-	YELLOW
O-	ORANGE
W/R-	WHITE/RED
Br/W-	BROWN/WHITE
W/L	WHITE/BLUE

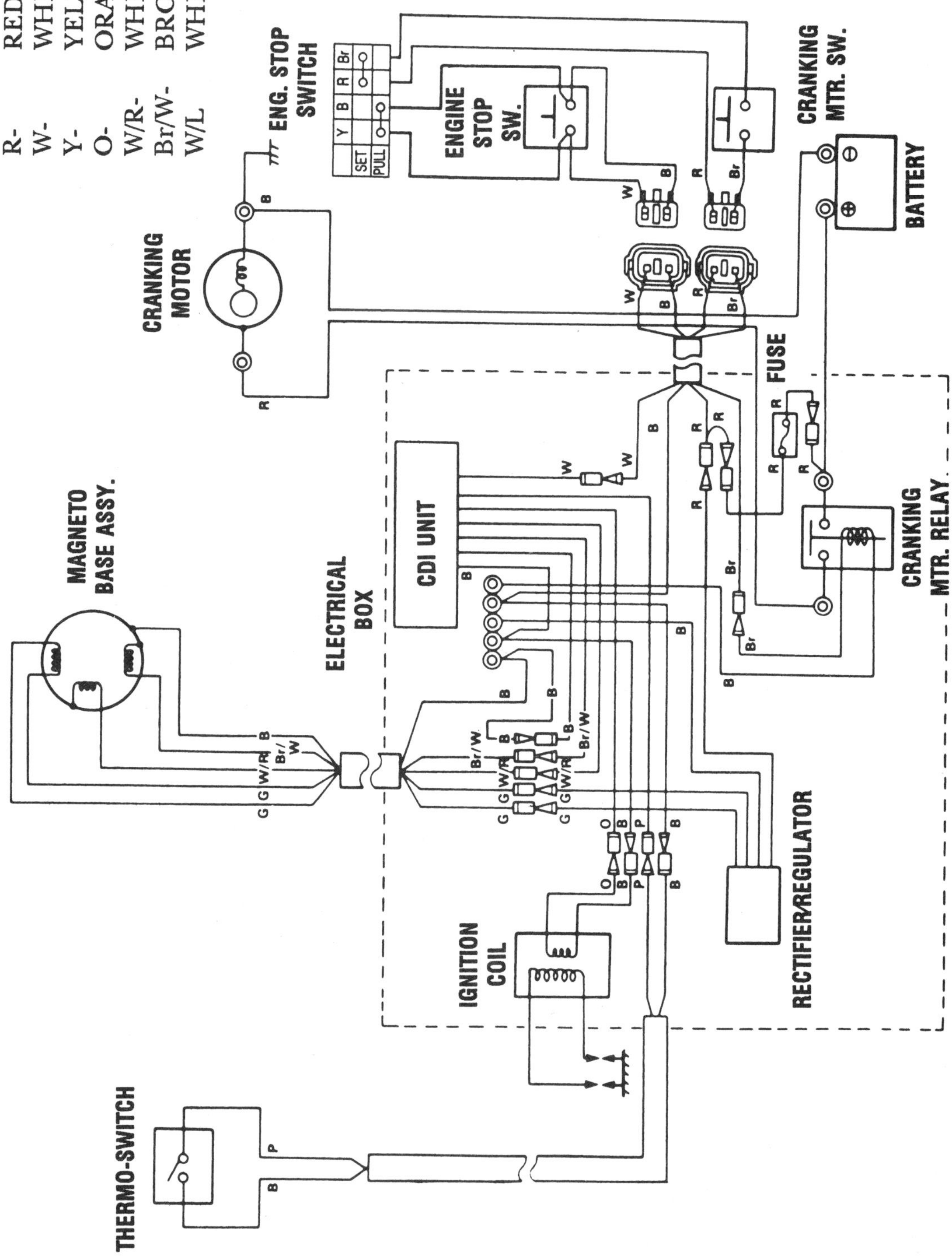

Electrical wiring diagram and wire color code for the ***WRB 650 and 700R/RA.*** *Further engine ID is "**FN8**". Major components of the system have been identified.*

B-	BLACK
Br-	BROWN
G-	GREEN
P-	PINK
R-	RED
W-	WHITE
Y-	YELLOW
O-	ORANGE
W/R-	WHITE/RED
Br/W-	BROWN/WHITE
W/L	WHITE/BLUE

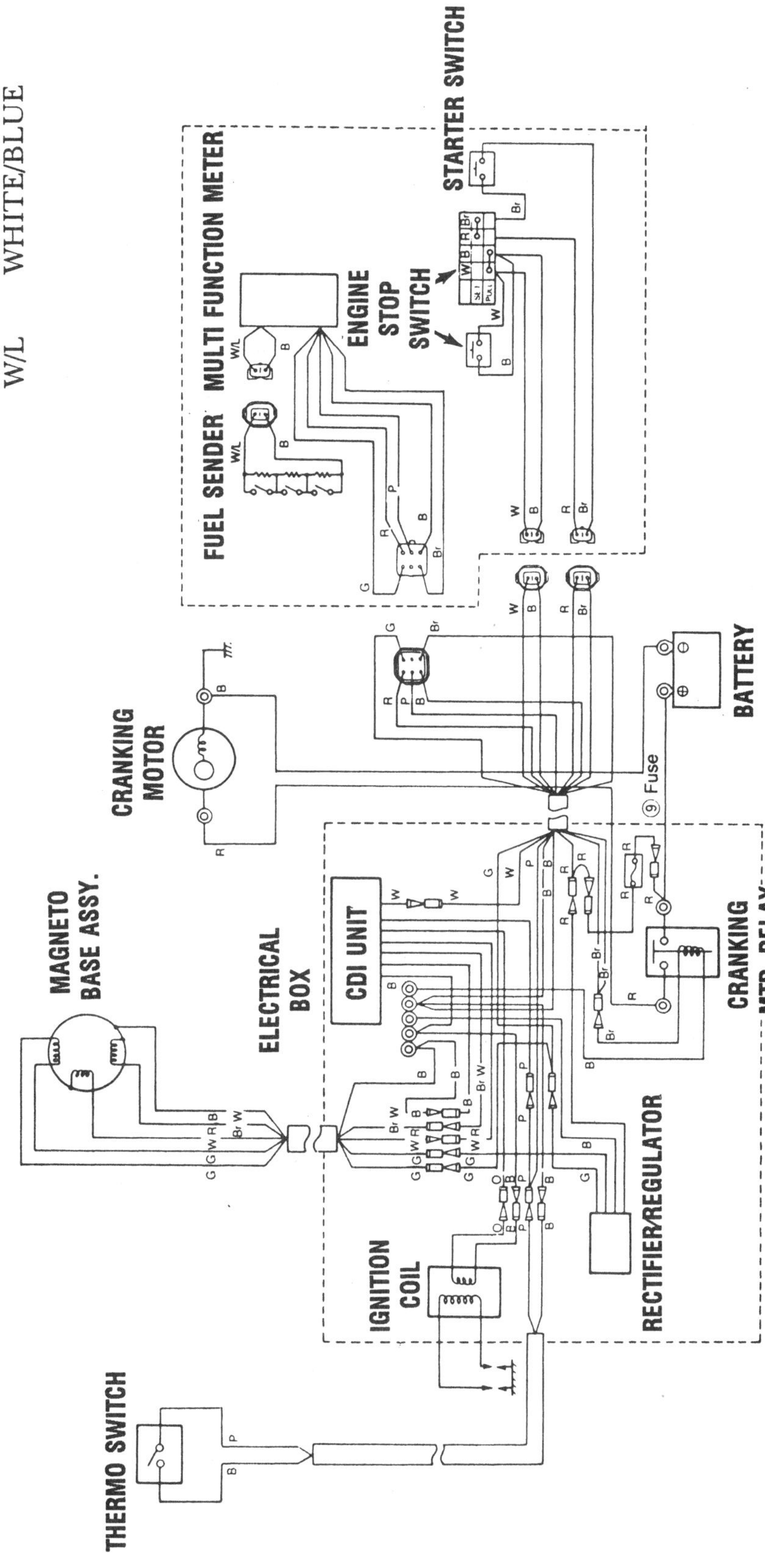

Electrical wiring diagram and wire color code for the ***WRB 650 and 700R/RA.*** *Further engine ID is "****GDO****". Major components of the system are identified.*

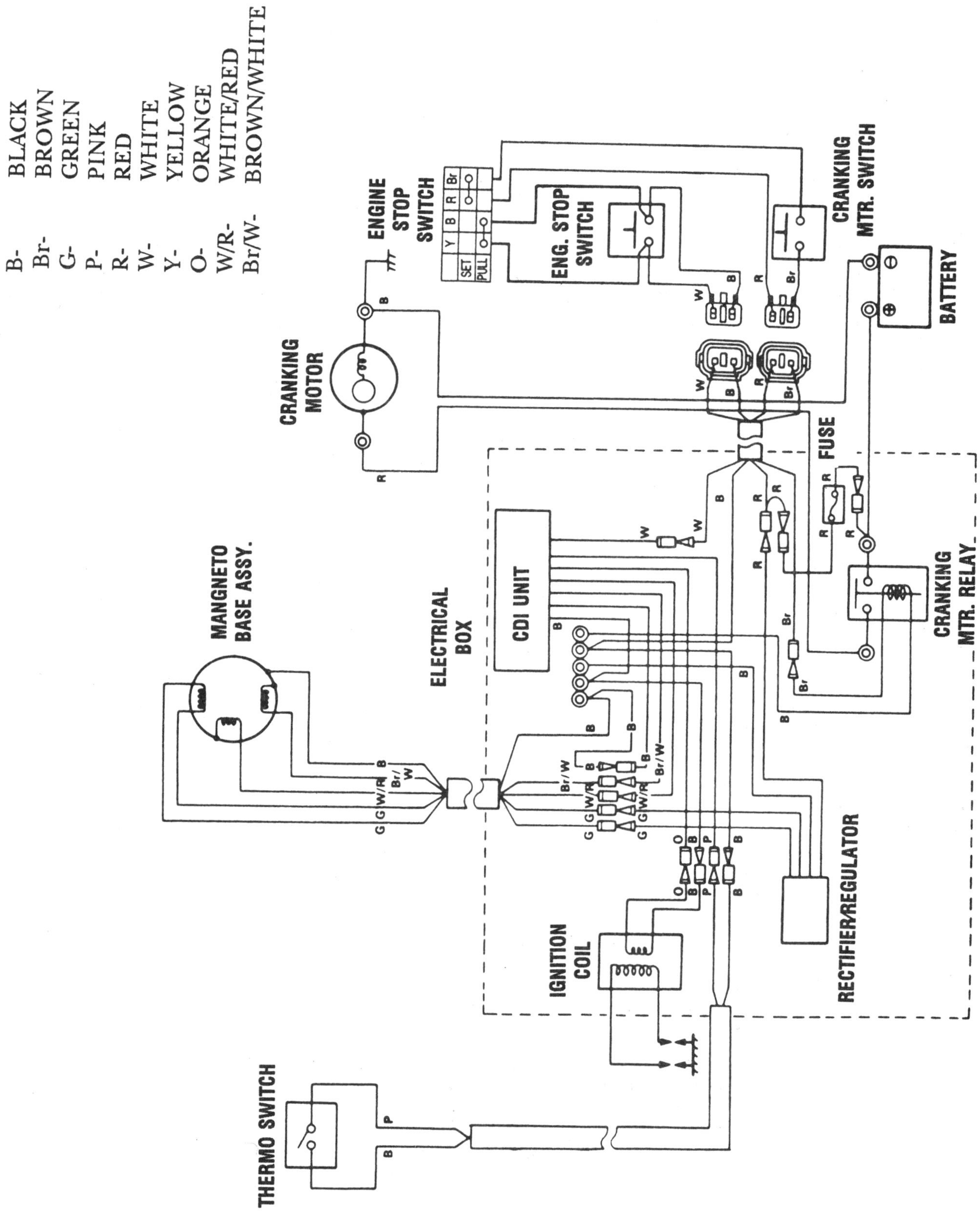

Electrical wiring diagram and wire color code for the ***WaveBlaster 700****. Major components are identified.*

B- BLACK
Br- BROWN/WHITE
O- ORANGE
P- PINK
W- WHITE
W/R WHITE/RED

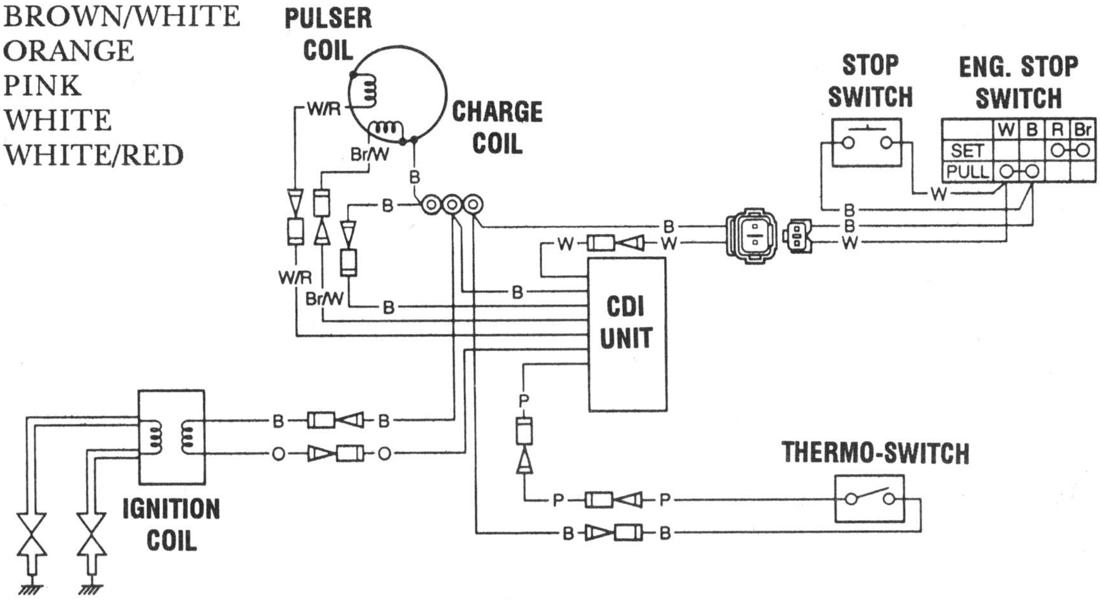

Ignition system wiring diagram and wire color code for the ***WaveVenture 700*** *and the* ***WaveRaider 700.***

B- BLACK
Br- BROWN
L- BLUE
O- ORANGE
P- PINK
W- WHITE
W/B- WHITE/BLACK
W/R WHITE/RED

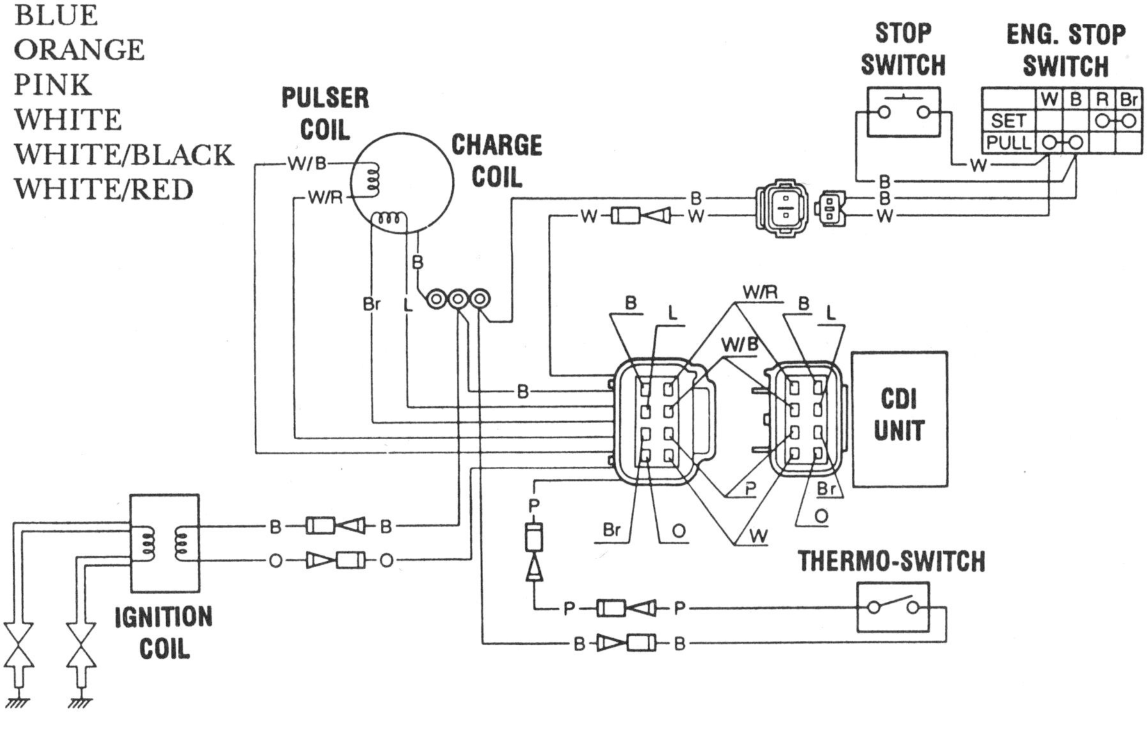

Ignition system wiring diagram and wire color code for the ***WaveBlaster II 760.*** *Major components have been identified.*

B-	BLACK
B/O-	BLACK/ORANGE
B/R-	BLACK/RED
B/W-	BLACK/WHITE
B/Y-	BLACK/YELLOW
Br-	BRFOWN
L-	BLUE
P-	PINK
W-	WHITE
W/B-	WHITE/BLACK
W/G-	WHITE/GREEN
W/R-	WHITE/RED

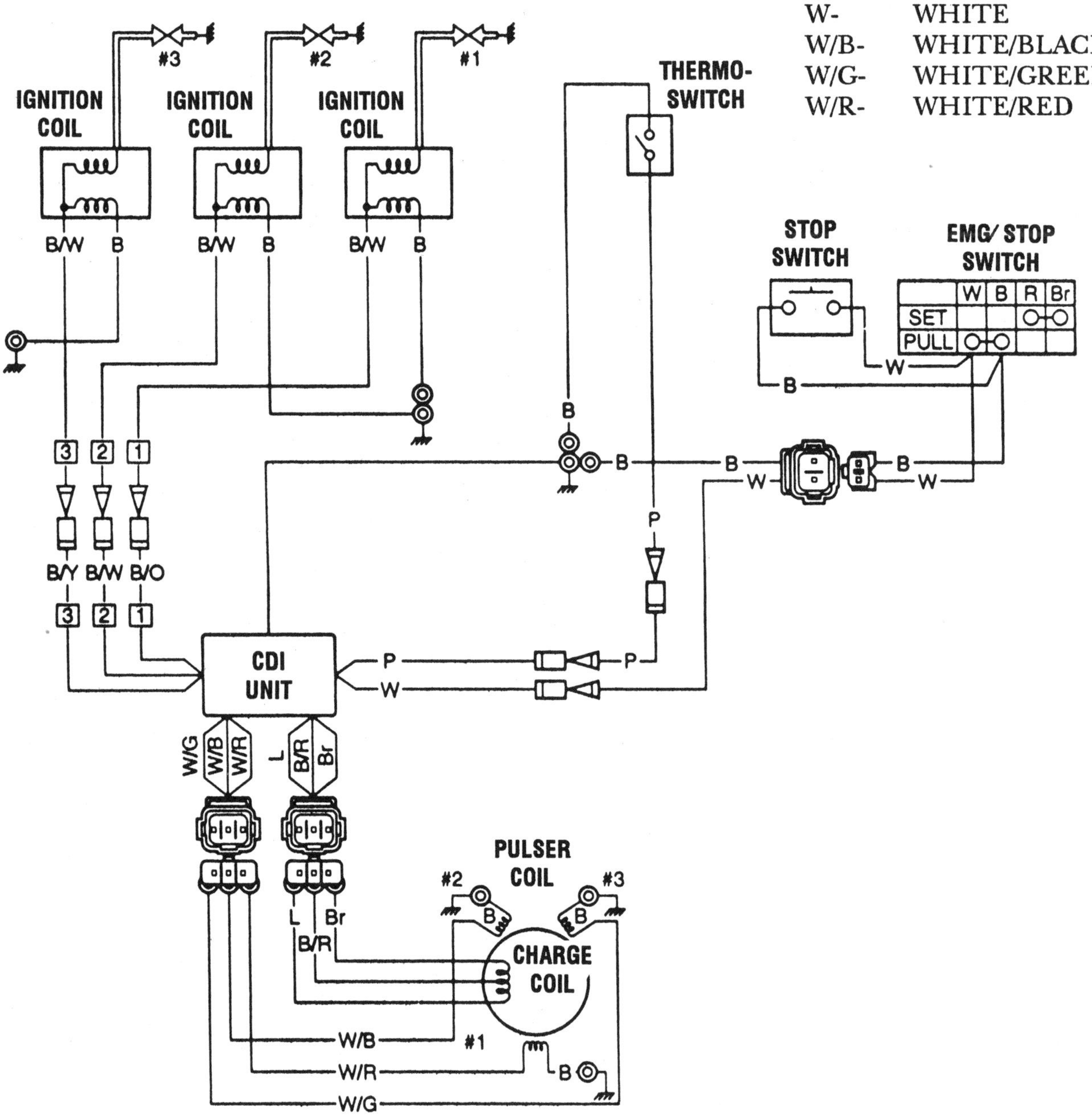

Ignition system wiring diagram and wire color code for the ***WaveVenture 1100 and WaveRaider 1100.*** *Major components have been identified.*

B-	BLACK
G-	GREEN
L-	BLUE
P-	PINK
R-	RED
R/W	RED/WHITE
W/L	WHITE/BLUE
Y-	YELLOW

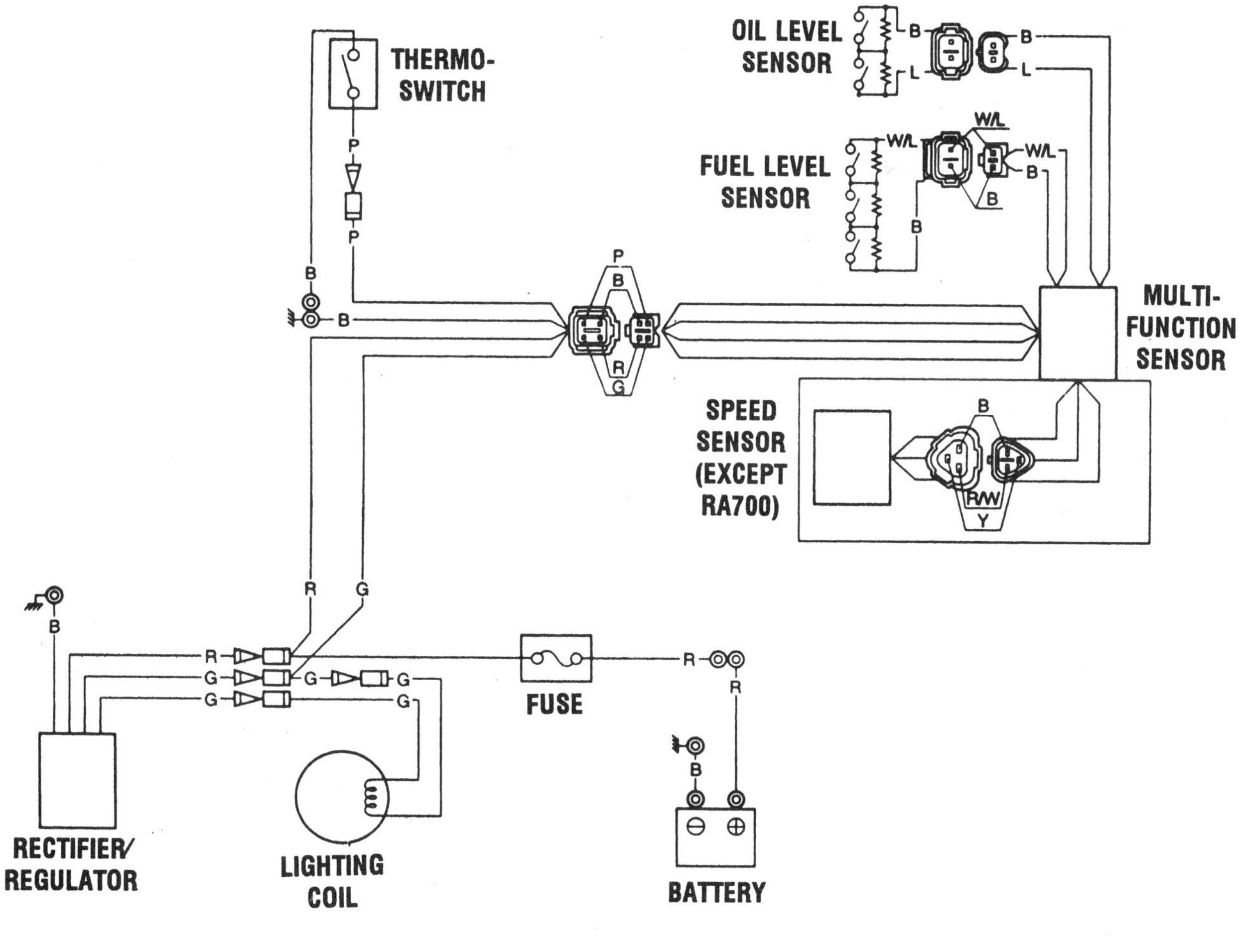

Electrical wiring diagram and color code for the ***INDICATION SYSTEM*** *on the* ***WaveVenture 700 and 1100.*** *Major components are identified.*

B- BLACK
Br- BROWN
R- RED

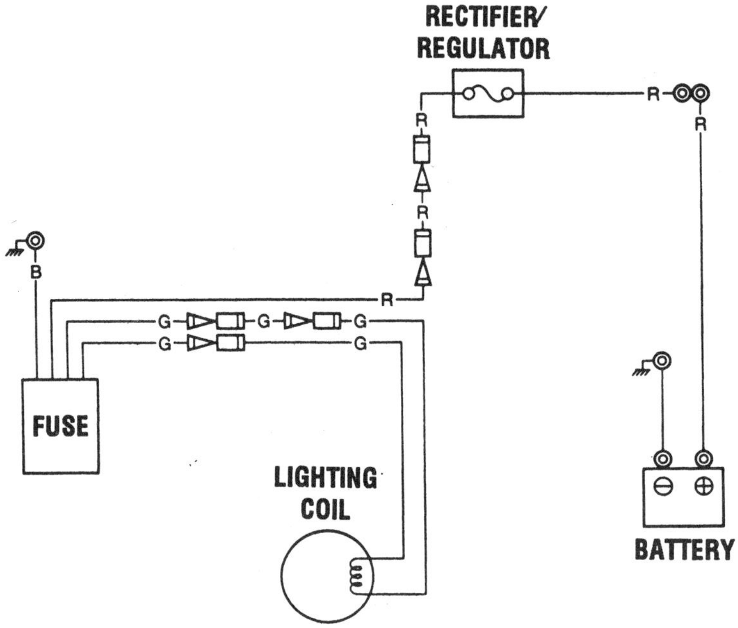

Electrical wiring diagram and color code for the ***Charging System*** *on the* ***WaveVenture 700 and 1100.*** *Major components in the system are identified.*

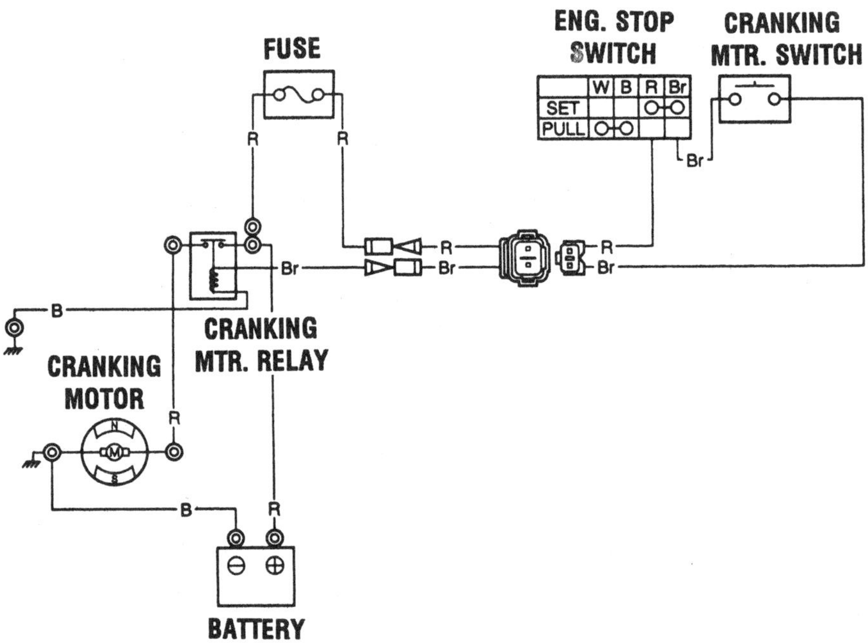

Electrical wiring diagram and color code for the ***Cranking Motor System*** *on the* ***WaveVenture 700 and 1100.*** *Major items in the system have been identified.*